MONOGRAPHS OF THE PHYSIOLOGICAL SOCIETY

Editors: H. Davson, A. D. M. Greenfield, R. Whittam,
G. S. Brindley, C. R. House

Number 25 VISCERAL AFFERENT FUNCTIONS OF
THE NERVOUS SYSTEM

Volumes marked * are now out of print.

VISCERAL AFFERENT FUNCTIONS
OF THE
NERVOUS SYSTEM

P. P. NEWMAN, M.D.

*Department of Physiology, School of Medicine,
University of Leeds*

LONDON

EDWARD ARNOLD (PUBLISHERS) LTD

© P. P. Newman, 1974

First published 1974
by Edward Arnold (Publishers) Ltd
25 Hill Street, London W1X 8LL

ISBN 0 7131 4227 8

Printed in Great Britain by
The Camelot Press Ltd, Southampton

PREFACE

THIS monograph is an expression of my pursuits in a field of research which has attracted successive workers at Leeds for nearly half a century. Interest in visceral afferents from the abdominal region began with McSwiney in 1926 when he traced impulses into the central nervous system and later, in collaboration with Bain, showed that afferents in the splanchnic nerves ascended to the oculomotor nucleus. Conduction pathways and their clinical implications were the subject of Goligher's well-known studies on the pelvic viscera. About the same time, ideas on the central control of the thoracic organs were being developed by Hemingway, Schweitzer & Neil and their lead opened up a new era in cardiovascular thinking which has since been actively promoted by Linden and his associates. It was in this background that I was encouraged to follow the course set by McSwiney for, at the time, very little was known about the cerebral destination of the visceral afferents or the part they played in reflex and regulatory mechanisms. Indeed, there was a curious reluctance on the part of many writers to admit that fibres travelling in the autonomic nerves belonged to a separate projection system which was sensory in function. Although the significance of the hypothalamus had long been recognized, there was no clear picture suggesting that the cerebral cortex might also serve in the neuro-endocrine adjustments of the body.

Notable progress was made in the year 1951 when it was shown that evoked potentials could be recorded from the sensory cortex after stimulating the central cut end of a splanchnic nerve and this was followed by the demonstration of cortical responses to over-distension of the gall bladder, stomach and other hollow viscera. In those days we lacked the advantages of modern equipment, but none of the pioneering spirit or enthusiasm that marked each disclosure and approach to the next problem. We constructed our own amplifying and recording systems, which now seem so primitive, and designed much of the hardware from the workshop bench. The introduction of microelectrode techniques was hailed by neurophysiologists everywhere and the literature during the next decade gave ample proof of its success in rediscovering the nervous system at a unitary level. It was certainly reassuring, if not entirely dramatic, when it was first shown that the discharge of a single brain cell could be influenced by impulses arising in abdominal viscera. The way was then open for a detailed analysis of the discharge properties of the units and to demonstrate their representation at every functional level. A new interpretation was given to the functions of the cerebellum and our knowledge of the reticular network in the brain stem was considerably advanced. It was also evident that feedback from corticofugal influences played an essential role in determining the outcome of complex interactions between afferents of somatic and visceral sources.

Another set of problems then emerged. Once it had been established that visceral afferents belonged to an organized projection system reaching to the cerebral cortex and utilizing feedback control, it was necessary to discover how such impulses could be integrated with the mass of information feeding into the hypothalamic and brain stem centres through which the reactions of the body were mobilized. At the present time it is believed that the limbic regions of the brain fulfil this role. Collectively, they exert a control over the entire autonomic nervous system and therefore make possible the widespread visceral reactions observed in conditions of emotion and stress. There are still many problems associated with emotional disturbances which may be relevant to the circuitry of the limbic system and only by the successful examination of the underlying physiological mechanisms can we hope to achieve a clearer understanding of functional changes in health and disease.

P. P. N.

CONTENTS

ACKNOWLEDGEMENTS

THE subject matter which provides the title of this book was derived in no small measure from discussions with colleagues throughout the world during the International Congresses of Physiology as well as at our own Society Meetings. From them came the inspiration and friendly contacts that are so important to the advance of our research. In particular, I am indebted to V. E. Amassian and his associates at the Albert Einstein College of Medicine, New York, to J. C. Eccles and to the late Warren McCulloch who spent some happy times in my laboratory at Leeds. Most of all I should like to thank J. H. Wolstencroft of Birmingham, and D. H. Paul of Manchester together with various colleagues who have worked with me over the years. I am also grateful to my colleague, Dr A. V. Holden, for reading and criticizing the manuscript and for many helpful suggestions. On the technical side I have been fortunate to have the expertise of Mr Eric French and the assistance of Mr Paul Armitage. Electronic developments have been in the hands of Mr Stanley Stainthorpe and his staff; workshop facilities, initially under the direction of the late Mr Albert Jepson, were cheerfully provided by Mr Stanley Pennington and Mr George Thompson; histological assistance by Mrs Barbara Royle. For the illustrations I am grateful to the late Mr Norman England and his successor, Mr Peter Hargreaves. The entire manuscript was kindly typed by Mrs Marian Stainthorpe. Finally, I should like to express my thanks to the Medical Research Council for many years of financial support.

A neurophysiological laboratory

1

INTRODUCTION

THE neurophysiologist is concerned with experiments designed to give information on the activities of the nervous system. He will generally begin by testing a hypothesis in a series of pilot experiments and the outcome may be of use to show him the direction for planning his future work. He will continue by observing and measuring the changes produced by a particular agent or stimulus, comparing such changes with those obtained under strictly controlled conditions. The inferences made from the experimental results can often be strengthened by using different methods of approach or using different techniques with appropriate forms of analysis. Eventually, as data accumulate, he may be tempted to express a point of view or to make a report which, although open to criticism, may give encouragement for further investigation. The objects of his research are to record the facts and to make tentative suggestions, leaving others to decide on their value and significance. Sometimes the facts are confirmed by contributions from other sources so that new ideas emerge and principles become established; in this way steady progress is made towards a further understanding of the problem. However, such is the competitive interest of scientific study that results are just as likely to give rise to controversy or doubt and the problem must then be investigated again, perhaps with the help of new techniques or a new approach or else await the attention of another generation of workers.

EXPERIMENTAL METHODS

The era of 'string, pulleys and smoked paper' has been superseded by a multitude of electronic and engineering devices, which have given the modern research worker a distinct advantage. Yet the possession of sophisticated instruments and knowledge of their application do not by themselves produce solutions to problems and in no way detract from the skill and insight of earlier workers. Many outstanding contributions have been made when only the most primitive equipment was available.

General rules of management

There are certain rules in the management of acute experiments which are designed to maintain the animal in good physiological condition. Availability and costs are usually the deciding factors in determining the species used. Cats have proved extremely valuable for investigations on the nervous system and there is a strong case for establishing more breeding farms to ensure standard sizes and weights. The kind of preparation employed will of course depend on the nature of a particular experiment. Decerebrate and spinal preparations have the advantage that they do not require an anaesthetic after completing all the operative procedures. On the other hand, they demand careful haemostasis, constant attention to airway and a watchful eye on the blood pressure. With intact animals, the success of an experiment often depends on the choice of the right anaesthetic and dosage. Commonly preferred anaesthetics are mixtures of Dial and urethane (0·7 ml/kg), chloralose (60–100 mg/kg), sodium pentobarbitone (Nembutal, 30–50 mg/kg) and sodium thiopentone (Pentothal, 45 mg/kg). An initial dose of barbiturate, given by intraperitoneal injection, acts slowly but safely and gives good surgical anaesthesia; thereafter small maintenance doses are given intravenously as required. When ether is used initially, followed by small doses of barbiturates, the skin wounds and pressure points should be infiltrated with a local anaesthetic (1% procaine HCl). In order to maintain the body temperature between 36 and 38°C an external source of heat is required such as an infra red lamp. The blood pressure is monitored at intervals during an experiment and may be prevented from falling below 80 mm Hg by intravenous drips of glucose or dextran.

Methods of stimulation

(i) Mechanical

Rubber balloons are widely used to effect distension of a viscus by expansion. They can be cut to size from a surgical glove and tied over the end of a glass cannula or polyethylene tube. A second tube inserted with the balloon can be used for measuring pressure in the viscus. The balloon is inflated with saline or air delivered from a motor-driven syringe or by hand. A two-way tap on the nozzle allows for rapid deflation. When experiments are performed on abdominal viscera, it is important to cause as little disturbance as possible to the mesentery, which is very sensitive to mechanical stimuli. After testing the action of the balloon, the connecting tubes are fixed to the skin of the abdominal wall, which is then closed in layers.

(ii) Thermal

Heat is an effective physiological stimulus. Many techniques have been described for raising intracranial temperature. In one method, the proximal end of one or both carotid arteries is cannulated and the blood passed through a spiral glass tube in a water-bath before being returned through a cannula inserted into the distal end of the artery. The temperature of the water is raised by an electric heater. The method avoids the danger of spread of heat to the vagi and other structures in the neck, which occurs when heating tubes are placed around the carotid arteries. The temperature of the carotid blood is monitored by a thermocouple inserted through the central end of the lingual artery. A second thermocouple, inserted into the brain, measures the change of temperature which occurs on heating. Irrigation of the cerebral ventricles with warm saline has also been used.

The application of heat to a localized region of the brain has been described in detail by Magoun, Harrison, Brobeck & Ranson (1938). These authors used a low-powered, high-frequency oscillator to pass current between two wire electrodes. A modification of their method uses a silver electrode, insulated except at the tip and mounted in a stereotaxic holder. The electrode is connected to the output of a diathermy or radio frequency unit; the indifferent electrode is a saline pad applied to one limb. The temperature in the region of the electrode tip is recorded by a thermocouple made by brazing together copper and constantan wires. Electrode placements are determined by histological studies in which the track of the electrode can be easily recognized.

The use of thermodes has the advantage of giving any desired temperature so that the effects of cooling can also be observed. Thermodes made from stainless steel tubes, insulated except at the tip, operate by the circulation of hot or cold water between two tanks. Thermal stimulation of surface structures may be effected by a stream of distilled water or saline emitted from the tip of a hypodermic needle. Rapid temperature changes can be accomplished by displacing the stream with fluid from a second needle (Poulos & Benjamin, 1968).

(iii) Chemical

Strychnine has proved a valuable aid in tracing pathways in the central nervous system. The method was introduced by Dusser de Barenne (1916) as an alternative to the method of extirpation for mapping cortical boundaries. He described the action 'setting on fire of the cortex by strychnine'. A small piece of filter paper, soaked in 1% strychnine sulphate and coloured with toluidine blue, is placed on the pial surface in proximity to a pair of recording electrodes. Cortical 'spiking' is observed about one minute after the application. If a second pair of recording electrodes is placed in another part of the brain, responses to strychnine stimulation suggest the existence of a direct functional pathway between the two areas. The method is simple, effective and avoids anatomical lesions.

Chemical substances, acting on the stomach, are introduced by means of an oesophageal catheter or by passing a polythene tube through the mouth. Alternatively, the abdomen is opened in the midline and the tube inserted into the pyloric antrum through a small incision in the wall of the duodenum, which is then tied. The resting contents of the stomach are washed out with warm saline solution before introducing the chemical stimulus. The effects of hyperacidity of the gastric mucosa have been studied in this way, using a solution of HCl which is first adjusted to any desired pH.

Substances introduced into the cerebrospinal fluid may be injected through the atlanto-occipital membrane or into one of the cerebral ventricles. It is possible to limit the action of a chemical to any part of the ventricular system by collecting the outflow through an implanted cannula, whilst other parts of the system are perfused separately. A method of multiple cannulation of the cerebral ventricles has been described by Carmichael, Feldberg & Fleischhauer (1964).

The application of a chemical substance to single neurones requires the use of a two-barrelled microelectrode. One barrel is filled with a solution of the substance to be tested and the other is used for recording the electrical response of the neurone. The technique of recording from single neurones will be described below. The chemical substance is released from the tip of the microelectrode by passing a current through the solution either constantly or in pulses. This electrophoretic method controls movement out of the tip by diffusion and obviously can only be used with ionic substances. Comis, Evans & Whitfield (1964) developed a micro-tap, consisting of two concentric pipettes, the outer filled with the chemical solution and the inner serving as the recording electrode. A screw-driven syringe advances the inner electrode towards the tip of the outer pipette and closes the tap. Multi-barrelled pipettes are also used for investigating the action of chemicals on single cells. They are made of fine glass tubes fused together, each containing a different substance. The tubes are arranged radially around a central pipette employed as the electrode recording the responses of the cell (Curtis & Eccles, 1958).

(iv) Electrical

Stimulating electrodes. A pair of silver wires, with tips 3–4 mm apart, is very satisfactory for peripheral nerve stimulation. They can be mounted with a second pair of silver wires for recording the nerve action potential; the part of the nerve between stimulating and recording electrodes is connected to the animal or grounded in order to reduce artifact. For abdominal work, it is useful to fix the multi-electrode assembly to the musculature of the body wall by sutures and also to hold the connecting leads in place before the abdomen is closed. This technique allows continuous stimulation and recording without loss of contact between nerve and electrodes, which may otherwise occur due to respiratory movements.

Bipolar silver wires with ball tips are suitable for stimulating surface areas of the brain. When a unipolar electrode is employed, the shock artifact may be quite large unless the indifferent electrode has a high resistance. Stimulation of structures deep to the surface is effected by a bipolar concentric needle electrode or by means of a fine steel wire, insulated with enamel except at the tip. Both these types of electrode allow a very localized region of stimulation.

Stimulus pulses. In many of the experiments to be described, peripheral nerves were stimulated by single shocks delivered through a 1 : 1 isolating transformer from a square wave pulse generator. Stimulus intensities ranged between 1 and 5 volts and the pulse duration was 0·01 msec. It is more useful to express the strength of a stimulus in terms of the nerve action potential, either as a fraction of the fibre groups excited or as multiples of the threshold response. The pulse generator is triggered to an oscilloscope, which displays a sweep on one channel and a time base on a second channel. The stimulus artifact can be displayed at any point along the sweep by means of a delay control. In order to study the effects of two stimuli applied to the same nerve or to a different nerve, a second pulse generator is triggered to the sweep. The time interval between the two stimuli can then be varied by operating the delay controls.

Experiments involving electrical stimulation of the cerebral cortex can give rise to conflicting results as the excitability of different areas of the cortex varies considerably. Much depends on the species, the choice of anaesthetic, the level of anaesthesia and the state of the circulation. Furthermore, the characteristics of the electrical stimulus—whether single shocks or repetitive shocks are employed—will be determined by the kind of response which is being investigated, e.g. changes in blood pressure, contraction of muscles or movements, neuronal discharges, etc. Consequently, many trials may be necessary in each experiment to determine the optimal parameters of stimulation. Surface anodal current pulses, 0·2 msec duration, have been found to stimulate selectively localized areas of the cortex. The intensity required is usually less than for surface cathodal stimulation (Livingstone & Phillips, 1957). Some investigators prefer repetitive stimulation delivered in short bursts; but the results are no more effective than single shock stimulation when the parameters are carefully chosen. In recent years, various forms of digital instruments have become available for the delivery of controlled stimulus pulses. They operate by counting impulses from a crystal generator to produce time-selected outputs over a wide range of settings. Pulse trains of precise duration and number pass through controlled gates and dividing circuits to trigger one or more battery-driven stimulators.

Methods of recording

(i) Recording electrodes

The type of recording electrode employed will be determined by the design of a particular experiment and by the input properties of the apparatus available. For recording action potentials in peripheral nerves, bipolar silver wires are commonly used; they may be embedded in a polythene block to shield them from surrounding structures. For long-term use, the nonpolarizable electrode is more satisfactory as it is less damaging to the nerve. The simplest in use is the silver—silver chloride wire. A silver electrode is connected to the positive pole of a battery. Anode and cathode are immersed in 0.9% NaCl and electrolysis is maintained for about an hour in the dark.

In electromyography, small silver disks filled with electrode jelly are attached to the skin overlying the muscle. They can also be used as scalp electrodes, although in animals, fine steel needles piercing the scalp are equally effective. When the brain is exposed, the simplest method of recording potentials is a saline wick in contact with the pial surface. When recording from deeper structures or if the electrode remains in the brain for any appreciable period, metal electrodes such as tungsten or platinum–iridium are the best choice; they have the necessary rigidity for stereotaxic work and are electrically stable.

Microelectrodes are employed for recording from single cells. They may be made from glass or metal. Glass micropipettes are manufactured from thin-walled Pyrex tubing supplied in 15 cm lengths. Although they can be pulled by hand when softened over a gas flame or by mechanical devices operated by springs, it is easier to acquire a puller in which the glass is melted by an electrically heated wire and pulled by a solenoid. The machine delivers with each pull two micropipettes with a fairly constant taper and tip diameter. For extracellular work, the micropipettes are filled with 3.5 M NaCl by heating in a flask under reduced pressure. Alternatively, they can be filled with methyl alcohol by boiling for a few minutes, placed in distilled water for ten minutes, followed by immersion in the electrolyte solution. Glass microelectrodes prepared in this way may be stored for several weeks; but the tips must be checked under a microscope before each experiment and the resistance measured.

Electrodes are selected with tips 0·5–3 µ, internal diameter, and a d.c. resistance of 5–10 megohms.

Metal microelectrodes give excellent results but are more difficult to prepare. The tungsten electrode described by Hubel (1957) is insulated to the tip with lacquer, then electropolished by dipping into potassium nitrate solution. A platinum–iridium wire coated with molten glass has exceptional durability and insulation.

(ii) Recording systems

Ink-writing pens give permanent records on continuously moving paper and provide simultaneous tracings for two or more input channels. Although developed to meet the requirements of clinical electroencephalography, they are equally suitable for electromyography and for recording strychnine spikes. The inertia of the pens, however, is too great for recording uniform responses at frequencies above 65 c/s.

Ultra-violet recorders can accommodate up to 50 input channels and faithfully reproduce data at very high frequencies. They utilize sensitive galvanometers and an optical system to give visible traces on print-out paper with a wide range of paper speeds. As photography is not required, they are very popular for experiments which involve simultaneous recording of multiple variables including blood pressure, visceral pressure, respiratory movements and nerve discharges.

Cathode-ray oscilloscopes record faithfully all potential changes including those picked up by microelectrodes. The amplified potentials appear as deflexions on a beam which sweeps across the display tube, whilst a second beam can be used for displaying the time marker. Each beam of the oscilloscope can be controlled independently or, by means of splitting and chopping devices, signals from several different input channels can be applied. A trigger circuit gives control of the repetition rate. In certain types of oscilloscope all the traces can be stored for a period of time, but permanent records require the use of photography.

Magnetic tape may now be regarded as an essential part of recording equipment if only for the time that is saved during an experiment. Unnecessary use of the camera is also avoided. All the data are stored until required, then played back for visual display on an oscilloscope and monitoring through a loud speaker; the signals can also be fed into a computer for averaging and analysis by means of histogram plots.

(iii) Extracellular recordings

When studying the activity of single cells, certain precautions must be taken to ensure successful and consistent results. After the operative procedures have been completed, the animal is transferred to a stereotaxic instrument and fixed in a rigid head-holder. Movements are eliminated by giving Flaxedil (gallamine triethiodide) intravenously and the animal is artificially ventilated with air or mixtures of oxygen. The microelectrode is held in a carrier which allows movements of the tip at any angle. The carrier itself is mounted on a micromanipulator provided with coarse and fine controls which guide the tip to the pial surface. Further advance of the microelectrode is controlled by a micrometer screw which also gives a reading of the depth below surface contact. Some workers prefer an oil-filled hydraulic drive for remote control of the electrode penetration. A fine silver wire, used as the recording lead, connects the microelectrode to a conventional cathode follower or to a transistorized source follower driving a differential preamplifier. The lead is kept as short as possible to reduce interference by fixing the cathode follower in close proximity to the electrode assembly.

The object of a good recording system is to maintain stable conditions over long periods of time. Cells are easily damaged or recordings of their discharges are lost by relatively slight movements. Several methods have been devised to overcome this difficulty. Artificial pneumothorax and drainage of the cerebrospinal fluid through the cisterna magna are helpful procedures. Cerebral pulsations may be controlled by utilizing a pressor foot (Amassian, 1953), which is essentially a small plate pressed against the pial surface and pierced by a hole to admit the microelectrode shaft. The elimination of brain movements is probably most successful when the cranial cavity is closed. In one technique, the microelectrode is surrounded by paraffin wax introduced into a polythene chamber; the latter can either be screwed into the skull or fixed in position with dental cement. The method limits the volume of brain which can be explored in any experiment, but is eminently suitable for investigations in the chronic preparation.

Methods of analysis

The techniques described above give an outline of the methods commonly used in experimental work on the nervous system. Examination of the tracings obtained from an experiment may give the answer to a simple question, for example, the presence or absence of blood pressure changes following stimulation of a viscus. However, in the more complicated responses of nervous activity, accurate analysis of the records is required for evaluation of the results. The following measurements include some of the standard methods of presenting data and apply, in particular, to the study of single unit discharges. Such information is indispensable before conclusions can be drawn about the underlying mechanisms of function:

1. Average response: the display of the summed responses from a large number of successive sweeps; when the signal is locked to the sweep the signal-to-noise ratio is improved.

2. Latency: a measurement of time between stimulus artifact and evoked response. In experiments on single units, the mean latency is perhaps more significant.

3. Amplitude: the size of a response, usually measured as peak-to-peak voltage.

4. Duration: a measurement of the time occupied by a potential waveform.

5. Spike count: a count of the number of potentials in a discharge.

6. Probability: a scale of response function indicating the level of probability (a) that a response will follow a stimulus or (b) that responses will occur at various time intervals following each stimulus. The scale of probability (P) is derived from the ratio between the number of responses evoked and the number of trials.

7. Temporal structure: the time intervals between spikes measured during a selected period of activity.

Whilst all the measurements can be made from films projected on a screen, the effort is both tedious and time-consuming and the results often inaccurate. The laboratory computer has been developed to meet the requirements of data analysis by processing signals as they emerge from the animal or from data stored on magnetic drums or punched paper. Two kinds of instrument are available: in one kind, the modes of operation are built-in to provide a means of averaging and a range of histograms; in the other kind, the instrument is far more versatile, but must be supplied with programmes compiled for each operation. Both kinds of computer accept experimental data directly, sample the events at selected intervals of time, convert the samples into a code of binary digits and store the result in memory registers. The output system permits the content of the store to be displayed on a cathode ray tube or to operate a teletypewriter at high speed.

Histological aids

At the end of an experiment the animal is given an overdose of anaesthetic; the parts to be examined are removed, then immersed in a fixative (10% formalin) for 2–3 days. Serial sections, 20–25 μ in thickness, are cut, mounted and stained with cresyl fast violet or thionin. Histological examination is necessary for precise location of stimulating and recording sites, for determining the position of microelectrode tips and for tracing the extent of experimental lesions.

ORGANIZATION OF THE VISCERAL AFFERENT SYSTEM

Visceral afferents originate in ganglion cells of the dorsal roots and cranial nerves; their peripheral processes terminate in receptors supplying the internal organs and their central processes enter the spinal cord or brain stem. Like somatic afferents, their projections are found at every level of the central nervous system. Like somatic afferents, they can influence the discharges of single cells or localized groups of cells. Their impulses may produce effects on somatic as well as on visceral structures and may cause the release of hormones, directly or indirectly, from most endocrine glands. Whilst the outflow to the viscera has been studied in great detail since Langley (1900) used the term 'autonomic' to describe it, knowledge of the afferent pathways and their central mechanisms is by no means complete. It is now clear that visceral afferents form a distinct and highly organized projection system and one that has many features in common with the classical somatosensory system.

Levels of visceral function

(a) Peripheral nerves

Afferent impulses from the viscera are conveyed to the central nervous system along pathways which follow, in the main, the distribution of vagal, splanchnic and pelvic nerves. The vagi supply the thoracic viscera and the stomach, the cells of origin being in the inferior or nodosal ganglion. Afferents in the splanchnic nerves supply most of the abdominal organs, the fibres passing through the sympathetic chain to their cell stations in the dorsal root ganglia. Afferents arising in the pelvic viscera traverse the network of sacral and hypogastric plexuses, taking a double route before entering the cord at either sacral or lumbar level. One difficulty in tracing the peripheral pathway of visceral afferents arises from the fact that they have no separate anatomical routes, but run in the distribution of the autonomic outflow to the viscera.

(b) Spinal cord

Various reflex functions in experimental animals and in man show that visceral centres of activity exist in the spinal cord. Stimulation of afferent pathways produces somatic as well as visceral reflexes indicating a great divergence of connecting neurones and irradiation of impulses. The reflex effects involve many different physiological systems, including cardiovascular, alimentary, endocrine and urogenital systems.

(c) Brain stem

The control of many visceral functions such as respiration, heart rate, vasomotor tone and gastrointestinal activity has long been assigned to centres in the medulla and pons. It appears that the brain stem reticular formation has an important role integrating these functions and that temperature regulation and endocrine secretions may also be concerned. A good deal of work has been done on the distribution of afferent fibres in the vagal and glossopharyngeal nerves and their participation in medullary reflexes, but less is known about the contribution to the reticular system of afferents derived from other visceral nerves.

(d) Cerebellum

It has been established in recent years that impulses originating in abdominal viscera project to circumscribed regions of the cerebellum. A splanchnic receiving area has been located in the culmen of the anterior lobe, just lateral to the paravermian vein. On the other hand, vagal afferents, stimulated directly or following distension of a viscus, produce more widespread effects in the vermis and posterior lobes of the cerebellum.

(e) Hypothalamus

The hypothalamus and its related structures in the diencephalon are concerned with autonomic reactions mediated by the parasympathetic and sympathetic outflow to the viscera. The nervous control of the pituitary and the release of its hormones are also functions of the hypothalamus. There is much less information on the sensory systems relaying impulses of visceral origin to the hypothalamus.

(f) Thalamus

Various authors have reported on the representation of splanchnic nerve afferents in the thalamus. Using the evoked potential technique, McLeod (1958) recorded from single units in the posterior ventral nucleus. The fast conducting A beta fibres in the splanchnic nerve gave responses in the contralateral thalamus alone, whereas the slower conducting A delta fibres yielded bilateral thalamic responses.

(g) Sensory cortex

Impulses initiated by distension of the gall bladder or stomach may give rise to potential changes in the sensory areas of the cerebral cortex. Surface positive responses following electrical stimulation of the splanchnic nerve have been recorded from limited but well-defined parts of somatosensory areas I and II. Single unit responses have also been recorded by microelectrodes in both sensory areas; a study of their discharge patterns has revealed a projection system comparable in many ways to the classical somatosensory system.

(h) Limbic regions

The neurological network, in which the hypothalamus is involved, includes three cortical areas known collectively as the limbic region:

1. The cingulate gyrus. At our present state of knowledge, the cingulate gyrus appears to be an important part of the limbic network although its functions and anatomical connexions are not precisely known. The reason for this lack of knowledge may be the conflicting results of stimulation experiments and the inconclusive effects of unilateral ablation. There is no doubt that the cingulate gyrus can influence many visceral functions such as blood pressure, respiration and gastrointestinal motility; but the changes observed depend to a great extent on the species, anaesthetic, stimulus parameters and other variables. Furthermore, in ablation experiments only bilateral removal furnishes any definite results.

2. The orbital gyrus. Similar observations may be applied to the role of the orbital gyrus in its relation to visceral function. Since Spencer (1894) reported on the effects produced by excitation of the cerebrum, there has been general agreement that stimulation of the orbital cortex inhibits respiration; the effects on blood pressure, however, are variable. Bailey & Bremer (1938) described changes in the electroencephalogram produced by stimulating afferents in the vagus nerve. This was an important beginning to an entirely new concept on the representation of visceral afferents in the cerebral cortex. Experimental work on animals and contributions from clinical data have emphasized the relationship between the orbital gyrus and the influence of vagal impulses on gastric functions.

3. The hippocampal formation. This part of the limbic system, comprising the hippocampal gyrus and related structures, receives impulses from visceral afferent projections in the brain stem. The vast network of its connexions with the hypothalamus, thalamus and cerebral cortex suggests that it may be a converging point of excitatory and inhibitory influences on the amygdaloid nuclei and hypothalamic centres. It is possibly the most important level of the entire visceral system.

IDEA OF A 'VISCERAL BRAIN'

Once it had been established that the central nervous system controlled the autonomic outflow to the viscera, attempts were made to discover afferent pathways between the viscera and the brain. It was recognized that the hypothalamic nuclei and associated pituitary gland had an important role in regulating the activity of visceral, endocrine and other systems of the body and were the principal centres for emotional expression. The problem which remained unsolved concerned the role of the cerebral cortex. Anatomical studies, supported by clinical evidence, had demonstrated a network of connexions between the hypothalamus and the structures known as the 'limbic lobe'. The problem, however, was made more difficult by the assumption that the limbic structures were purely olfactory in function. Since Papez (1937) published his theory of central emotion, proposing that 'the hypothalamus and its cortical circuit constituted a harmonious mechanism', the idea has been suggested that a ring of cortex involving the rostral part of the forebrain and temporal lobes may be regarded as the region which integrates the visceral functions of the nervous system. MacLean (1949) applied the descriptive term 'visceral brain' to this region, although the term should also include a number of subcortical structures and their numerous anatomical interconnexions. There is now considerable evidence that the so-called rhinencephalic or limbic structures have little olfactory function in primates and that their role is concerned largely with visceral activity and emotional behaviour. The 'visceral brain' may be regarded as comprising (1) a receptive region for visceral afferent impulses, (2) a distribution centre for directing influences within the network and (3) a motor region for controlling the patterns of hypothalamic discharges. In addition, following the proposals expressed by Papez, the 'visceral brain' is the most likely anatomical site in which neuronal activity may be integrated for the expression of emotional states. Acceptance of these views would provide a framework on which the control of visceral functions could be based: visceral afferents have representation at all levels of the cerebrospinal system; the central organization uses sensory and motor areas and association regions for integration analogous to those of the somatic nervous system; the autonomic nerves act exclusively as a motor system innervating peripheral organs.

REFERENCES

Amassian, V. E. (1953). Evoked single cortical unit activity in the somatic sensory areas. *Electroen. Neurophysiol.* 5, 415–438.
Bailey, P. & Bremer, F. (1938). A sensory cortical representation of the vagus nerve. *J. Neurophysiol.* 1, 405–412.

Carmichael, E. A., Feldberg, W. & Fleischhauer, K. (1964). Methods for perfusing different parts of the cat's cerebral ventricles with drugs. *J. Physiol.* **173**, 354–367.

Comis, S. D., Evans, E. F. & Whitfield, I. C. (1964). A micro-tap for controlling the application of drugs to single neurones. *J. Physiol.* **173**, 4P.

Curtis, D. R. & Eccles, R. M. (1958). The excitation of Renshaw cells by pharmacological agents applied electrophoretically. *J. Physiol.* **141**, 435–445.

Dusser de Barenne, J. G. (1916). Experimental researches on sensory localizations in the cerebral cortex. *Quart. Jl exp. Physiol.* **9**, 355–390.

Hubel, D. H. (1957). Tungsten microelectrode for recording from single units. *Science,* **125**, 549–550.

Langley, J. N. (1900). The sympathetic and other related systems of nerves. In *Textbook of Physiology,* edited by Schäfer, E. A. Vol. 2. Young & Pentland, Edinburgh and London.

Livingston, A. & Phillips, C. G. (1957). Maps and thresholds for the sensorimotor cortex of the cat. *Quart. Jl exp. Physiol.* **42**, 190–205.

Maclean, P. D. (1949). Psychosomatic disease and the 'visceral brain'. *Psychosom. Med.* **11**, 338–353.

Magoun, H. W., Harrison, F., Brobeck, J. R. & Ranson, S. W. (1938). Activation of heat loss mechanisms by local heating of the brain. *J. Neurophysiol.* **1**, 101–114.

McLeod, J. G. (1958). The representation of the splanchnic afferent pathways in the thalamus of the cat. *J. Physiol.* **140**, 462–478.

Papez, J. W. (1937). A proposed mechanism of emotion. *Archs Neurol. Psychiat.* **38**, 725–743.

Poulos, D. A. & Benjamin, R. M. (1968). Response of thalamic neurons to thermal stimulation of the tongue. *J. Neurophysiol.* **32**, 28–43.

Spencer, W. G. (1894). The effect produced upon respiration by faradic excitation of the cerebrum in the monkey, dog, cat and rabbit. *Phil. Trans.* **185B**, 609–657.

2

VISCERAL SENSIBILITY

IT may be taken as established that the viscera and their attachments
are supplied with receptors sensitive to a variety of stimuli including
pain-producing agents. Nerve impulse discharges are conveyed
centrally by three different groups of afferent fibres: large myelinated
fibres of the A beta group; smaller myelinated fibres of the A delta
group and non-myelinated C fibres. Whilst there are difficulties in
identifying the type of fibre supplying a particular receptor, especially
those which function as nociceptors, the activity set up by natural
stimulation accounts for a vast number of reflex responses. The
function of many receptors may be served by spinal reflexes alone; on
the other hand, afferent discharges from the viscera may produce their
effects at all levels of the central nervous system and also contribute to
conscious experience.

VISCEROCEPTORS

(1) Chemical

Gastric receptors sensitive to change in pH are distributed in all
parts of the stomach. In the cat, the threshold of excitation for acid
receptors is about pH 3; for alkali receptors, above pH 8. Both kinds
of receptors are located in the gastric mucosa and are supplied by
terminals of vagal afferents. As destruction of the mucosa abolishes
their activity, they can be distinguished from tension receptors found
in other layers of the stomach (Iggo, 1957). Impulses in vagal afferent
fibres can be detected after intra-aortic injections of phenyl diguanide.
This method was used by Paintal (1954a) to determine the presence of
chemoreceptors in abdominal viscera. The possible role of serotonin
(5-HT), normally present in the alimentary tract, has been discussed
by Douglas and Ritchie (1957). They showed that small doses of
serotonin injected into the circulation caused a high rate of firing in

non-myelinated afferent fibres in the vagus nerve. As no activity was
seen after removal of the stomach, they considered that more than
one-third of the abdominal vagal fibres had been activated by the
chemical stimulant. Possible chemoreceptor activity in the small
intestine was reported by Sharma & Nasset (1962). These workers
perfused segments of gut with different solutions, e.g. glucose, glycine,
histidine, and found increased frequency of impulse discharge
recorded from mesentric nerves; they suggested that intestinal
chemoreceptors might be concerned with the absorption of food.

(2) Mechanical

Pacinian corpuscles are found in large numbers in the cat
mesentery and embedded along the mesenteric nerves and vessels.
They are readily excited by slight mechanical stimuli such as tapping
or blowing a puff of air and are rapidly adapting. In the intact body,
natural stimulation provided by movements of the intestine may set up
a stream of impulses in the fibres supplying them. The fibres belong to
the A beta group of splanchnic nerve afferents (Gernandt &
Zotterman, 1946).

The responses of stretch receptors in the stomach have been studied
in detail by Paintal (1954b), who recorded afferent discharges in single
vagal units following distension of the stomach with a balloon. The
frequency of impulse discharge was roughly linear in relation to the
degree of distension and the mean conduction velocity was about 9
m/sec. Their mode of action has been examined by Iggo (1955) who
showed that all the receptors which were excited by distending
different parts of the stomach were also excited by contractions of the
stomach wall. He concluded that the gastric receptors were tension-
signalling devices 'in series' with the contractile elements in the smooth
muscle. They were unaffected by removal of the mucosa and
submucosa.

Receptors responding to mechanical stimulation are also present in
the wall of the intestine and urinary bladder. Impulse discharges
recorded from single afferent fibres show similar properties to gastric
recordings. The receptors are slowly adapting and respond to passive
distension or active contraction of the viscus.

Intestinal receptors signalling movement within the abdomen have
been described by Bessou & Perl (1966) in the cat. Although the sense

organs themselves or their axon terminals could not be identified structurally, their discharge properties and characteristics could be distinguished in several ways from those of other kinds of mechanoreceptors in the small bowel or mesentery. From a study of the action potentials in single mesenteric nerves the fields of distribution were determined by light pressure with a fine probe or by distension with a balloon. Sensitive points were found close to the surface of the intestine and along the mesenteric vessels. In the absence of stimuli, a background discharge was evident. The receptors were excited, typically, by mechanical events such as spontaneous or evoked movements of the intestine; but they were also sensitive to distension or traction upon the mesentery. The fibres supplying the receptors were small in diameter, usually myelinated and with conduction velocities between 5 and 15 m/sec. The authors regarded these receptors as 'sensors of movement' following any kind of mechanical change in the abdomen, whether caused by posture, respiration, circulation or intestinal activity. In confirming the existence of these movement receptors Morrison (1972) has suggested that they may have a much wider distribution and much larger receptive fields.

Receptors concerned with the local distribution of blood in the splanchnic circulation were described by Andrews, Andrews & Orbach (1972) in the rabbit and cat. When the venous pressure was increased by mechanical obstruction of the portal vein, there was a proportional increase in the frequency of afferent potentials and an increased efferent discharge in the sympathetic nerves supplying the small intestine. The reflex activity persisted after bilateral vagotomy and transection of the spinal cord at the cervical level.

(3) Nociceptive

There are no clear cut boundaries to distinguish nociceptors from other visceral receptors. It is likely that the same receptor units are excited by 'innocuous' as well as by nociceptive stimuli. The viscera are supplied with free nerve endings arranged in a plexus of fine non-myelinated axons ramifying in the muscular walls and mucous membranes. They are not exclusively nociceptive, but search for a specific pain receptor has not been fruitful.

Adequate stimulus

Abdominal operations performed under local anaesthesia cause little distress or pain to the conscious patient. Yet the routine acts of exploration, manipulation and clamping of viscera must set up a barrage of impulse discharges with no apparent conscious reactions. No painful sensations are produced by crushing the bowel wall, cutting or even burning, as the viscera are not sensitive to these forms of stimulation. The adequate stimuli are those which result from excessive activity in the viscera themselves. Adequate stimuli include strong acids, alkalis or chemical irritants acting on chemoreceptors in the mucosa and over-distension or vigorous contraction of the muscular walls in the various organs. Thus in spite of the apparent insensitivity of the viscera to ordinary forms of stimulation, severe abdominal discomfort and pain are only too frequently a common experience in health and disease.

(4) Thermal

The importance of peripheral receptors in the maintenance of body temperature has generally been studied from the panting response of animals placed in a heated chamber. In experiments on the sheep, Bligh (1959) found that the onset of panting could occur in the absence of any rise in temperature of the blood supplying the brain. Subsequently he suggested that thermal receptors in the region of the vena cava might contribute to the response since a depression of respiratory frequency occurred during intravenous infusion of cold saline (Bligh, 1963). Support for this hypothesis may be found in the experiments of Rawson & Quick (1972) who also worked on the sheep. These authors demonstrated that heating the abdominal viscera was followed by a rapid increase in respiratory frequency and that the response was entirely independent of temperature changes in the skin, spinal cord or hypothalamus. Furthermore, they showed that the response could be abolished by section of the splanchnic nerves. The existence of abdominal thermoreceptors could be affirmed from their results; the experiments indicated that the stimulated sites were not in the wall of the vena cava but probably located in the intestine and mesenteric veins. The afferent pathway for these receptors was in the splanchnic nerves.

TYPES OF FIBRES

Visceral afferent fibres are found in the parasympathetic and sympathetic divisions of the autonomic nerves. The task of identifying afferent fibres, many of which are non-myelinated, has been approached by several different methods. Using histological techniques, Daly & Evans (1953) identified myelinated afferents which had their cells of origin in the nodose ganglion. The cervical vagus of the cat was cut and the fibres allowed to degenerate. After fixing and staining with pyridine–silver, transverse sections were photographed and subsequently enlarged. Measurements of the fibres showed that they belonged to the group 1–14 μ. In an extension of this work (Agostoni *et al.*, 1957), the fibres in the abdominal branches of the vagus were counted in order to estimate the relative number of afferent and efferent fibres. Their results demonstrated that over 90 per cent of the fibres were afferent in function and that the great majority were non-myelinated and below 6 μ in diameter. Paintal (1954), as already mentioned, identified afferent fibres in the cervical vagus by recording impulse discharges during distension of the stomach with a balloon. Under the dissecting microscope the nerve trunk was divided into small strands and subdivided with needles until single action potentials were recorded. Conduction velocities were calculated from a range of fibres between 6 and 14 μ in diameter. Also using the single fibre technique, Iggo (1955) reported on vagal afferent discharges from the stomach with conduction velocities less than 2·5 m/sec, i.e. the afferent fibres were non-myelinated. Conduction velocities of the same order were obtained for afferent discharges recorded in the pelvic plexus during distension or active contraction of the urinary bladder. A technique developed by Douglas & Ritchie (1957) has given further information on the mass of non-myelinated afferent fibres in the vagus nerve. This technique depends on the observation that antidromic impulses evoked by electrical stimulation are extinguished by impulses initiated at the nerve endings. They found that spontaneous activity in the sensory nerves or the activity induced by stimulation of their endings caused a reduction in the size of the C wave of the compound action potential. No such reduction was found after removal of the alimentary tract and the authors considered that the majority of vagal C fibres arose from the abdominal viscera.

It is clear from the above investigations that the stomach is supplied with vagal afferent fibres, the majority of which are non-myelinated, and that they contribute to the C wave of the compound action potential. The fibres belong to the smallest diameter group with slow conduction velocities.

THE SPLANCHNIC NERVE COMPOUND ACTION POTENTIAL

When the splanchnic nerve is stimulated electrically and its action potential recorded on an oscilloscope, four main deflexions may be seen (Fig. 2.1).

1. A beta wave. The earliest wave to appear has a very low threshold. Some of the fibres are excited with stimulus intensities less than 1·0 V and duration 0·01 msec. As the intensity of the stimulus is increased above threshold a greater number of A beta fibres are excited until the maximum amplitude of the wave is reached. A beta fibres have the fastest conduction velocities (70–75 m/sec) and belong to the fibre group 6–10 μ in diameter. A small deflexion, representing a

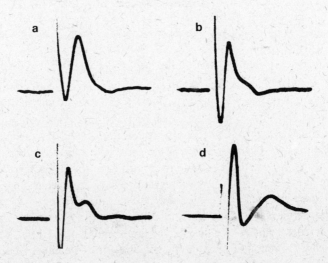

FIG. 2.1. Splanchnic nerve compound action potential. Various stages in the development of the A fibre potentials as the strength of stimulus is progressively increased. Further description in text.

slower conducting component, sometimes appears on the descending slope.

2. *A gamma–delta wave.* When the intensity of the stimulus is increased to above 2·0 V (0·01 msec duration) a second wave appears after the A beta is completed. The conduction velocity of the fibres ranges between 30 and 35 m/sec and the amplitude of the wave is smaller.

3. *B wave.* This is a large amplitude wave requiring a stimulus intensity of about 4·0 V and 0·05 msec pulse duration. The fibres belong to the range 1–3 μ in diameter with a conduction velocity of about 10 m/sec. The B wave represents activity in the preganglionic efferent fibres of the splanchnic nerve.

4. *C wave.* Seen only with high stimulus intensities and a pulse duration over 0·1 msec. The fibres are non-myelinated with a maximum conduction velocity of about 1–2·5 m/sec.

The compound action potential demonstrates that afferent fibres in the splanchnic nerve fall into three main groups—A beta, A delta and C—a classification originally suggested by Gernandt & Zotterman (1946).

THE PATHWAYS OF AFFERENT FIBRES IN THE SPLANCHNIC NERVES

In the cat, the splanchnic nerves leave the ganglia of the sympathetic trunk in a series of six to ten small branches. The first of this series corresponds to the greater splanchnic nerve in man. Some of the fibres originate from segments as high as the fifth thoracic and descend in the sympathetic trunk before emerging. Early efforts to trace the afferent component of the splanchnic nerves were made by histological examinations. Ranson & Billingsley (1918) showed that splanchnic afferents do not arise from the sympathetic ganglia but have their cells of origin in spinal ganglia. After section of the dorsal roots, all the preganglionic efferent fibres degenerated, but the afferent fibres were left intact; many of these were seen to be non-myelinated.

One of the difficulties in physiological investigation of afferent pathways was to find a reliable index which could be used to identify these pathways. Many workers examined the reflex changes produced by visceral stimulation including those involving the pathways for pain. Thus Schrager & Ivy (1928) reported that distension of the gall bladder in conscious dogs caused marked distress, inhibition of respiration and even vomiting. When, however, the right splanchnic nerve was cut or blocked with 70% alcohol, the distress was completely relieved. Attempts to trace the pathways from abdominal viscera were not very successful until the pupillary reactions were employed, although McDowall (1925) had already pointed out the value of the pupil as a physiological index.

In cats under chloralose anaesthesia, the pupil becomes constricted and any change in size can be readily detected through a low-power microscope. Stimulation of the central cut end of the splanchnic nerve causes immediate dilatation of the pupil. Using this response as an index of visceral activity, Bain, Irving & McSwiney (1935) demonstrated that afferent impulses are conducted into the spinal cord from the 3rd thoracic to the 1st lumbar segments inclusive. The afferent fibres pass through the sympathetic ganglia without any synapse, ascend in the splanchnic nerves or sympathetic chain to the spinal ganglia and thence via the dorsal roots of spinal nerves into the cord. They believed that pupillary dilatation was due mainly to inhibition of the oculomotor nucleus.

In an extension of this work Irving, McSwiney & Suffolk (1937) established that the stomach, duodenum and small intestine were sensitive to moderate degrees of distension produced by inflating a balloon with air. Dilatation of the pupil and reflex changes in blood pressure were observed in cats anaesthetized with chloralose and also in decerebrate and spinal animals. They failed to obtain pupillary reactions after the applications of 1% cocaine to the mesenteric border of the stomach and all the responses were abolished after section of the splanchnic nerves. The authors concluded that distension was an adequate stimulus and that the right and left splanchnic nerves were the main afferent pathway for impulses concerned in these reactions.

Downman (1952) investigated the distribution of afferent fibres in the mesenteric nerve bundles connecting the intestine to the spinal cord. He found that gentle pinches to the wall of the bowel elicited reflex pupillary dilatation and changes in arterial blood pressure. The nerve supply to a loop of small intestine was served by neurovascular bundles containing three functional types of fibres, namely, the reflexogenic afferent, and the vasoconstrictor and inhibitory efferent fibres. Whilst there was considerable overlap of the fields supplied by the primary mesenteric bundles, the territory of visceral afferent innervation in any loop was confined to a limited region between the centres of adjacent arterial arcades.

AFFERENT PATHWAYS FROM THE LARGE INTESTINE

The main function of the large intestine is to act as a terminal reservoir and to propel the contents to the exterior. It is insensitive to many forms of stimulation, but can give rise to a vague sensation of discomfort when moderately distended and to pain when over-distended. The sensations of fullness and discomfort might be caused simply by stretching of the mesentery. However, the pain of intestinal colic is more likely to arise from the bowel itself. The presence of chemical irritants in the bowel or drastic purgation results in vigorous peristalsis and excitation of nerve endings in the gut wall or mucosa.

Impulses from the large intestine reach the spinal cord by two routes:

1. From the colon, afferents are conveyed in the sympathetic system (a) fibres from the caecum, ascending colon and transverse colon pass through the coeliac and superior mesenteric ganglia; (b) fibres from the descending and pelvic colon pass through the inferior mesenteric and aortic ganglia. Both sets of fibres are conveyed by the splanchnic nerves to their cell stations in the dorsal root ganglia of the spinal nerves. Ray & Neill (1947) have described some clinical experiments which support the above statements. They introduced balloons into different segments of the colon in conscious patients and found that the pain caused by distension was abolished after bilateral sympathectomy. In spite of the fact that branches of the vagal nerves are distributed to the coeliac ganglia and mesenteric plexus, there is no evidence that afferent fibres from the colon are carried in the parasympathetic.

2. From the rectum, impulses are conveyed in the sacral division of the parasympathetic. The afferent pathway was investigated by Goligher & Hughes (1951). They demonstrated that rectal sensation was unaffected after bilateral sympathectomy but was abolished by low spinal anaesthesia which blocked the entrance of impulses in the pelvic nerves at the second and third sacral segments.

AFFERENT PATHWAYS FROM THE URINARY BLADDER

The nerves supplying the urinary bladder are derived from two sources:

(1) Sympathetic. The hypogastric nerves are formed from a collection of fibres lying in front of the sacrum, receiving contributions from the presacral nerve and lumbar ganglia. Each nerve ends in a corresponding hypogastric ganglion.

(2) Parasympathetic. The pelvic nerves arise from the second and third sacral segments and also join the hypogastric ganglia. Branches from the hypogastric ganglia are distributed to the pelvic organs.

Afferent fibres from the urinary bladder travel along both of these supply routes to gain access to the spinal cord. The surgical anatomy is of practical importance in operations on the pelvic viscera as the nerves are easily damaged and bladder sensation may be lost. Learmonth (1931) studied the effects of such injuries in patients, including lesions of the spinal cord, and classified his results as follows:

(i) Information regarding the degree of distension of the bladder is served by fibres which follow both of the routes described above.

(ii) Impulses set up by over-distension of the bladder generally follow the hypogastric route to reach the 12th thoracic and 1st lumbar segments of the cord. The hypogastric route is the principal route for all sensations culminating in pain, although a small proportion of the fibres may take the pelvic route to the sacrum.

(iii) Afferent fibres for tactile and thermal impressions are conveyed in the pelvic nerves to the sacral segments.

(iv) Afferent fibres concerned in the micturition reflex travel exclusively in the pelvic nerves. The hypogastic pathway is not essential for micturition.

There is good agreement between these results and those derived by other workers from laboratory experiments. Talaat (1937) investigated the responses of the bladder to different levels of intravesical pressure. In one series of experiments, the pelvic nerves of the dog were cut in a preliminary operation and allowed to degenerate. When electrodes were subsequently placed on the hypogastric nerves, slowly adapting discharges were recorded following a considerable rise of bladder pressure. In another series, the hypogastric nerves were cut and recordings obtained from the pelvic nerves in response to smaller but rapid changes in bladder pressure. Talaat concluded that afferents entering the sacral cord via the pelvic nerves were concerned with bladder function in micturition, whilst the main function of the hypogastric pathway was to carry impulses for pain. Iggo (1955) confirmed these observations, working with single fibre recordings in the cat. He found that passive distension of the bladder evoked a brief discharge of impulses in the pelvic nerves. As the fibres also responded to active contraction of the bladder wall, he thought that the role of slowly and rapidly adapting discharges was open for further investigation. Recently it has been shown that A delta afferents from the bladder take part in two kinds of reflexes which may be concerned in the regulation of bladder function—excitatory reflexes mediated by the sacral cord through the pelvic nerves and supraspinal inhibitory reflexes involving the hypogastric nerves (De Groat & Lalley, 1972).

SENSATIONS FROM ABDOMINAL VISCERA

The principal sensations aroused from abdominal viscera are hunger, fullness, discomfort, tenderness and pain.

Hunger

Hunger is associated with an empty or fasting stomach. If food is presented to a hungry animal it will usually feed. A measure of food intake is not, however, a reliable guide to the degree of hunger as feeding is regulated centrally. The sensation of hunger is the result of a complex interplay of many factors including the presence or absence of thirst, appetite, body temperature, environment and species behaviour. The question considered here concerns the role of the stomach itself—whether impulses originating in the stomach contribute more than a sensory stimulus to feeding reflexes.

Sherrington (1900) believed that the sensory nerve channel for the local sensation of hunger was the vagus nerve, but he could not rule out the splanchnic afferent channel. He emphasized that neither channel was essential for the occurrence of hunger, suggesting the possibility that the sensitivity of medullary neurones might be influenced by the nutritive condition of the circulating blood. Cannon & Washburn (1912), dismissing the idea that hunger might be of central origin, stated that hunger pangs were due to contractions of the stomach and other parts of the gut. This view was supported by the experiments of Carlson (1913) on the dog, who showed that hunger contractions were present in the empty stomach after complete section of splanchnic and vagal nerves. In reviewing the origin of hunger contractions, Alvarez (1950) expressed some doubt whether the records made by balloons were in fact due to genuine contractions of an empty stomach and whether they could be distinguished from the waves of normal digestion. Perhaps stomach contractions were not essential in order to experience hunger sensations. Additional support for these arguments comes from studies on patients who have been subjected to bilateral vagotomy for the treatment of peptic ulcer. Grossman & Stein (1948) observed that hunger sensations were unaltered after the operation. Even intense hunger, induced by the injection of insulin, continued to occur. Yet the operation had abolished all gastric contractions. They concluded that no pathways exist in the vagus nerves for the gastric origin of hunger sensation.

At the present time, the controversy is unresolved. Hunger is a very real sensation which is promptly relieved by food. On the one hand, there is evidence that gastric contractions stimulate sensory nerve endings in the stomach. As a result, a local sensation of 'emptiness' is referred to the epigastrium and interpreted as hunger. Impulses from the stomach are believed to travel in the vagal nerves; but hunger may occur in patients after bilateral vagotomy. There remains the possibility that the impulses are conveyed in splanchnic afferent pathways without, however, much evidence to support the idea. On the other hand, hypothalamic neurones are sensitive to changes in blood sugar concentration. When the blood sugar is lowered by starvation or by the administration of insulin, the activity of the hypothalamus is increased with consequent adjustments to the mechanisms under its control. Hunger sensation may be elaborated purely as a central effect without involving the stomach, as Sherrington suggested, or may be derived from gastric contractions following augmented vagal activity. Lack of agreement may have resulted from a failure to appreciate the complex nature of hunger sensation. Local reflexes from the stomach and hypothalamic sensory discharges are intimately bound up with each other. Loss of one source of stimulation, e.g. vagotomy, does not necessarily impair the experience of hunger.

Pain

A sensation of fullness or discomfort is commonly experienced after a large meal, when the bladder is full or the rectum loaded. It appears that the organs are sensitive to mild physiological stimuli, such as natural distension, although the symptoms are quickly relieved by emptying. If the stimulus becomes too great, discomfort is acute and the subject experiences pain. Any abdominal organ may give rise to pain when the parietal peritoneum is involved, e.g. inflammatory conditions which stimulate somatic sensory nerves. The viscera themselves, which possess a different form of innervation, and especially the hollow organs, are sensitive to increased tension in their muscular walls. Thus excessive distension or powerful muscular contractions may give rise to severe pain. The mesentery is also sensitive to stimuli which produce pain. Morley (1931) believed that the mesentery of the small intestine was supplied by somatic nerves up to a point close to its attachment to the bowel. This would explain the pain produced by adhesions or by traction on the roots of the mesentery when operations are performed under local anaesthesia. Morley's theory is supported by the fact that free nerve endings of myelinated nerves are found in the mesentery. Sheehan (1933) demonstrated their presence in the cat after dividing the vagi and splanchnic nerves and allowing them to degenerate. It could only be concluded that the nerve endings were somatic in origin. It is clear that abdominal pain is derived from a double innervation—somatic and visceral. Somatic pain originates from impulses in the parietal peritoneum and mesentery. Like cutaneous pain its character is sharp and accurately localized; it is often associated with tenderness and reflex muscular rigidity.

Visceral pain arises in nerve endings of small myelinated and non-myelinated fibres supplying the organs and the visceral peritoneum which covers them. It is characterized, initially, as a vague, deep-seated sensation, tending to become more violent unless relieved, but poorly localized or else referred to the mid-line of the abdomen; it is unaccompanied by tenderness or muscular rigidity. The plexus of non-myelinated fibres are terminals of afferents following the distribution of the splanchnic nerves, as demonstrated in the dissections made by Sheehan. However, animal experiments are unsatisfactory in the study of pain mechanisms and more reliable information has been obtained from clinical work. Thus Alvarez (1931) investigated the nerve pathways which must be cut or blocked by local anaesthesia to relieve abdominal pain in patients. He found that pain was promptly relieved by splanchnic blocking and permanent relief from pain was afforded by cutting the appropriate posterior nerve roots. Alvarez recognized the possibility of other pathways being concerned, e.g. vagal fibres from the stomach, phrenic fibres from the gall bladder, nerve plexuses accompanying blood vessels and entry into the spinal cord via anterior nerve roots. However, the role of these alternative pathways appeared to be negligible since operations on the upper part of the abdomen could be performed painlessly after splanchnic blocking. He concluded that vagal afferents and splanchnic afferents were no different from sensory nerves anywhere else in the body, but happened to travel in the same sheaths as the autonomic nerves. Numerous animal and clinical studies have since confirmed that the afferents for visceral pain from the abdomen do in fact travel in the splanchnic nerves.

SUMMARY

There can be little doubt that the abdominal viscera and their attachments are endowed with a high degree of sensitivity and possess a peripheral apparatus concerned with the conduction of impulses to the brain and spinal cord. Receptors, which are readily excited by mechanical and chemical stimuli, have been located by means of single fibre recordings. Pacinian corpuscles lie embedded in the substance of the mesentery and in the peritoneum covering the anterior and posterior abdominal walls. They are excited by slight, non-nocuous mechanical stimuli and their afferent discharges are carried in the splanchnic nerves. Tension-signalling receptors are found 'in series' with the contractile elements of smooth muscle, especially in the walls of the alimentary tract and urinary bladder. They are stimulated by passive distension or active contraction of the muscle. Other receptors, responding to chemical stimulation, have been traced in the gastrointestinal mucosa. Free nerve endings have also been located in the muscular walls and the mucous membranes; they give rise to a plexus of fine, non-myelinated fibres which mostly serve impulses for painful sensations. Visceral afferent fibres are conducted to the central nervous system within the sheaths of the parasympathetic and sympathetic division of the autonomic nerves. A high proportion of non-myelinated afferent fibres is found in the vagal branches from the stomach; a similar spectrum of afferent fibres in the pelvic nerves supplies the rectum and urinary bladder. Afferents in the splanchnic nerves, which supply most of the abdominal organs, have a broader spectrum of fibres ranging from large myelinated A beta fibres to small non-myelinated C fibres. Their cell stations are found in the dorsal root ganglia of the spinal nerves, but many devious routes are taken to reach them. The afferent pathways may enter the aortic and mesenteric plexuses or may pass through several ganglia of the sympathetic chain before joining the dorsal roots.

Some of the visceral afferent fibres take part in reflex adjustments of the autonomic and endocrine systems, acting either independently of or in conjunction with the somatic nervous system; others mediate the sensations of hunger and abdominal pain. Hunger is a psychological drive to eat, a subjective experience influenced by many diverse factors. Epigastric hunger sensation may be regarded as a local component of a complex process set up by nerve impulses originating in the stomach. The exact nature of the stimulus is still undecided. One hypothesis related hunger pangs to waves of gastric contractions; but hunger may be experienced in the absence of contractions after complete bilateral vagotomy.

Abdominal pain arises from somatic and visceral nerve endings. Somatic nerve endings are found in the mesentery and parietal peritoneum and the character of the pain is accordingly similar to that of the body wall—sharp and accurately localized. In contrast, pain sensation arising from the viscera is dull initially, deep-seated and poorly localized. Impulses for visceral pain are conducted in the A delta and C groups of splanchnic nerve afferents. The fibres follow the course of the sympathetic nerves, taking devious routes before reaching their cell stations and make no synapses outside the spinal cord. The distribution of splanchnic nerve afferents is the only peripheral route of practical importance in the surgical relief of pain.

REFERENCES

Agostoni, E., Chinnock, J. E., Daly, M. de Burgh & Murray, J. G. (57). Functional and histological studies of the vagus nerve and its branches to the heart, lungs and abdominal viscera in the cat. *J. Physiol.* **135**, 182–205.

Alvarez, W. C. (1931). Abdominal pain. *Am. J. Surg.* **14**, 385–394.

Alvarez, W. C. (1950). *An Introduction to Gastro-enterology,* Heinemann, London.

Andrews, C. J. H., Andrews, W. H. H. & Orbach, J. (1972). A sympathetic reflex elicited by distension of the mesenteric venous bed. *J. Physiol.* **226**, 119–131.

Bain, W. A., Irving, J. T. & McSwiney, B. A. (1935). The afferent fibres from the abdomen in the splanchnic nerves. *J. Physiol.* **84**, 323–333.

Bessou, P. & Perl, E. R. (1966). A movement receptor of the small intestine. *J. Physiol.* **182**, 404–426.

Bligh, J. (1959). The receptors concerned in the thermal stimulus to panting in sheep. *J. Physiol.* **146**, 142–151.

Bligh, J. (1963). The receptors concerned in the respiratory response to humidity in sheep at high ambient temperature. *J. Physiol.* **168**, 747–763.

Cannon, W. B. & Washburn, A. L. (1912). An explanation of hunger. *Am. J. Physiol.* **29**, 441–454.

Carlson, A. J. (1913). A study of the mechanisms of the hunger contractions of the empty stomach by experiments in dogs. *Am. J. Physiol.* **32**, 369–397.

Daly, M. de Burgh & Evans, D. H. L. (1953). Functional and histological changes in the vagus nerve of the cat after degenerative section at various levels. *J. Physiol.* **120**, 579–595.

De Groat, W. C. & Lalley, P. M. (1972). Reflex firing in the lumbar sympathetic outflow to activation of vesical afferent fibres. *J. Physiol.* **226**, 289–309.

Douglas, W. W. & Ritchie, J. M. (1957). On excitation of non-medullated afferent fibres in the vagus and aortic nerves by pharmacological agents. *J. Physiol.* **138**, 31–43.

Downman, C. B. B. (1952). Distribution along the small intestine of afferent, vasoconstrictor and inhibitory fibres in the mesenteric nerve bundles. *J. Physiol.* **116**, 228–235.

Gernandt, B. & Zotterman, Y. (1946). Intestinal pain: An electrophysiological investigation on mesenteric nerves. *Acta physiol. scand.* **12**, 56–72.

Goligher, J. C. & Hughes, E. S. R. (1951). Sensibility of the rectum and colon. *Lancet* **1**, 543–547.

Grossman, M. E. & Stein, I. F. (1948). Vagotomy and the hunger-producing action of insulin in man. *J. appl. Physiol.* **1**, 263–269.

Iggo, A. (1955). Tension receptors in the stomach and urinary bladder. *J. Physiol.* **128**, 593–607.

Iggo, A. (1957). Gastric mucosal chemoreceptors with vagal afferent fibres in the cat. *Quart. Jl exp. Physiol.* **42**, 398–409.

Irving, J. T., McSwiney, B. A. & Suffolk, S. F. (1937). Afferent fibres from the stomach and small intestine. *J. Physiol.* **89**, 407–420.

Learmouth, J. R. (1931). A contribution to the neurophysiology of the urinary bladder in man. *Brain* **54**, 147–176.

McDowall, R. J. S. (1925). The reaction of the pupil in the chloralosed animal. *Quart. Jl exp. Physiol.* **15**, 177–180.

Morley, J. (1931). *Abdominal Pain.* Livingstone, Edinburgh.

Morrison, J. F. B. (1972). Mechanoreceptors in the region of the mesentery with A delta and C fibres in the splanchnic nerves of cats. *J. Physiol.* **226**, 100–101P.

Paintal, A. S. (1954a). A method of locating the receptors of visceral afferent fibres. *J. Physiol.* **124**, 166–172.

Paintal, A. S. (1954b). A study of gastric receptors. Their role in the peripheral mechanism of satiation of hunger and thirst. *J. Physiol.* **126**, 255–270.

Ranson, S. W. & Billingsley, P. R. (1918). An experimental analysis of the sympathetic trunk and greater splanchnic nerve in the cat. *J. comp. Neurol.* **29**, 441–456.

Rawson, R. O. & Quick, K. P. (1972). Localization of intra-abdominal thermoreceptors in the ewe. *J. Physiol.* **222**, 665–677.

Ray, B. S. & Neill, C. L. (1947). Abdominal visceral sensation in man. *Ann. Surg.* **126**, 709–724.

Schrager, V. L. & Ivy, A. C. (1928). Symptoms produced by distension of the gall bladder and biliary ducts. *Surgery Gynec. Obstet.* **47**, 1–13.

Sharma, K. N. & Nassett, E. S. (1962). Electrical activity in mesenteric nerves after perfusion of gut lumen. *Am. J. Physiol.* **202**, 725–730.

Sheehan, D. (1933). The afferent nerve supply of the mesentery and its significance in the causation of abdominal pain. *J. Anat.* **67**, 233–248.

Sherrington, C. S. (1900). In *Textbook of Physiology*, edited by Schafer, E. A., Vol. 2, p. 991. Young J. Pentland, Edinburgh and London.

Talaat, M. (1937). Afferent impulses in the nerves supplying the urinary bladder. *J. Physiol.* **89**, 1–13.

3

VISCERAL REFLEXES MEDIATED
BY THE SPINAL CORD

DURING the last decade research on the functional organization of the spinal cord has led to a revival of interest in the classical work of Sherrington and his pupils on the principles of reflex action. The clinical application of these studies deals with the recovery of function after the cord has been damaged or severed from its connexions with the brain; the need for research into the management of such casualties has unfortunately increased. Immediately after a complete transection there is loss of all neurological signs below the level of the lesion. This is the period of inactivity known as acute spinal shock, which, though of relatively short duration in animals, may last up to three weeks in man. Depression of spinal centres may be due to a combination of factors:

(i) Interruption of facilitatory influences especially those in the reticulo-spinal and cortico-spinal tracts.
(ii) Persistence of inhibitory influences in the isolated cord.
(iii) Progressive degeneration of internuncial neurones.

The clinical picture tends to vary according to the level of the lesion and the extent of damage. At first, there is absence of tone in all affected muscles, including the smooth muscles of blood vessels, bowel and bladder. The distal part of the cord carries out no reflex activities; skeletal muscles are paralysed, voluntary movement and micturition are impossible and there is complete loss of sensation. Recovery of reflex activity emerges with the appearance of the ipsilateral flexor response, elicited by a strong stimulus and, shortly afterwards, reflex contraction takes place in the bladder, accompanied by relaxation of the sphincters. The result is that the bladder is emptied without knowledge of its distension or conscious control by the patient—a condition known as 'automatic bladder'. Tone may also return to the lower bowel and rectum with regular attempts at reflex evacuation. Recovery of vasomotor activity allows the blood pressure to return to normal levels and sweating occurs in the previously dry skin. Obviously, the re-establishment of visceral reflexes is of great importance not only to those responsible for the management and after-care of the patient, but also for assessment of his progress and eventual rehabilitation.

Experimental studies of visceral reflexes are carried out on intact animals under general anaesthesia, on decerebrated animals when the anaesthetic has worn off, on spinal animals under anaesthesia and on chordotomized animals after decerebration. Other methods of study employ local cooling of the spinal cord and animals with chronic spinal lesions. It is important to exercise care in drawing conclusions from laboratory investigations as reflexes elicited in the spinal animal are not necessarily examples of normal mechanisms, whilst the act of decerebration results in a loss of both excitatory and inhibitory effects. Two kinds of reflex responses have been found most useful in the investigation of visceral afferent functions in the cord—viscero-vascular and viscero-motor reactions. Other possible actions, such as temperature changes and sweating, have also been described. Thus, stimulating an abdominal organ or the afferent nerves supplying it may bring about vasoconstriction and rise in arterial blood pressure; in addition, the impulses may elicit reflex contraction of skeletal muscle and movements of limbs.

CHANGES IN ARTERIAL BLOOD PRESSURE FOLLOWING STIMULATION OF THE GALL BLADDER

To investigate this response in cats under sodium pentobarbital anaesthesia or in decerebrate and spinal preparations, the gall bladder was distended by means of a balloon whilst recording the blood pressure from a femoral or carotid artery. No significant change in blood pressure occurred until a threshold degree of distension was reached; thereafter, as the distension of the gall bladder increased, a progressive rise in blood pressure was recorded (Fig. 3.1). The maximum rise of blood pressure observed was about 50 mm Hg. On deflation of the balloon, the blood pressure returned slowly to its original level. The procedure could be repeated many times. It was not dependent on impulses in the vagus nerves, but the reflex was abolished after section of the right splanchnic nerve. If only the left splanchnic nerve was cut, the blood pressure response was reduced by about a half. The response was also modified by evisceration, the results depending on the extent of the operation. For example, excision of the alimentary tract from the duodenum to the rectum had only a small effect on the response. A further reduction occurred after total evisceration of the gut, including the mesentery, omentum and spleen.

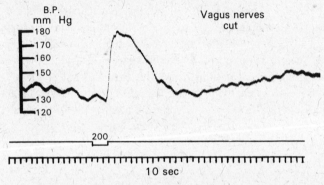

FIG. 3.1. Blood pressure response to distension of the gall bladder. Anaesthetized cat. Vagi cut. On inflation of the balloon there is a marked rise in arterial blood pressure which is partly reflex and partly due to the discharge of adrenaline.

In experiments in which the adrenal glands alone were tied or removed, distension of the gall bladder still produced a rise in blood pressure; but the rise was not as great and the response was not maintained. On the other hand, removal of the adrenal glands together with total evisceration of the gut abolished the reflex changes altogether. It was concluded that impulses set up by distension of the gall bladder proceed in the right splanchnic nerve to the spinal cord where the vasomotor reflex arcs are excited. Since the splanchnic vascular bed and adrenal glands are supplied bilaterally by the efferent pathways, the rise in blood pressure represents initial vasoconstrictor activity reinforced by the discharge of adrenaline.

Viscero-vascular reflexes have been described in many experimental studies on spinal autonomic mechanisms. Downman & McSwiney (1946) elicited the response by pinching the intestine with forceps, squeezing the bowel or pulling on the mesentery. They examined the differences in decerebrate cats before and after cutting the spinal cord, observing the relatively increased activity of the visceral reflex in spinal animals. This observation is important because somatic reflexes are generally reduced in the spinal animal and increased in the decerebrate. The idea that visceral reflexes have a central organization somewhat different from that of somatic reflexes has been further developed by Franz, Evans & Perl (1966). These authors applied single shocks to the central cut end of the splanchnic nerve and recorded from sympathetic preganglionic fibres. The discharges evoked by the splanchnic nerve were similar to those evoked by cutaneous stimulation, but the latency was considerably longer due to greater internuncial delay. Monosynaptic responses were not seen. Splanchnic impulses may spread through many segments of the cord by a relatively fast-conducting pathway in the sympathetic chain; if this is cut, the intraspinal route can be shown to be slower and complicated. Hence splanchnic evoked discharges are characterized by prolonged after-discharge whilst cutaneous evoked discharges are not. Another difference was the fact that, following the effects of asphyxia, the splanchnic evoked discharges persisted for some minutes after the cutaneous reflexes had failed.

VISCERO-MOTOR REFLEXES

Afferent impulses from abdominal viscera can reflexly elicit contractions of skeletal muscle. Muscular rigidity in visceral disease affords protection to the underlying inflamed organs. The patient frequently draws up his legs to diminish intra-abdominal pressure and relieve pain. These actions may be regarded as protective reflexes. To test their reflex origin Miller (1924) made myographic recordings of the diaphragm, muscles of the abdominal wall and hind limb muscles in the spinal cat. He showed that faradic stimulation of mesenteric nerves or distension of the stomach caused increased tone or contraction of the muscles involved. To test the hypothesis that antagonistic muscles in a spinal reflex would be inhibited, Dusser de Barenne & Ward (1937) investigated viscero-motor responses in the chronic spinal monkey. They found that distension of the gall bladder or a loop of intestine resulted in disappearance of the knee jerk. Thus the effects were analogous to inhibition of extensor reflexes by antagonistic flexors.

Downman & McSwiney (1946) believed that the viscero-motor reflexes did not involve the same spinal arcs as the viscero-vascular reflexes but were dependent upon a comparable spinal organization. In subsequent work Downman (1955) recorded the reflex response from intercostal nerves in the decerebrate and acute spinal cat. When a threshold stimulus was delivered to the splanchnic nerve, discharges were found only in the lower intercostal nerves, whereas a stronger stimulus allowed the spread of impulses into upper thoracic levels and even to the opposite side of the cord. The irradiation of impulses was much faster and more extensive than similar responses produced by stimulating an adjacent intercostal nerve. Interaction between splanchnic and cutaneous afferents was also demonstrated. The results suggested that afferent fibres in the splanchnic nerve had widespread polysynaptic connexions in the spinal cord; activity was conducted rapidly through the internuncial system to spinal motoneurones innervating the musculature of the trunk.

The effects of splanchnic afferent impulses on the hind-limb reflexes in the cat have been studied by Evans & McPherson (1958). The reflex discharge elicited by the sciatic nerve were recorded from a lumbar ventral root. Using the splanchnic nerve for conditioning and the sciatic nerve for testing, they found that the monosynaptic test response was almost invariably facilitated. From Fig. 3.2 it will be seen that facilitation began when the interval between conditioning and testing stimuli was about 25 msec; maximal effects were observed at 35–40 msec whilst the effects disappeared with intervals longer than 60 msec. In contrast, when a polysynaptic reflex was elicited, the test response was partially or totally inhibited by a preceding splanchnic stimulus. No explanation was offered by the authors to account for the opposite effects observed.

It has already been noted that descending impulses from the brain stem have an important influence on spinal reflex arcs and that while somatic reflexes are facilitated, visceral reflexes are generally inhibited. In order to demonstrate this difference between decerebrate and spinal animals, Downman & Hussain (1958) attempted to locate the inhibitory spinal pathway involved. They compared the size of the reflex response before and after cutting through the dorsal half of the cord at the level of the 6th cervical segment. They found that the response was greatly enhanced after dorsal hemisection and that no further change occurred when the ventral half was subsequently cut.

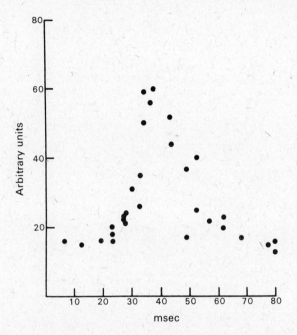

FIG. 3.2. Graph showing facilitation of the monosynaptic test response by a conditioning stimulus applied to the splanchnic nerve. The amplitude of the responses is plotted against the time-interval between the two stimuli. Facilitatory effects occur at C–T intervals between 25 and 60 msec with maximal responses at 35 msec. (Evans & McPherson, 1958, Fig. 3.)

The authors concluded that spinal cord transection caused release of reflex arcs from an inhibitory pathway in the dorsal part of the cord. In other experiments, they confirmed the different effects of interaction between afferents in decerebrate and spinal preparations, but did not extend their investigations to include the activity of interneurones. The conclusion which may be drawn from all these experiments is that splanchnic afferents converge with cutaneous and proprioceptive afferents in an extensive network of neurones involving the cells of the dorsal horn and their internuncial connexions.

SPLANCHNIC AFFERENT PATHWAYS

Methods of investigation

There are many ways in which the spinal pathways of the visceral reflexes can be studied. Histological examination has revealed variation in size, shape and distribution of the cell populations in the grey matter and their functional correlation has been attempted by observing the responses evoked in a particular group of cells when a peripheral nerve was stimulated. Electrophysiological techniques for the study of individual cell discharges offer the advantage of allowing extremely accurate measurements of reflex events and a good deal of information has been derived from recordings of the current fields during the intraspinal course of the action potentials. By means of conditioning stimuli it can be shown that the same cell may be influenced from more than one afferent source and this relates directly to synaptic convergence along the path of the reflex. Although the interpretation of electrical recordings is often dependent upon a host of experimental variables, this method of investigation is at present being most successfully pursued. By comparison, the more traditional methods for tracing visceral pathways in the cord may seem crude and indirect. All the same, the pupillo-dilator response, mentioned in the previous chapter, is still usefully employed as an index of activity following afferent volleys in the splanchnic nerve. More commonly, the cord may be explored for evoked potentials by inserting electrodes at different sites until a consistent response to stimulation is obtained. Successive lesions are then made below the level of the recording electrode until the response is completely abolished. In this way it is possible to ascertain the channels or tracts through which the response operated. Another method of tracing the pathways of splanchnic afferent impulses is by making sections through the cord in a conditioning-testing experiment. For example, apply a conditioning stimulus to the splanchnic nerve and a testing stimulus to a cutaneous nerve. Adjust the interval between the stimuli (e.g. 40 msec) until the test response is completely inhibited. Now make discrete lesions through the cord at different sites below the recording electrodes until the test response is restored. In this way the route taken by the splanchnic impulses can be determined.

The arrangement of cells in the dorsal horn

Rexed (1952), reporting on the various types of cells found in the spinal cord of the cat, described 9 laminations subdividing the grey matter from dorsal to ventral surfaces. Cells in laminar 5 of this classification belong to the projections of A delta splanchnic fibres. It is generally assumed that A beta splanchnic fibres do not terminate in the region of the dorsal horn and have no share in generating local visceral reflexes. Pomeranz, Wall & Weber (1968) studied the electrical properties of laminar 5 cells by recording the activity of single units responding to splanchnic nerve stimulation. Their results showed that splanchnic afferent impulses reached the ventral part of the dorsal horn at a conduction velocity of 10–30 m/sec. Many units responded to single shock stimulation by firing repetitively for as long as 16 msec. In studying the effects of interaction, a splanchnic conditioning stimulus usually inhibited a cutaneous test response for periods lasting up to 150 msec. Yet it was interesting to note that on reversing the sequence of stimulation, cutaneous conditioning failed to inhibit splanchnic-evoked responses—an observation that certainly does not apply to the cerebellum or cerebral cortex. One explanation for this finding may be that the cells belonging to different laminations in the dorsal horn have distinct physiological properties. Good evidence in support of laminar separation may be deduced from the work of Armett, Gray & Palmer (1961), who described both short and long-latency units in the dorsal horn indicating the existence of separate groups of cells. A latency difference of 1·5 msec between the responses of laminar 4 and laminar 5 was described by Wall (1967) and if it is accepted that cutaneous afferents terminate on cells in laminar 4, they could excite the cells of laminar 5 by means of short interneurones. Thus convergence of cutaneous and splanchnic afferents on the cells in laminar 5 is satisfactorily explained.

Activity of spinal interneurones

Interneuronal activity may be defined as the activity of connecting elements between input and output systems. In the spinal cord they form simple or complex chains extending from the dorsal surface of the cord to the ventral borders of the anterior horns. Whilst they may discharge impulses in the absence of applied stimulation, the resting discharge can be readily modified by descending influences or by impulses from the periphery. Much of the information on the properties of interneurones has been derived from studies of somatic reflexes elicited by cutaneous and muscle nerves. Thus Frank & Fuortes (1956) found that the majority of spinal interneurones could be excited by afferent stimulation. The typical response to a single shock was a short high-frequency burst or sustained firing at 200/sec. Some interneurones were inhibited by prolonged stimulation, followed by an excitatory burst when the stimulus ceased. All sensory information is offered opportunities for excitatory or inhibitory action at each synaptic relay during transmission through interneuronal pathways. There is evidence that impulses take different routes through the network according to their modality, but considerable convergence must also occur. Thus low-threshold muscle afferents concerned with the control of movement have a virtually independent pathway to alpha and gamma motoneurones. A second system, including cutaneous and high threshold muscle afferents, operates a different part of the network (Eccles, Kostyuk & Schmidt, 1962a). There is no evidence that a third system for visceral afferent fibres actually exists and it can only be assumed that they converge on the same interneurones by separate synapses. Presynaptic inhibition can occur at these sites. Selzer & Spencer (1967) have shown that A delta afferents in the caudal sympathetic chain can depolarize presynaptic cutaneous fibres resulting in a prolonged depression lasting up to 300 msec. There are as yet no reports that A beta afferents have similar actions on interneurones.

Activity in the dorsal columns

Electrophysiological observations on sensory activity in the dorsal columns began with the evidence of Gasser & Graham (1933) that an afferent volley in a dorsal root produced a slow negative–positive wave extending over the dorsum of the cord. The origin and analysis of this electrical change have been investigated subsequently by systematic examination of the various components generating current flow within the spinal cord. There is general agreement that all varieties of afferent flow produce dorsal cord potentials (Bernhard, 1953; Coombs, Curtis & Landgren, 1956; Fernandez de Molina & Gray, 1957) and that the positive phase is recorded dorsally, the negative phase ventrally. Eccles, Kostyuk & Schmidt (1962a) constructed a diagram of the field potentials produced by active depolarization of cutaneous fibres entering the cord from the dorsal roots. The negative phase was recorded at a depth of 1 to 2 mm below the surface in the region corresponding to the cells of origin of ascending tracts.

Cord potentials produced by splanchnic afferent volleys have been described by Widen (1955) in attempting to trace the pathways of splanchnic impulses to the cerebellum. He found that the slow negative potential from the dorsum of the cord was a product of the high threshold A delta fibres and concluded that the A beta group of splanchnic afferents made no contribution to this pathway. In support of Widen's statement, it had already been calculated that the conduction velocity of the splanchnic impulses was in the range 22–36 m/sec (Aidar, Geohegan & Ungewitten, 1952). However, it is now well established that the faster conducting fibres in the splanchnic projections are also conveyed in the dorsal columns. Amassian (1951) described the representation of splanchnic afferent impulses in the cerebral cortex. The primary waves evoked by stimulation of the A beta group of fibres were permanently abolished after section of the dorsal columns at the level of C2, but remained unaltered if only the anterior and lateral columns were sectioned. By recording the cord potentials, he found that the A beta afferents were located in a narrow strip of the ipsilateral dorsal column, close to the mid-line. The conduction velocity ranged between 45 and 54 m/sec. Amassian also made the interesting observation, which has recently been confirmed (Newman & Paul, 1969), that at least 30 per cent of the A beta group of splanchnic afferents did not ascend in the dorsal columns. Further confirmation of the splanchnic afferent pathways in the spinal cord of the cat has come from the work of Downman & Evans (1957) using microelectrode recordings. These authors found that the response evoked by stimulating A beta fibres in the splanchnic nerve had a centre of maximum activity in a compact region partly in fasciculus gracilis, partly in fasciculus cuneatus and that the region was entirely ipsilateral. Evidence that the A beta and A delta fibre groups form two independent projection systems will be presented in Chapter 5.

Activity in the ventrolateral columns

Unlike the dorsal column pathway, the distribution of splanchnic afferents elsewhere in the cord is widely scattered. The location of points where splanchnic impulses have been detected has shown that many alternative routes are available and destruction of some of these routes will often leave many others intact. Hence the difficulty in accurate mapping of splanchnic afferent pathways. Thus the route taken by splanchnic impulses to the cerebellum may be quite different from the splanchnic projections to the cerebral cortex. As suggested above, the A beta fibres may form an independent system distinct from the A delta group of fibres, whilst the ascending pathway of high threshold C fibres is still relatively unknown. It may well be that the organization of splanchnic projections is not discretely anatomical and studies might be more profitably directed to determining systems rather than pathways.

There is nevertheless general agreement that impulses originating in the A delta group of splanchnic afferents ascend on both sides of the spinal cord. Amassian (1951) recorded bilateral evoked potentials in the ventrolateral region of the cervical cord close to the grey matter. Essentially similar results were obtained by Widen (1955), recording from different segmental levels of the spinal cord. At a stimulus strength capable of exciting the delta fibres of the splanchnic nerve, the fastest conduction velocity was about 20 m/sec. Downman & Evans (1957) explored the ventrolateral columns at the level of the 2nd and 3rd cervical segments: responses were recorded bilaterally, but appeared to be more concentrated in the contralateral column and all had conduction velocities between 20 and 30 m/sec. The evidence, therefore, points to the existence of at least two projection systems which carry impulses from abdominal viscera to the brain:

1. A fast-conducting pathway occupying a discrete region of the ipsilateral dorsal column; the fibres comprising this pathway have the largest diameter, the lowest threshold and belong to the A beta group of afferents in the splanchnic nerve.

2. A slower conducting, diffuse pathway ascending bilaterally in the ventrolateral columns; this pathway comprises the A gamma-delta group of splanchnic afferents. In subsequent chapters, an account will be found of the central organization of the splanchnic projections, together with their terminal destinations and functions.

VISCERAL REFLEXES FROM PELVIC ORGANS

The pelvic viscera have a double afferent innervation. Fibres distributed with the parasympathetic outflow enter the spinal cord at the level of the sacral segments; other afferent fibres traverse the hypogastric plexus and sympathetic chain to join the splanchnic nerves (see Chapter 2). In the spinal cord, pelvic afferents have considerable action on local reflexes, influencing changes in blood pressure, heart rate, sweating, skin and body temperature; they are also capable of producing facilitatory and inhibitory effects on somatic reflex arcs.

Vasomotor reflexes

Changes in arterial blood pressure have been reported by various authors following distension of a pelvic organ, especially the bladder and rectum. Frequent clinical observations have also been made on the fall of blood pressure which may follow sudden emptying of the chronically distended bladder. Watkins (1938) observed a rise of blood pressure in cats on distending the bladder with warm saline; on the other hand, distension of the rectum by means of a balloon produced a fall in blood pressure. These reflex effects were not altered by cutting the vagi or tying the adrenal glands. Similar changes in blood pressure were reported by Talaat (1937), who recorded a steady impulse discharge in the hypogastric nerve of the anaesthetized dog when the bladder was over-distended; cutting the pelvic nerve had no effect, but section of the hypogastric nerve abolished the reflex. Guttman & Whitteridge (1947) studied the effects of bladder distension on patients with severe lesions of the spinal cord. The bladder was filled through a suprapubic drainage tube with saline or 0·5% acetic acid solution at body temperature. They found that in all spinal lesions above L2 distension of the bladder caused reflex vasoconstriction in the toes; in patients with complete transections above the level of T5, there was vasoconstriction of fingers and toes accompanied by a large rise in blood pressure. In addition, they observed that marked sweating in the upper extremities and face was a prominent feature. Extending these observations to the acute spinal cat Mukherjee (1957a) demonstrated that the vasopressor response involved reflex vasoconstriction of the splanchnic and renal vascular beds.

It is evident from all these experiments that the isolated spinal cord is capable of carrying out a large-scale redistribution of the blood by means of reflex responses to pelvic afferent stimulation. The rise in blood pressure, however, is not so marked in the intact animal since the vasomotor reflexes are probably modified by the 'buffer' action of the carotid sinus and aortic baroceptors. After denervation of the baroceptors the rise in blood pressure might be increased by over 50 per cent (Taylor, 1963).

Viscero-somatic reflexes

Head & Riddock (1917) and Riddock (1917) have given a classical description of the automatic bladder and rectum in their studies on military patients suffering from gross injuries to the spinal cord. Injecting fluid into either of these organs evoked characteristic flexor spasms of the abdominal muscles and lower limbs. Barclay & Franklin (1937) reported on the reflex contraction of the diaphragm and abdominal muscles when the bladder was manually compressed or when the rectum was suddenly distended. Similar observations were made by Mellanby & Pratt (1940) on anaesthetized or decerebrate cats. The reflex contractions which they studied were those elicited by changes of the bladder from the isotonic to the isometric state and involved the shoulder girdle in addition to the muscles of the abdominal wall. All the reflex contractions were abolished after section of the pelvic nerves.

Further studies on viscero-somatic reflexes and their underlying mechanisms have been carried out in a long series of experiments by Evans & McPherson (1958, 1959). The earlier part of their work, which dealt with myographic recordings of hind-limb muscles in the cat, emphasized the differences between anaesthetized, decerebrate and acute spinal preparations. In animals under chloralose anaesthesia, moderate distension of the bladder caused diminished amplitude of flexor and crossed extensor reflexes with decrease of muscle tone while, in decerebrate animals, reflex activity and muscle tone were enhanced. If high intravesical pressures were used, the reflexes were diminished in the decerebrate animal, but increased in the spinal animal. These results suggested that impulses set up by distending the bladder could exert both excitatory and inhibitory effects on spinal motoneurones and that the excitatory effects produced by over-distension of the bladder were due to inherent spinal mechanisms released from the influence of higher centres.

In later experiments, Evans & McPherson (1960) investigated the effects of interaction between pelvic afferent impulses and mono-synaptic and polysynaptic reflex responses recorded from lumbar and upper sacral ventral roots. They found that the somatic reflexes were facilitated by a preceding conditioning stimulus delivered to the pelvic nerve and obtained maximal effects when the interval between the two stimuli was about 40 msec. With intervals greater than 65 msec between conditioning and testing stimuli, the reflex responses were inhibited. Thus the effects on somatic motoneurones were similar to those observed when the splanchnic nerve was used for conditioning. In subsequent work Evans & McPherson (1963) suggested that some of the effects produced might be due to a direct visceral influence on the gamma efferent discharge to skeletal muscles. By recording action potentials from small fascicles of motor nerves or from single unit pre-parations of the lumbo-sacral dorsal roots, the authors demonstrated a reduction in gamma efferent activity when the bladder was distended, followed by a return of activity as soon as the bladder was emptied. These changes occurred in decerebrate preparations and also when the animal was under sodium pentobarbitone anaesthesia. Depression of gamma activity, sometimes lasting several minutes, was the dominant change observed. Occasionally, however, bladder distension caused an increase of gamma activity especially with low intravesical pressures. This was an interesting observation as different results had already been reported by Abdulla & Eldred (1959), working on unanaesthetized spinal cats. The latter authors had studied the activity of gamma efferents supplying hind-limb flexor muscles during filling of the bladder with warm saline. Their results showed an increased frequency of gamma efferent discharge with increasing degrees of bladder distension. The response appeared to be consistent; it could be maintained for periods lasting over 15 minutes and it was also present in the decerebrate animal.

Variability in experimental results can be partly explained by differences in techniques. In considering results based on the acute spinal animal, attention should be paid to the level of blood pressure,

which may be considerably reduced, to the persistence of depression
due to spinal shock and to the possibility that the cord has not been
cleanly divided. After recovery from spinal shock, the isolated spinal
segments may exhibit heightened excitability due to release from
higher centres. The decerebrate animal maintains a more stable blood
pressure; but the brain stem mechanisms, reinforced by those of the
cerebellum, can exert a powerful and variable influence on spinal
reflex arcs. In studies based on the intact animal, much depends on the
choice of anaesthetic and the depth of anaesthesia at the time of
recording. Bearing these points in mind a search of the literature will
frequently reveal evidence of conflicting data. There is obviously no
simple relationship between the input from the viscera and the reflex
responses mediated by the spinal cord.

The part played by reflexes in the regulation of bladder function has
recently been re-examined by De Groat & Lalley (1972) in
experiments performed on chloralosed cats. These authors showed
that electrical stimulation of A delta afferent fibres or distension of the
urinary bladder by injection of small volumes of fluid elicited reflex
responses in the lumbar sympathetic outflow; the afferents reached the
sacral cord via the pelvic nerves. The response was observed in
animals with an intact spinal cord and also in acute spinal and chronic
spinal animals. In experiments with the spinal cord intact, low
frequency stimulation of the central end of the pelvic nerve always
elicited a lumbar sympathetic discharge, but at higher frequencies or
during active bladder contraction (mediated by firing the sacral
parasympathetic), the reflex was markedly reduced or completely
suppressed. When, however, the spinal cord was transected at level
T10–T12 inhibition of the reflex was no longer obtained and the
micturition reflexes were also absent. Instead, the vesico-sympathetic
reflex was enhanced. These findings indicated that facilitation as well
as depression of sympathetic firing accompanied reflex micturition.
The authors accordingly concluded that two populations of neurones
were concerned in the responses to impulses from the bladder: one
population being excited through a spinal pathway, the other
depressed by processes which were cut off after spinal transection.

SUMMARY

All the essential features of reflex visceral activity can be demonstrated in man after complete transection of the spinal cord. Some weeks after the injury the patient is able to maintain a reasonable level of blood pressure, sweating occurs over areas of skin innervated by isolated spinal segments and tone returns to the bladder and rectum, allowing reflex evacuation of these organs. As influences from higher centres are eliminated, the reflex functions are mediated entirely by spinal arcs. If the reflex mechanisms are examined in the spinal animal it is found that synaptic excitability is increased for most visceral inputs. Thus a rise in arterial blood pressure occurs when a viscus is distended, stimulation of a visceral afferent nerve causes considerable irradiation of impulses over many segments of the cord, viscero-somatic responses are facilitated and widespread 'mass reflexes' may follow a single stimulus.

Vascular changes are brought about mainly by vasoconstriction of the splanchnic and renal blood vessels. The impulses set up by moderate distension or light mechanical stimuli are conveyed in the afferent fibres of the hypogastric and splanchnic nerves to the dorsal roots. Reflex arcs are completed by complex pathways involving many segments on both sides of the cord. The efferent fibres pass in the vasomotor nerves supplying the blood vessels and adrenal glands. Viscero-somatic reactions may be regarded as protective reflexes involving muscles of the abdominal wall, diaphragm and lower extremities. At some point in the reflex network impulses from visceral and somatic nerves converge on the same motoneurones with the result that large interaction fields can be demonstrated. Facilitation occurs with monosynaptic test responses elicited by stimulation of muscle afferents; maximal effects are seen when activation of each pathway is separated by an interval of about 40 msec, the effects persisting for as long as 65 msec. Inhibitory interaction occurs with polysynaptic test responses elicited by stimulating cutaneous afferents. There are indications from work involving cutaneous and high threshold muscle afferents that prolonged depression of the test response may be an example of presynaptic inhibition (Eccles et al., 1962b).

Investigations on the action of afferent volleys in the splanchnic nerve have led to the conclusion that A beta and A delta afferents belong to functionally different systems. The A beta group of splanchnic afferents does not terminate on cells in the dorsal horn and apparently takes little or no part in the mediation of spinal reflexes. The majority of the fibres occupies a circumscribed part of the ipsilateral dorsal columns and represents a fast-conducting pathway destined for localized points in the cerebellum and cerebral cortex. The A delta splanchnic afferents, on the other hand, are widely scattered in the cord. Their fibres converge on cells in the ventral part of the dorsal horn from which arises a vast network of connexions through interneurones, many of which are common to the reflex pathways of cutaneous and muscle afferents. Ascending tracts in the ventrolateral columns of the cord provide a separate, slower conducting route to various parts of the brain.

Afferents from the pelvic viscera exert a powerful influence on vascular and somatic spinal reflexes. Two pathways have been distinguished. One traverses the hypogastric plexus to join the sympathetic chain and splanchnic nerve; the other follows the distribution of the parasympathetic outflow to the sacral segments. Both are capable of modifying synaptic potentials by facilitation or inhibition. Vascular reflexes can be elicited by distension of the bladder. In man, after severe injuries to the cord above L2, there is a marked rise of blood pressure accompanied by vasoconstriction of splanchnic and skin vessels. At the same time, impulses passing into the sacral segments produce reflex contractions of skeletal muscle. There are indications that visceral impulses have a direct influence on gamma efferent discharges, although more investigations are required before a general statement can be made. The establishment of automatic emptying of bladder and rectum occurs after one or two weeks following acute transection of the cord. The return of reflex activity is thought to involve some kind of reorganization of spinal connexions cut off from long-loop reflexes to the brain stem (De Groat & Ryall, 1969).

REFERENCES

Abdullah, A. & Eldred, E. (1959). Activity in gamma efferent circuits induced by distension of the bladder. *J. Neuropath. exp. Neurol.* **18**, 590–596.

Aidar, O., Geohegan, W. A. & Ungewitter, L. H. (1952). Splanchnic afferent pathways in the central nervous system. *J. Neurophysiol.* **15**, 131–138.

Amassian, V. E. (1951). Fiber groups and spinal pathways of cortically represented visceral afferents. *J. Neurophysiol.* **14**, 445–460.

Armett, C. J., Gray, J. A. B. & Palmer, J. F. (1961). A group of neurones in the dorsal horn associated with cutaneous mechanoreceptors. *J. Physiol.* **156**, 611–622.

Barclay, A. E. & Franklin, K. J. (1937). Reflexes from the bladder and large intestine. *J. Physiol.* **90**, 478–481.

Bernhard, C. G. (1953). The spinal cord potentials in leads from the cord dorsum in relation to peripheral source of afferent stimulation. *Acta physiol. scand.* **29**, Suppl. 106, 1–29.

Coombs, J. S., Curtis, D. R. & Landgrend, S. (1956). Spinal cord potentials generated by impulses in muscle and cutaneous afferent fibres. *J. Neurophysiol.* **19**, 452, 467.

De Groat, W. C. & Lalley, P. M. (1972). Reflex firing in the lumbar sympathetic outflow to activation of vesical afferent fibres. *J. Physiol.* **226**, 289–309.

De Groat, W. C. & Ryall, R. W. (1969). Reflexes to sacral parasympathetic neurones concerned with micturition in the cat. *J. Physiol.* **200**, 87–108.

Downman, C. B. B. (1955). Skeletal muscle reflexes of splanchnic and intercostal nerve origin in acute spinal and decerebrate cats. *J. Neurophysiol.* **18**, 217–235.

Downman, C. B. B. & Evans, M. H. (1957). The distribution of splanchnic afferents in the spinal cord of cat. *J. Physiol.* **137**, 66–79.

Downman, C. B. B. & Hussain, A. (1958). Spinal tracts and supraspinal centres influencing visceromotor and allied reflexes in cats. *J. Physiol.* **141**, 489–499.

Downman, C. B. B. & McSwiney, B. A. (1946). Reflexes elicited by visceral stimulation in the acute spinal animal. *J. Physiol.* **105**, 80–94.

Dusser de Barenne, J. G. & Ward, Jr., A. A. (1937). Reflex inhibition of the knee-jerk from intestinal organs. *Am. J. Physiol.* **120**, 340–344.

Eccles, J. C., Kostyuk, P. G. & Schmidt, R. F. (1962a). Central pathways responsible for depolarization of primary afferent fibres. *J. Physiol.* **161**, 237–257.

Eccles, J. C., Kostyuk, P. G. & Schmidt, R. F. (1962b). Presynaptic inhibition of the central actions of flexor reflex afferents. *J. Physiol.* **161**, 258–281.

Evans, M. H. & McPherson, A. (1958). The effects of stimulation of visceral afferent nerve fibres on somatic reflexes. *J. Physiol.* **140**, 201–212.

Evans, M. H. & McPherson, A. (1959). The effects of distension of the bladder on somatic reflexes in the cat. *J. Physiol.* **146**, 438–458.

Evans, M. H. & McPherson, A. (1960). The effects of electrical stimulation of visceral afferent nerve fibres on monosynaptic and polysynaptic reflex responses. *J. Physiol.* **150**, 105–113.

Evans, M. H. & McPherson, A. (1963). Alterations in activity of gamma efferents during distension of the bladder in the cat. *J. Physiol.* **165**, 358–367.

Fernandez de Molina, A. & Gray, J. A. B. (1957). Activity in the dorsal spinal grey matter after stimulation of cutaneous nerves. *J. Physiol.* **137**, 126–140.

Frank, K. & Fuortes, M. G. F. (1956). Unitary activity of spinal interneurones of cats. *J. Physiol.* **131**, 424–435.

Franz, D. N., Evans, M. H. & Perl, E. R. (1966). Characteristics of viscero-sympathetic reflexes in the spinal cat. *Am. J. Physiol.* **211**, 1292–1298.

Gasser, H. S. & Graham, H. T. (1933). Potentials produced in the spinal cord by stimulation of the dorsal roots. *Am. J. Physiol.* **103**, 303–320.

Guttmann, L. & Whitteridge, D. (1947). Effects of bladder distension on autonomic mechanisms after spinal cord injuries. *Brain* **70**, 361–404.

Head, H. & Riddoch, G. (1917). The automatic bladder, excessive sweating and some other reflex conditions in gross injuries of the spinal cord. *Brain* **40**, 188–263.

Mellanby, J. & Pratt, C. L. G. (1940). The reactions of the urinary bladder of the cat under conditions of constant volume. *Proc. R. Soc.* B. **128**, 186–201.

Miller, F. R. (1924). Viscero-motor reflexes. *Am. J. Physiol.* **71**, 84–89.

Mukherjee, S. R. (1957a). Effect of bladder distension on arterial blood pressure and renal circulation in acute spinal cats. *J. Physiol.* **138**, 300–306.

Mukherjee, S. R. (1957b). Effect of bladder distension on arterial blood pressure and renal circulation: role of splanchnic and buffer nerves. *J. Physiol.* **138**, 307–325.

Newman, P. P. & Paul, D. H. (1969). The projection of splanchnic afferents on the cerebellum of the cat. *J. Physiol.* **202**, 223–237.

Pomeranz, B., Wall, P. D. & Weber, W. V. (1968). Cord cells responding to fine myelinated afferents from viscera, muscle and skin. *J. Physiol.* **199**, 511–532.

Rexed, B. (1952). The cytoarchitectonic organization of the spinal cord in the cat. *J. comp. Neurol.* **96**, 415–466.

Riddoch, G. (1917). The reflex functions of the completely divided spinal cord in man, compared with those associated with less severe lesions. *Brain* **40**, 264–402.

Selzer, M. & Spencer, W. A. (1967). Convergence and reciprocal inhibition of visceral and cutaneous afferents in the lumbar spinal cord. *Fed. Proc.* **26**, 433.

Talaat, M. (1937). Afferent impulses in the nerves supplying the urinary bladder. *J. Physiol.* **89**, 1–13.

Taylor, D. E. M. (1963). Some effects of slow bladder distension on the arterial blood pressure of the cat. *J. Physiol.* **166**, 51–52P.

Wall, P. D. (1967). The laminar organization of dorsal horn and effects of descending impulses. *J. Physiol.* **188**, 403–423.

Watkins, A. L. (1938). Reflex responses of the nictitating membrane and the blood pressure to distension of the bladder and rectum. *Am. J. Physiol.* **121**, 32–39.

Widen, L. (1955). Cerebellar representation of high threshold afferents in the splanchnic nerve. *Acta physiol. scand.* **33**, Suppl. 117, 1–69.

4

VISCERAL AFFERENT
REPRESENTATION IN THE
CEREBELLUM

THOMAS WILLIS (1664) was the first to suggest that the cerebellum exerted some influence on visceral functions. He drew attention to the fact that such functions as the heart beat and alimentary movements were performed 'silently and unperceivedly without our knowledge or care.' Thus he made the distinction between voluntary and involuntary actions that led eventually to the concept of a motor organization which comprised both volitional and reflex mechanisms. This concept was elaborated by Rolando (1809) in a series of experiments showing that cerebellar ablations caused disturbances of voluntary movement. By the end of the nineteenth century Sherrington had begun his classical researches on the nervous system and later published a series of papers which helped to elucidate many of the problems connected with balance, posture and the coordination of movement. The cerebellum was regarded as the 'head ganglion of the proprioceptive system', receiving contributions from receptors in joints, muscles, ligaments, tendons, viscera, etc. Following this pioneer work came the contributions from the field of electrophysiology and three important aspects of cerebellar function were developed:

1. It became obvious that different parts of the body were represented in different parts of the cerebellum. Bremer (1922) was largely responsible for the idea of functional localization in the anterior and posterior lobes.

2. It was found, largely through the work of Adrian (1944), that functional pathways existed between the sensorimotor cortex of the cerebrum and the contralateral cerebellar hemisphere.

3. The idea was developed of an outward drive from the cerebellum which could influence the motor system through its action on the

excito-motor cortex and brain stem nuclei. Thus the conclusion was reached that the cerebellum was concerned in a two-way system, deriving information from a wide variety of receptors and influencing in turn the motor discharges of descending tracts.

Modern ideas on cerebellar function began when Dow (1939) recorded responses in the cerebellum after stimulating cutaneous nerves. This finding was confirmed by Adrian (1943) who inserted a wire electrode into the substance of the cerebellum in order to study the degree of localization of the cerebellar responses. He showed that potentials evoked by stimulation of tactile and pressure receptors in the skin were not uniformly distributed, but were concentrated at points which had a fixed anatomical relation with different parts of the body. Other evidence of cutaneous representation in the cerebellum was provided by Snider & Stowell (1942, 1944) who found that stimulating the skin caused localized responses in the anterior lobe. These authors also showed that auditory and visual stimuli could activate the cerebellar cortex, thus confirming earlier observations on electrical activity in the cerebellum by Gerard, Marshall & Saul (1936). Interaction between auditory and cutaneous afferent volleys in the decerebrate cat was reported by Bonnet & Bremer (1951). Evidence of visceral representation in the cerebellum has only been forthcoming since Widen (1955) described surface potentials evoked by electrical stimulation of the delta fibres in the splanchnic nerve. These and similar observations reported by Bratus (1960) suggested that there was considerable overlap of the projection areas for different afferent systems.

The conclusion to be drawn from all these investigations is that the cerebellum can no longer be considered in terms of the proprioceptive system alone. It receives impulses from almost every kind of sense organ, including the eye and the ear, and is therefore in a position to analyse a wide range of information and even to 'learn' the context of the incoming signals. It can make use of the information by sending out a new code of signals or set of instructions to the output circuits with which it is linked. Some of the problems and theories relating to these aspects of cerebellar function will be discussed in the next chapter. The evidence presented here will describe the contributions made by impulses of visceral origin and the effects of their interaction with cutaneous afferent volleys.

EXPERIMENTAL METHODS

1. Anaesthesia

Adult cats were anaesthetized with an initial dose of sodium thiopentone (45 mg/kg) administered by intraperitoneal injection. This was usually sufficient to carry out the operative procedures, but maintenance doses (5–10 mg/kg) were given at intervals through an intravenous cannula. The level of anaesthesia could be ascertained by a monitoring electrocorticogram or by reference to the pupils which should remain constricted. The skin was infiltrated with 1% procaine solution at all operative sites. Many workers favour the use of sodium pentobarbital for mapping the distribution of localized responses, as it tends to reduce the background activity; others prefer the decerebrate unanaesthetized animal.

2. Operative procedures

These may be described in four stages:

(a) Insertion of cannulae. A vein on the medial side of the forepaw was used for the administration of drugs, anaesthetics and infusions. Blood pressure was recorded from the femoral artery and a cannula was tied into the trachea for artificial ventilation.

(b) Balloons and electrodes. With the animal on its back, the abdomen was opened through a mid-line incision and the gall bladder gently manipulated to allow insertion of a small balloon with attached tubing. The balloon was held in place by a purse-string suture and the tubing fixed to the skin after closing the abdomen. In some experiments, balloons were also inserted into various parts of the alimentary tract. The splanchnic nerves were exposed by resection of the lowest three ribs. The nerves are seen running obliquely on the bodies of the vertebrae and can be traced through the diaphragm to the coeliac ganglion. After covering with mineral oil and freed from connective tissue, the central cut end was arranged on a bank of silver electrodes comprising a distal pair for stimulation, a proximal pair for recording and an earthed electrode between them. The electrode assembly was then fixed by sutures to the body wall to prevent loss of contact due to respiratory movements.

(c) Craniotomy. With the head of the animal in a rigid holder, an incision was made through the scalp, the temporal muscles detached on each side and the occipital bone cleared down to the foramen magnum. Craniotomy was performed with fine bone nibblers, the extent of the exposure depending on the needs of the experiment. It was usually necessary to dissect away the bony tentorium or, if access was required to the anterior limits of the cerebellum, the occipital lobes were removed by suction. Great care must always be taken on opening the venous sinuses to prevent undue loss of blood and to preserve the local circulation in a healthy state.

(d) Pulsations. In order to minimize brain pulsations due to cardiac and respiratory movements and to prevent reflexes, the following procedures were adopted routinely:

   (i) The cerebrospinal fluid was drained by an incision into the cisterna magna.

   (ii) A pressor foot attached to the micromanipulator was applied to the pial surface while the shaft of the recording microelectrode passed through the lumen.

   (iii) The animal was given an intravenous injection of gallamine triethiodide (Flaxedil, May & Baker) and artificially ventilated with air or oxygen.

3. Recording procedures

When all the above preparations were completed, the animal was transferred to a stereotaxic assembly, the dura was deflected and the recording site covered with warm mineral oil. Rectal temperature was maintained between 37 and 38°C. Action potentials in the splanchnic nerve were passed through an a.c.-coupled differential preamplifier and displayed on an oscilloscope. Figure 4.1 shows that when the gall bladder was stimulated, a rapid burst of spike potentials appeared in the right splanchnic nerve during the period of distension, but ceased immediately the balloon was deflated. The spike amplitude was about 100 µV. Activity recorded from the surface of the cerebellum was monitored by a pair of silver contacts in the base of the pressor foot; the latter also recorded the surface primary responses evoked by electrical stimulation of the splanchnic nerve. Points from which recordings were made were plotted on a large print of the cerebellar surface during the experiment. Single cell discharges were recorded

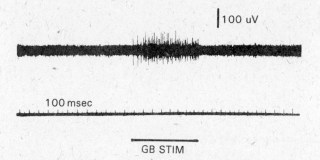

100 uV

100 msec

GB STIM

FIG. 4.1. Action potentials recorded by electrodes on the right splanchnic nerve during distension of the gall bladder.

with capillary microelectrodes filled with 2·5 molar sodium chloride and having a resistance of 4–10 MΩ. Unit responses were displayed after amplification and samples fed into the input of a Biomac computer for storage and analysis. The track of the microelectrode was afterwards identified by histological examination.

PROJECTION AREA IN THE ANTERIOR LOBE

The cerebellum of the adult cat consists of a central vermis with lateral hemispheres. Roman numerals I–X are used to designate the various subdivisions or lobules. According to Larsell (1953) lobules I–V belong to the anterior lobe, VI–IX belong to the posterior lobe and lobule X is the flocculo-nodular lobe. As the grey matter of the cortex dips into the surface, each lobule has several folia. In the anterior lobe, lobule I is relatively small, corresponding to the lingula in man; lobules II and III form the centralis and lobules IV and V the culmen. The folia of lobule V are labelled a–f. The primary fissure which separates the anterior and posterior lobes is formed by folia d, e and f of lobule V and the rostral part of lobule VI or simplex.

The majority of points responding to visceral stimulation are found in the posterior culmen, lateral to the paravermian vein; very few are found in the vermis or simplex. Using Larsell's classification; the responsive area corresponds to lobule Vb, Vc on the surface and Vd, Ve and Vf deep in the primary fissure (Fig. 4.2). Although there is

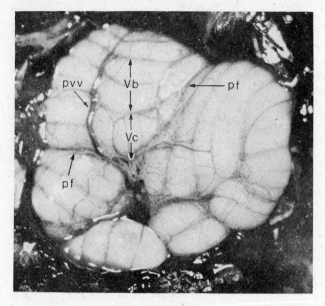

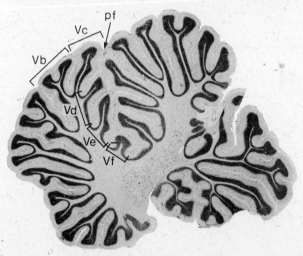

FIG. 4.2. A photograph showing the dorsal surface of cat cerebellum on the right side: pf, primary fissure between culmen and simplex; pvv, paravermian vein running between vermis and intermediate part of anterior lobe. Lobules Vb, Vc indicate sites of maximal evoked splanchnic responses. The section below illustrates responsive points deep in the primary fissure.

considerable overlapping with points responding to tactile stimuli from the trunk and extremities, the position is largely in agreement with the findings of Widen (1955) and Bratus (1960) for evoked surface potentials. The posterior culmen may therefore be described as the 'visceral receiving area' of the cerebellum.

Stimulation of abdominal viscera

The activity of single units in the culmen of the cerebellum has been explored by recording microelectrodes during distension of abdominal viscera. Figure 4.3 shows the increase of discharge frequency produced by distending the gall bladder or loop of intestine. As the

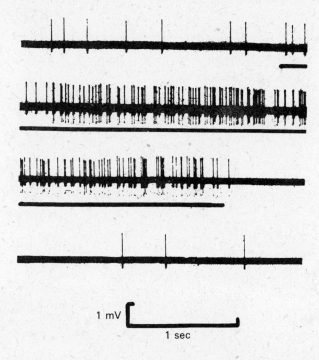

1 mV

1 sec

FIG. 4.3. Effect of stimulating the gall bladder on a spontaneously active cerebellar unit. Continuous record showing increased frequency of discharge during period of stimulation. Signal line in lower trace marks distension of gall bladder by a balloon. In this and subsequent figures a relative positivity of the microelectrode is recorded as a downward deflexion.

microelectrode was driven into the cerebellar cortex, many units were encountered which were unaffected by visceral stimulation but continued to yield spontaneous discharges. Other units were silent in the absence of stimulation, discharging only during the period of distension and ceasing immediately the balloon was deflated (Fig. 4.4). If the right splanchnic nerve was cut all unit discharges evoked by

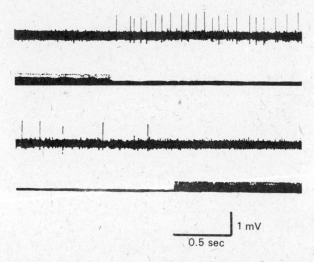

1 mV

0.5 sec

FIG. 4.4. Continuous record showing evoked activity of a single unit in cerebellar cortex. Signal line in lower trace indicates period of distension by a balloon in gall bladder. No spontaneous activity.

distending the gall bladder were abolished. In a third group of units the discharge frequency was reduced or the unit ceased to fire altogether during the period of stimulation (Fig. 4.5). It was also found that many units responded to light pressure on the viscera applied through the abdominal wall or to pulling on a loop of intestine or attached mesentery. Such units failed to respond to other forms of stimulation, including distension of the gall bladder, stroking the abdominal wall or movement of the limbs; on the other hand they could usually be excited by electrical stimulation of the splanchnic nerves.

It may be concluded from the above experiments that cerebellar units responding to visceral stimulation have certain distinguishing properties:

1. Units responding to visceral distension but otherwise silent. Such units fired initially at about 10/sec, maintained firing during distension at a reduced frequency then ceased when the balloon was deflated.

2. Units firing spontaneously at low discharge rates. In this group, irregular firing at about 4/sec was immediately increased to about 25/sec on distending a viscus.

3. Units firing spontaneously at high discharge rates (30–40/sec). The frequency of discharge was reduced or the unit was completely inhibited during the period of distension.

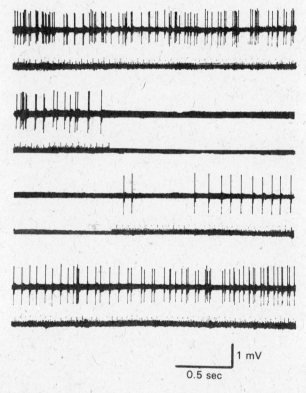

1 mV

0.5 sec

Fig. 4.5. Inhibition of single cerebellar unit discharging spontaneously at high frequency. Continuous record showing complete cessation of firing during period of stimulation. Signal marker in lower trace is switched off to mark distension of loop of small intestine by a balloon. Note gradual return to original frequency on deflation (signal marker on).

In summary it may be said that impulses set up by mechanical stimuli and manipulation of viscera can influence the activity of single units in three different ways: the silent cell may become active, the persistently discharging cell may become more active or else its discharge rate is reduced or blocked.

Stimulation of the splanchnic nerve

As the majority of impulses originating in abdominal viscera are conveyed to the spinal cord by the splanchnic nerves, a study has been made of the properties and characteristics of cerebellar responses following electrical stimulation of the splanchnic nerve. Examination of the deflexions recorded in the compound action potential reveals that the afferent fibres fall into two main categories, fast conducting, low threshold A beta fibres and slower conducting, high threshold A delta fibres. In the spinal cord, both groups have bilateral ascending pathways, although the majority of A beta fibres occupy the ipsilateral dorsal columns while the majority of A delta fibres ascend the antero-lateral columns. Thus some degree of organization is maintained between the two groups. It is not surprising, therefore, that the threshold of the cerebellar responses was also found to fall into two categories (Newman & Paul, 1966a).

Primary waves

When the tip of the microelectrode made contact with the pial surface of the cerebellum, primary waves were recorded following each stimulus delivered to the splanchnic nerve. These waves were evoked without difficulty in the posterior culmen on the rostral side of the primary fissure. The latency of response was about 20 msec, the duration 10–15 msec and the polarity surface-positive. When the microelectrode was inserted into the substance of the cerebellum, a negative or reversed primary wave was recorded at depths ranging from 0·5 to 3·0 mm below the pial surface. With further advancement of the electrode a second positive wave was usually recorded with similar latency and duration. The deep positive wave could be reversed, giving a deep negative wave, by advancing the electrode tip about 60 µ (Fig. 4.6). The primary waves represent localized potential changes set up by activity in the terminals of projection systems; they constitute physiological evidence of a nervous pathway between the point of stimulation and the recording site. The successive reversals of polarity are characteristic of recordings from the cerebellum where the cortex is thrown into folds and several layers encountered as the microelectrode is advanced.

Single unit discharges

The effects of an electrical stimulus applied to the splanchnic nerve

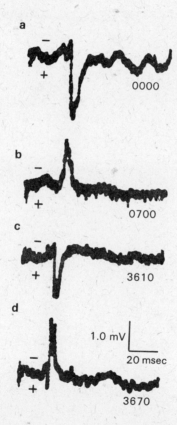

FIG. 4.6. Evoked primary responses recorded from posterior culmen of cerebellum following electrical stimulation of ipsilateral splanchnic nerve: (a) initially positive primary wave at pial surface; (b) reversed primary wave, 700 μ below pial surface; (c) deep positive wave, 3610 μ below pial surface; (d) deep negative wave at 3670 μ below surface. The response characteristic at each depth can be demonstrated as the microelectrode is advanced or withdrawn.

were (a) the silent cell discharged one or more spikes and (b) the spontaneously active cell responded to the afferent volley followed by a period of silence (Fig. 4.7). The characteristic form of the spike was a diphasic positive-negative deflexion, 1–3 mV in amplitude,

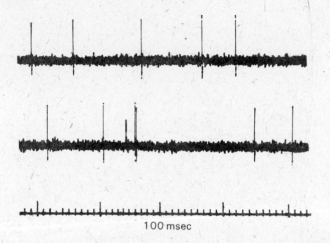

100 msec

FIG. 4.7. Effect of a single shock to splanchnic nerve on a spontaneously active cerebellar unit. Cat under sodium thiopentone anaesthesia. Continuous record. Note period of post-excitatory depression.

superimposed on the primary wave. Smaller, initially negative spikes were also seen when the electrode was not actually in contact with the cell membrane. The latency of the response was measured on the oscilloscope by the interval between the stimulus artifact and the first spike of the discharge. The mean latencies of a large number of evoked responses were given by teleprinter write-out after computation.

As stated above, the threshold of all units evoked by splanchnic nerve stimulation fell into two categories according to the fibre spectrum of the compound action potential and intensity of the stimulus:

Low threshold cells. In this group, the cells were usually silent or fired irregularly in the absence of stimulation. The mean latency for the first spike of the discharge was about 15 msec. Some of the cells had a very low threshold, responding to a stimulus of less than 1 V and 0·01 msec duration. On inspection of the splanchnic nerve action potential it was evident that only a fraction of the A beta fibres were excited.

High threshold cells. In this group, the cells responded to stimulation of the splanchnic nerve only when the A delta fibres were excited, e.g. 2 V, 0·1 msec. The latency for the first spike of the discharge ranged from 20 to 25 msec (Fig. 4.8).

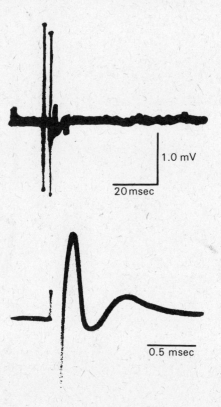

1.0 mV

20 msec

0.5 msec

Fig. 4.8. Extracellular recording from high-threshold unit in cerebellar cortex. Upper trace, evoked unit response to electrical stimulation of the splanchnic nerve; latency, 20 msec. Lower trace, simultaneous recording of splanchnic nerve action potential showing A beta and A delta deflexions.

Effects of varying stimulus intensity

The discharge properties of single units in the cerebellum can be studied by finding the threshold of the response to a single stimulus and then observing the effects of progressive increase of intensity. It was found that increasing the intensity of stimulation resulted in:

1. Reduction in the mean latency for the first spike. With weak intensities of stimulation the latency of the discharge varied greatly from unit to unit under identical conditions. The effects of increasing the stimulus intensity by progressive steps above the threshold are shown in Fig. 4.9. In both low-threshold and high-threshold units the

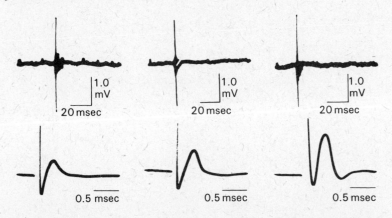

FIG. 4.9. Relation between strength of stimulus and latency of response. Upper traces, response of single unit in posterior culmen to increasing stimulus intensities. Lower trace simultaneous recording of splanchnic nerve action potential. Note shortening of latency of evoked spike and increasing height of A beta action potential with increasing strength of stimulus.

mean latency for the first spike was reduced, the longer latencies dropped out and a greater incidence of the shorter latencies was observed.

2. Increase in the number of spikes. The total number of spikes discharged by a single unit in response to stimulation of the splanchnic nerve was also found to vary. The records in Fig. 4.10 illustrate the increase in number of spikes with increasing stimulus intensities. The

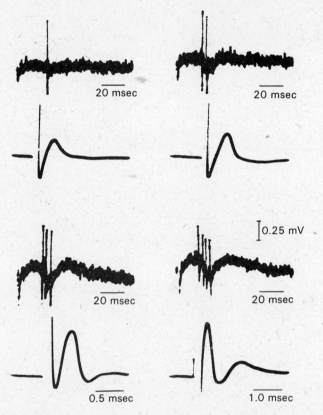

FIG. 4.10. Relation between number of spikes and strength of stimulus. Upper traces, cerebellar response. Lower trace, splanchnic nerve action potential simultaneously recorded. Unit in posterior culmen isolated at depth 2·66 mm below pia.

size of the nerve action potential was simultaneously recorded. In spite of variability in response, a small increase of stimulus intensity generally converted a one-spike discharge to a two-spike discharge, while multiple bursts of six or seven spikes were observed with stronger stimulation.

3. Increase in the probability of response. Discharges of cerebellar units evoked by the splanchnic nerve did not always follow each successive stimulus. However, increasing the intensity of the stimulus increased the probability that the unit would discharge at least one spike. The probability P was derived from the ratio between the number of times the unit responded by discharging a spike and the total number of trials. The graph in Fig. 4.11 presents this relationship

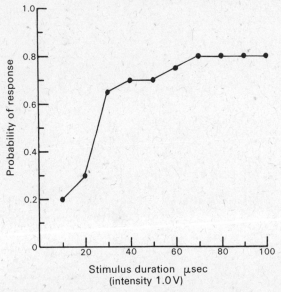

FIG. 4.11. Relation between probability of response and strength of stimulus. The probability factor represented on the ordinate was calculated from the number of times the unit fired a spike in thirty successive trials. Stimulus intensity constant at 1·0 V. Note increase of probability as the duration of the stimulus increased. In this example, probability did not reach unity with maximal excitation of the A beta group of fibres.

for a given unit isolated in the culmen, but its general form is typical of the series. It will be seen that probability may not always reach unity even with maximal excitation of the nerve.

In summary, it may be said that fluctuations in the response characteristics of individual units are significantly related to the parameters of stimulation. At low intensities of stimulation, there is a relatively long and variable latency, a one-spike discharge and a low level of probability. At higher intensities of stimulation, the mean latency is reduced, the number of spikes per discharge is increased and the probability that the unit will respond to a given stimulus is also increased.

INTERACTION BETWEEN CUTANEOUS AND SPLANCHNIC AFFERENTS

The experimental data described above have shown that impulses set up by electrical stimulation of the splanchnic nerve can influence the discharge patterns of single units in the anterior lobe of the cerebellum. The region of maximal activity is located in lobules Vb–f of the posterior culmen. This region overlaps in part that described by Snider & Stowell (1944) for cutaneous representation. Since impulses of visceral origin apparently have the same cortical destination as impulses of somatic origin it is likely that afferents from both sources converge and interact. This possibility has been studied by the technique of conditioning and testing stimuli, a stimulus to one pathway being followed by a stimulus to the other over a wide range of time intervals. The results have revealed striking inhibitory effects on the response to the second or testing stimulus in the majority of units sampled (Newman & Paul, 1966b).

Primary waves

A conditioning stimulus was applied to the skin of the abdominal wall and a testing stimulus delivered to the splanchnic nerve. When the interval between conditioning and testing stimuli was 70 msec or more, a primary wave was recorded from the cerebellum in response to each stimulus. As the interval was reduced by adjusting a delay control on the stimulator, there was a decrease in amplitude of the primary wave response to the testing stimulus. At an interval of 50 msec the amplitude was reduced by half and at 40 msec between the two stimuli, the response to the testing stimulus was absent, reappearing when the conditioning stimulus was switched off (Fig. 4.12).

Single unit responses: effects of varying the C–T interval

Figure 4.13 shows the response of a single unit to a conditioning stimulus followed by the response of the same unit to a testing stimulus. The interval between the two stimuli was 60 msec. It can be seen in the lower traces of the figure that, when the interval was reduced to 40 msec, the unit responded to the conditioning stimulus as before, but failed to respond to the testing stimulus. The figure also

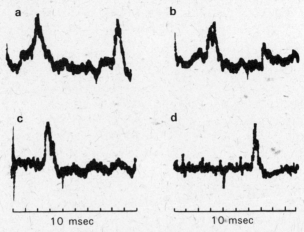

FIG. 4.12. Interaction between cutaneous and splanchnic afferent impulses revealed by effect on test primary wave. (a–c) test stimuli to splanchnic nerve given respectively at 70, 60 and 40 msec after a conditioning stimulus to the skin. Note reduction of test primary wave in (b) and its absence in (c). The same test stimulus produces the response in (d) when conditioning stimulus is switched off.

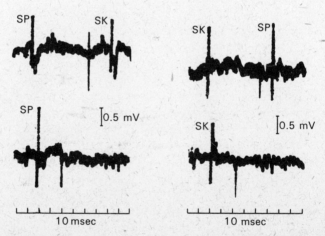

FIG. 4.13. Effect of interaction between cutaneous and splanchnic afferents on single cerebellar unit. On the left, upper trace shows that the unit responds to both splanchnic and skin stimuli when interval between stimuli is 70 msec; lower trace illustrates complete blocking of test response with C–T interval at 40 msec. Traces on right show comparable results when sequence of stimuli is reversed. SP, response to splanchnic nerve stimulation; SK, response to skin stimulation.

demonstrates that the sequence of stimulation was not important—it did not matter which afferent pathway was stimulated first. Inhibition of the test response was sometimes observed with a weak conditioning stimulus which was below threshold and therefore did not evoke a spike discharge. However, a primary wave was usually evident (Fig. 4.14).

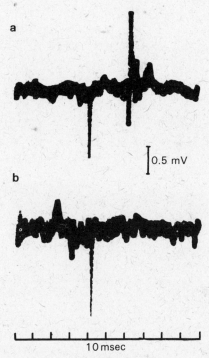

Fig. 4.14. Effect of subthreshold conditioning stimulus on evoked discharge of cerebellar unit. (a) response to a testing stimulus applied to the splanchnic nerve alone; (b) subthreshold conditioning stimulus applied to abdominal skin 40 msec before testing stimulus. Note conditioning stimulus evokes only a primary wave without discharging the unit but the test response is inhibited.

The presence or absence of a response to the testing stimulus can best be described in terms of probability statements. The variability of successive responses to identical peripheral stimuli has already been emphasized. The probability of response to a testing stimulus must therefore be computed for a large number of trials at each time interval. The results of one experiment are plotted in the graph of Fig. 4.15 but the curve is typical of all the experiments; it shows the relationship between the probability of response to a testing stimulus and the interval between conditioning and testing stimuli. It can be seen that when the interval was 90 msec or more the unit discharged

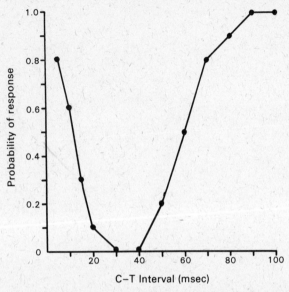

FIG. 4.15. Graph to show relationship between probability of response to a testing stimulus and the conditioning-testing (C–T) interval. Probability = 1·0 when C–T interval is 90 msec or longer. Note diminishing probability as the C–T interval is reduced and complete cessation of the test response (probability = 0) with intervals between 40 and 25 msec. With intervals shorter than 25 msec probability rises again, i.e. inhibition is less intense at the briefer intervals.

every time it was stimulated ($P = 1$). Response probability to the testing stimulus was progressively reduced as the intervals were reduced until, at an interval of 40 msec between the two stimuli, the unit ceased to discharge ($P = 0$). Inhibition of the test response was maintained for intervals as short as 25 msec, but the effect was less intense with briefer intervals. The graph illustrates an important aspect of cerebellar function—when two pathways converge on a single neurone, activity in one pathway can block the influence of the other pathway, the effect depending on the time interval between the two sets of impulses.

Single unit responses: effects of varying the parameters of stimulation

In addition to the C–T interval, the relative intensities of the two stimuli have an important bearing on the results. This fact is illustrated in the following experiments:

A conditioning stimulus was applied to the skin and a testing stimulus to the splanchnic nerve. The cerebellum was explored for a unit which responded to both stimuli with a high level of probability. The interval between the two stimuli was then kept constant, whilst the intensity of either the conditioning stimulus or of the testing stimulus was altered.

Varying the conditioning stimulus. In Fig. 4.16 the C–T interval

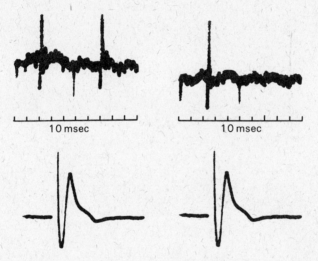

FIG. 4.16. Effect on test response of increasing conditioning stimulus. Upper traces show unit response on a time course of 100 msec; lower traces show the splanchnic nerve action potential simultaneously recorded. On the left of the figure, unit responds to both cutaneous conditioning and splanchnic testing stimuli; on the right, intensity of conditioning stimulus is increased whilst that of test stimulus remains unchanged. Note absence of test response. C–T interval is constant at 50 msec.

was 50 msec. The intensity of the testing stimulus was such that the unit discharged a spike with maximum probability ($P=1$) in the absence of conditioning. When the conditioning stimulus was switched on, the unit responded to each stimulus; but as the intensity of the conditioning stimulus was increased, the probability of the unit discharging to the testing stimulus was reduced and eventually reached zero.

Varying the testing stimulus. The C–T interval was again 50 msec. The conditioning stimulus was now set for maximum probability and kept constant. When the testing stimulus was switched on, a response was evoked as before; but as the intensity of the testing stimulus was reduced, the response was diminished until its probability was zero ($P=0$). It will be noticed from Fig. 4.17 that the splanchnic nerve

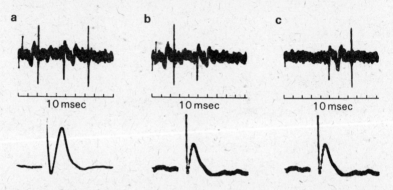

FIG. 4.17. Effect on test response of reducing the testing stimulus. Upper traces, responses of cerebellar unit on time course of 100 msec; lower traces, splanchnic nerve action potential. Intensity of conditioning stimulus remains unchanged. In (a) the unit responds to both conditioning and testing stimuli. In (b) the test response is absent; note reduced amplitude of splanchnic nerve action potential. (c) Same testing stimulus as (b) but conditioning stimulus switched off. C–T interval is constant at 50 msec.

action potential (testing stimulus), recorded when probability was zero, was only about one third of its maximum amplitude. However, the stimulus was still strong enough to excite the unit in the absence of conditioning.

The conclusion drawn from these experiments was that alteration of the relative intensities profoundly influenced the interaction: when the testing stimulus was constant, increasing the intensity of the conditioning stimulus resulted in more powerful inhibition; conversely, when the conditioning stimulus was constant, inhibition was more pronounced with decrease of the testing intensity.

DISCUSSION

During recent years there has been a growing interest in the functional organization of the cerebellum and an interpretation of its mode of action will be discussed in the next chapter. Here it is convenient to make certain statements of a general nature from the work described above and to arrive at some conclusions.

The information which is fed into the cerebellum comes from widely different sources; indeed, from almost every kind of sense organ in the body. The contribution from the muscular system has been known for some time and this may account for the fact that disturbances of muscle tone, balance and voluntary movement, including disturbances of speech and gait have been much emphasized in the clinical literature. On the other hand, the contributions from cutaneous structures, the eye and the ear, have not been so clearly documented while those from the internal organs of the body seem to have been neglected altogether. In the normal functioning of the cerebellum the uniformity of its structure must be of great significance. Nevertheless, any acceptable theory of cerebellar function must consider the extremely wide representation of the sensory input.

The degree of overlap between afferents of different modalities conforms with the principle of fibre economy found elsewhere in the nervous system, where sharing of neurones provides the structural basis for synaptic convergence and opportunities for facilitation or inhibition. In the anterior lobe, cutaneous and splanchnic projections share to a large extent the same population of neurones. This situation favours studies on interaction by the technique of conditioning and testing: a stimulus to one afferent source being followed by a stimulus to a second afferent source at different time intervals. When recording from large groups of cells, each peripheral input evokes a primary wave response in its field of activity; if the primary wave is reduced or suppressed by previous conditioning, this suggests the possibility of inhibitory interaction. When similar studies are applied to individual cells, the most prominent change observed is a reduction in the probability of discharge of the test response. The depression occurs over a wide range of intervals, but is maximal between 25 and 40 msec. Recovery may not be complete even at intervals as long as 100 msec or more. Another factor which can influence the state of depression concerns the strength of the incoming volleys. It is a common finding that increasing the intensity of conditioning or decreasing the intensity of testing results in a more powerful and prolonged period of inhibition.

There has been much speculation on the synaptic levels at which convergence can take place. As mentioned in the last chapter, such a possibility exists in the spinal cord where splanchnic and cutaneous fibres terminate on cells in the dorsal horn. Evidence that interaction may occur during transmission through interneuronal pathways is not very convincing, at least as far as visceral afferents are concerned. Another possibility is that cutaneous and splanchnic afferents may converge on cells in the inferior olive and project by climbing fibres to the cerebellum. The various spinal paths which terminate as climbing fibres from the inferior olive have several synaptic relays which might help to explain the long latencies of the evoked responses. Many of the fibres travelling in the lateral funiculus of the cord converge extensively on the same olivary neurone. However, they are activated predominantly by cutaneous and high threshold muscle afferents, while their role in conveying information from the viscera is uncertain. Furthermore, it is believed that the climbing fibre system does not respond very effectively to natural stimulation or to receptors of specific modality (Larson et al., 1969). An alternative view is that convergence may occur in the cerebellar cortex itself. The Purkinje cells, which control the output from the cerebellum, are influenced not only by the projections from the olive, but indirectly by granule cells through the mossy fibre system. If impulses of visceral origin follow different spinal pathways from those of cutaneous origin, it is possible that the two afferent systems—mossy fibre and climbing fibre—form the anatomical basis for convergence in the cerebellum. The view is attractive because the mossy fibre–granule cell relay has a remarkable built-in mechanism for inhibitory interaction.

An outstanding feature of the cerebellar unit responses to visceral stimulation is the high degree of specificity observed. Units responding to distension of the gall bladder are apparently unaffected by intestinal stimulation; other units responding to manipulation of the gut or mesentery are not influenced by gall-bladder stimulation. In addition, the response patterns of individual units are found to be consistent. If the response is an increase of discharge frequency, inhibition is not encountered with the same unit. Conversely, when a persistently discharging unit is inhibited, that response is also consistent. Thus there is very strong evidence for supposing that viscero-cerebellar pathways form a discrete and independent projection system.

REFERENCES

Adrian, E. D. (1943). Afferent areas in the cerebellum connected with the limbs. *Brain*, **66**, 289–315.

Adrian, E. D. (1944). Localization in cerebrum and cerebellum. *Brit. med. J.* **2**, 137–140.

Bonnet, V. & Bremer, F. (1951). Interaction between auditory and tactile volleys in decerebrate cats. *J. Physiol.* **114**, 54–55P.

Bratus, N. V. (1960). O predstavile'stve v mozzhechke nekotorykh vischeral'nykh nervov. *Fiziol. zh. SSR* **46**, 179–184.

Bremer, F. (1922). Contribution à l'étude de la physiologie du cervelet et la fonction inhibitrice du paleo-cérébellum. *Arch. int. Physiol.* **19**, 189–226.

Dow, R. S. (1939). Cerebellar action potentials in response to stimuli of various afferent connections. *J. Neurophysiol.* **2**, 543–555.

Gerard, R. W., Marshall, W. H. & Saul, L. J. (1936). Electrical activity of the cat's brain. *Arch. Neurol. Psychiat.* **36**, 675–738.

Larsell, O. (1953). The cerebellum of the cat and the monkey. *J. comp. Neurol.* **99**, 135–199.

Larson, B., Miller, S. & Oscarsson, O. (1969). Termination and functional organization of the dorsolateral spino-olivocerebellar path. *J. Physiol.* **203**, 611–640.

Newman, P. P. & Paul, D. H. (1966a). The representation of some visceral afferents in the anterior lobe of the cerebellum. *J. Physiol.* **182**, 195–208.

Newman, P. P. & Paul, D. H. (1966b). The effects of stimulating cutaneous and splanchnic afferents on cerebellar unit discharges. *J. Physiol.* **187**, 575–582.

Rolando, L. (1809). *Saggio sopra la vera struttura del cervello. Sassari, Stamp. Priv.*

Snider, R. S. & Stowell, A. (1942). Evidence of a representation of tactile sensibility in the cerebellum of the cat. *Fed. Proc.* **1**, 82.

Snider, R. S. & Stowell, A. (1944). Receiving areas of the tactile, auditory and visual systems in the cerebellum. *J. Neurophysiol.* **7**, 331–357.

Widen, L. (1955). Cerebellar representation of high threshold afferents in the splanchnic nerve. *Acta physiol. scand.* **33**, Suppl. 117, 1–69.

Willis, T. (1664). *Cerebri anatome.* J. Martyn and J. Allestry, London.

5

IDEAS ON CEREBELLAR
FUNCTION

In the preceding chapter it was shown that impulses from abdominal viscera make a significant contribution to the stream of afferents flowing into the cerebellum. An account was given of the location and discharge properties of single cells or groups of cells responding to visceral distension or to electrical stimulation of the splanchnic nerve. Three different kinds of responses were observed: activation of the so-called silent cell, facilitation of persistently discharging cells and inhibition of cells firing spontaneously at high frequencies. On the basis of the characteristic field potentials generated in the cerebellar cortex, it was concluded that the fibre spectrum of splanchnic afferents was divided into two functional groups. It was stated further that, because of overlap between cutaneous and visceral afferent projections and synaptic convergence, the excitatory influence in one pathway produced a prolonged inhibitory depression in the other. This chapter is devoted to the interpretation of these events. A detailed study of the structural elements has given functional meaning to the whole complex organization, which will now be discussed.

STRUCTURE OF THE CEREBELLUM

The track made by a microelectrode as it passes through the substance of the cerebellum can be demonstrated histologically from serial prints of cut sections. It will be seen from Fig. 5.1 that successive layers of grey and white matter were penetrated by the electrode tip in its advance from the surface to a depth of about 5 mm. The cerebellar cortex covers the whole of the visible surface and dips into the various fissures of the interior. The white matter forms a central core, projecting into the cortex in the form of laminations. When recording, the position of the electrode tip can often be followed on the auditory monitor since the background noise of the cellular

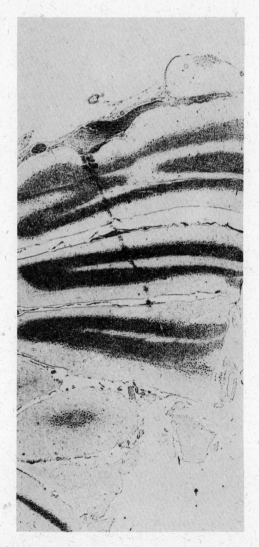

FIG. 5.1. Section through posterior culmen of anterior lobe, constructed from prints of serial transverse sections, to show microelectrode tract. Note the numerous folia through which the penetration was made. The vermis is to the right of the tract.

elements gives way to relative silence as the white matter is reached. Penetrations oblique to the surface are likely to sample a greater number of cells in each layer and when the angle of the recording electrode is fairly steep, several Purkinje cells may be identified in a single penetration. Primary waves evoked by afferent stimuli reveal changes in polarity as the electrode is advanced or withdrawn through the layers of grey matter and deep positive waves are characteristic of cerebellar recordings.

The cortex shows complete uniformity of structure. Its three histological layers are well-defined. A review of the various cell types found in the cerebellar cortex has been given by Eccles, Ito & Szentagothai (1967) and reference should be made to this publication for further information.

1. The molecular layer is densely packed with dendrites and axons but has relatively few cells. The dendrites belong to the branching processes of Purkinje and Golgi cells whilst the axons are derived mainly from granule cells. In addition, there are numerous terminal filaments of climbing fibres distributed from the white matter. Two kinds of cells are found in the molecular layer—basket and stellate.

Basket cells are about 20 μ in diameter. Their dendrites form a rich arborescence in the deep part of the molecular layer and make synaptic contacts by means of spines; their axons run parallel to the cortical surface, giving off many collaterals. Each basket cell supplies about eight Purkinje cells.

Stellate cells are smaller than basket cells and are located more superficially, but otherwise have similar dendritic processes with spiny contacts. Their axons may be short and thin, running a horizontal course, or somewhat longer with ascending and descending terminal filaments.

It is sometimes found that the activity of single units is difficult to record in the region just below the pia. This may be partly due to the low density of cells compared with the mass of fibre material. Other causes of inactivity may be due to a fall in systemic blood pressure or body temperature. There may be inadequate circulation in the pial vessels, possibly caused by damage during the exposure or by local anaemia from the pressure of recording instruments. However, in good preparations, the superficial layers of the cortex will remain responsive for many hours.

2. The Purkinje cells form a single layer of flask-shaped bodies wedged between the molecular and granular layers. Dendrites arise from the neck of the flask to extend through the molecular layer as a broad, flat, branching sheet, parallel with the transverse plane of a folium. The axon of each Purkinje cell descends from the bottom of the flask and soon becomes myelinated; it gives off abundant collaterals as it traverses the granular layer to end in the deep nuclei of the cerebellum. Quantitative histological investigations reveal that Purkinje cells have a mean density of $330/mm^2$ with an estimated total number of about $1 \cdot 2$–$1 \cdot 3$ million in adult cats (Palkovits, Magyar & Szentagothai, 1971).

The electrical activity of Purkinje cells is readily recorded under light barbiturate anaesthesia. There is often a continuous rhythmic discharge at rest. Purkinje cells can sustain high rates of firing often followed by short intervals of silence.

3. The granular layer contains round, closely packed cells about 5–8 μ in diameter. These are the granule neurones. Dendrites radiating from a cell body have characteristic claw-shaped tufts which together with the terminal filaments of a mossy fibre form a complex synaptic arrangement called a 'cerebellar glomerulus'. The axons of the granule cells ascend to the molecular layer where they bifurcate and give rise to the parallel fibres. In addition to granule neurones there are large stellate neurones or Golgi cells mostly in the superficial part of the granular cortex. Each Golgi cell has an expansive dendritic tree in the molecular layer, but its axon descends to form profuse terminal synapses on the granule cells. The composition of a cerebellar glomerulus is therefore as follows:

(a) Presynaptic terminal endings of a mossy fibre, often described as a 'clump of rosettes'.
(b) Presynaptic terminals of a Golgi cell.
(c) Postsynaptic dendritic tufts of a granule cell.

The synaptic functions involved in a glomerulus will be discussed later, but it can be stated here that the mossy fibre–granule cell synapse is entirely excitatory whilst the Golgi cell serves essentially as an inhibitory interneurone.

4. The white matter contains two systems of afferent fibres terminating in the cerebellar cortex:
(a) Mossy fibres originate from the brain stem and spinal cord.

They carry impulses from a wide variety of sense organs. On reaching the granular cortex, each mossy fibre innervates about 20 glomeruli in addition to supplying numerous collaterals.

(b) Climbing fibres originate mainly from cells in the inferior and accessory olives. The majority ascend undivided through the white matter to reach the dendritic tree of the Purkinje cells; others give off collaterals.

5. *The deep nuclei* embedded in the white matter constitute cell stations on the efferent pathways from the cerebellar cortex:

(a) The fastigial nucleus is found close to the mid-line above the roof of the fourth ventricle. It receives the axons terminals of those Purkinje cells which are situated in the vermis and it also receives an important contribution from the mossy fibres.

(b) The intermediate nuclei receive Purkinje projections from the paravermian zones of the cerebellum.

(c) The dentate or lateral nucleus appears as a double fold of grey matter in transverse section. Afferent fibres enter the nucleus from the outer border and break up into fine arborizations. These are the terminals of Purkinje axons derived from the lateral zones of the cerebellum. In addition, the dentate nucleus receives collaterals from climbing fibres and possibly also from other afferent systems.

The above account of the structure of the cerebellum describes the various types of cell and their principal connexions. Details of cerebellar organization based on comparative and embryological material have been published by Jansen & Brodal (1954). Information on cerebellar function derived from physiological evidence will now be discussed. It will be clear that the cerebellar cortex has two distinct input systems—mossy fibre and climbing fibre—but only one output system, the Purkinje cell axons to the deep nuclei.

FUNCTIONAL ARRANGEMENTS IN THE CEREBELLUM

1. The mossy fibre input

Impulses reach the cerebellum from almost every kind of sense organ including those from the viscera. The spinal pathways are exceedingly varied and not all of them have been defined. This is because many fibres give off collaterals or cross and recross the cord as they ascend, with the result that identification is difficult. However, it is believed that the following spinal pathways conveying afferents to the cerebellum terminate as mossy fibres:

The dorsal spino-cerebellar tract occupies the dorsal half of the lateral funiculus. It has relatively large myelinated fibres with conduction velocities between 85 and 160 m/sec (Grundfest & Campbell, 1942; Grant, 1962). The fibres originate from proprio-ceptors of hind-limb muscles and terminate in the rostral part of the cerebellar vermis, mainly in the ipsilateral centralis. It was found that cerebellar responses evoked by electrical stimulation of the tibial nerve had a mean latency of 4–6 msec. From the evidence of the conduction rates and distribution of this pathway, it is unlikely that it serves as a route for visceral afferents.

The ventral spino-cerebellar tract occupies the ventrolateral part of the lateral funiculus. The fibres originate from muscular and cutaneous nerves supplying the fore-limb and hind-limb and after one synapse in the grey matter of the cord, cross to the opposite side. Second-order neurones ascend to the superior peduncle, then cross again in the vermis of the cerebellum to be distributed to the centralis and anterior culmen. The result is that impulses from one side of the body reach the granular cortex of the ipsilateral anterior lobe. Carrea & Grundfest (1954) found latencies between 4 and 8 msec for evoked cerebellar responses and estimated conduction velocities between 30 and 80 m/sec. Again it is unlikely that visceral afferent impulses are conveyed in this tract.

The cuneo-cerebellar tract arises from cells in the external cuneate nucleus which derives its fibres from the dorsal column of the cord. It transmits impulses from the cervical and upper thoracic segments for distribution to the cerebellar vermis. The tract enters the cerebellum through the inferior peduncle, terminating as mossy fibres in the anterior and posterior lobes. Lesions involving the vermis are followed by degenerative changes in the cuneate nucleus whilst other lesions restricted to the intermediate and lateral zones of the cerebellum do not produce changes in the cuneate (Jansen & Brodal, 1954). Thus on anatomical grounds alone, it would seem that visceral afferent fibres make no contribution to this tract.

The spino-reticular tract ascends in the lateral funiculus of the cord, receiving collaterals at all segmental levels. It maintains a somatotopical pattern all the way to the terminal synapses in the lateral reticular nucleus of the medulla. Cerebellar projections from the nucleus pass as mossy fibres to the vermis of the anterior lobe. The functional role of this tract is as yet undetermined although the delayed timing of its conduction may be significant.

Spino-pontine projections have been traced by Walberg & Brodal (1953) using histological methods following lesions placed in the cortico-spinal tracts. In the pontine nuclei, synaptic contacts are established between the spinal and pontine-cerebellar projections, but the function of these pathways is uncertain.

The dorsal columns form part of the classical sensory system conveying impulses from the skin, muscles and viscera to the opposite thalamus and sensory cortex. The majority of the fibres are large, myelinated and fast conducting and ascend without interruption to the gracile and cuneate nuclei in the medulla. Second-order neurones either take part in the sensory decussation or course towards the cerebellum via the inferior peduncle. According to studies by Newman & Paul (1969) the A beta group of splanchnic afferents are conveyed in the dorsal columns. In order to trace the spino-cerebellar pathways, single unit responses were recorded from the cerebellum following electrical stimulation of the splanchnic nerve. Lesions were made through different tracts in the cord until the evoked response was abolished. The diagram in Fig. 5.2 shows where the A beta pathway was interrupted by a lesion placed in the dorsal column close to the mid-line.

Action of granule cells

The various afferent systems terminating in the cerebellum as mossy fibres form excitatory synaptic contacts with the dendrites of granule cells. A single mossy fibre may divide into many terminal rosettes capable of exciting several hundred granule cells. The axon of each granule cell bifurcates into the parallel fibres, which in turn make excitatory synaptic contacts with all the cell types of the molecular layer—Golgi, basket, stellate as well as Purkinje cells. Thus one mossy fibre has a very wide dispersion of activity in the cerebellar cortex.

Activation of a granule cell may give rise to the following events:
1. A large number of Purkinje cells are excited. This is due to

postsynaptic excitation of parallel fibres ending on the dendritic tree. According to Fox & Barnard (1957), each parallel fibre makes contact with about 300 Purkinje cells or more. As the parallel fibres run superficially in the cerebellar cortex they are readily stimulated by a concentric electrode resting on the pial surface.

2. Golgi cells are excited. This is due to the action of parallel fibres on the upper dendritic branches. As stated above, the axons of Golgi

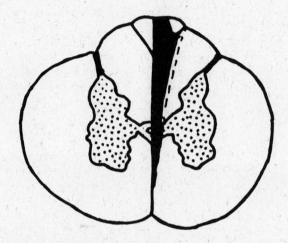

Fig. 5.2. Diagram of transverse section through spinal cord of cat at upper cervical level. The A beta splanchnic pathway is interrupted by a lesion in the ipsilateral dorsal column close to the mid-line. The lesion is effective in abolishing cerebellar potentials evoked by stimulation of the splanchnic nerve.

cells terminate inside a mossy fibre glomerulus where they form inhibitory synapses with granule cell dendrites. Thus the granule cell has its own negative feed-back control.

3. Basket cells are excited by means of their spiny contacts with the parallel fibres. The axons terminate around the bodies of Purkinje cells on which they exert a powerful inhibitory action. One basket cell can inhibit as many as 50 Purkinje cells.

4. Stellate cells are excited. They are found in the outer part of the molecular layer and have similar characteristics to basket cells. Their axons are distributed in two kinds of terminal ramifications, establishing inhibitory synaptic contacts with the primary and secondary dendrites of the Purkinje cells.

Action of Golgi cells

It is believed that the Golgi cell synapses in the cerebellar glomeruli cause inhibition of the granule cell discharges. As the Golgi cells are driven by the granule cells the action can be interpreted as a device for limiting the influence of the mossy fibre input. It was shown in the previous chapter that a test response evoked by stimulation of the splanchnic nerve could be inhibited by preceding stimulation of a cutaneous nerve. Inhibition remained complete for about 40 msec whilst full recovery could take as long as 100 msec or more. Almost identical interaction times were reported by Eccles, Llinas & Sasaki (1966b) when investigating inhibition of granule cell discharges evoked by stimulating the superficial radial nerve. The Golgi cells may thus be regarded as an important control system limiting the excitation of Purkinje cells by mossy fibre impulses. Relatively weak inputs are suppressed and only granule cells which are strongly excited have access to the output lines.

Action of basket and stellate cells

These cells are considered to be inhibitory interneurones lying on the pathway between the parallel fibres and the Purkinje dendritic tree. They have the task of controlling the threshold of the Purkinje cells. If the parallel fibres are stimulated by an electrode placed on the surface of the cerebellum, the Purkinje cells are first excited by direct action of parallel fibre axons then inhibited by the activity of the interneurones. The inhibition may be both powerful and prolonged. Thus, the basket and stellate cells form a second inhibitory system controlling the mossy fibre influence on Purkinje cell discharges.

2. The climbing fibre input

The climbing fibres are axons arising from cells in the inferior olive and accessory olives. After crossing the mid-line, they ascend through the inferior peduncle to be distributed to all parts of the contralateral cerebellum. Each climbing fibre ends on the dendritic tree of a Purkinje cell where excitatory synaptic contacts are established. The pathway from olive to Purkinje cell is monosynaptic. It is important to note that a climbing fibre and its chosen Purkinje cell form a functional pair, although many collaterals also extend to adjacent Purkinje cells and to basket and stellate cells. Since it is now accepted that climbing fibres belong to the olivo-cerebellar projections, a brief account will be given of the various afferent systems that are known to relay in the olive. In general, two groups of afferents are described, spinal and pontine.

Spino-olivo-cerebellar pathways

The existence of fibres from the spinal cord to the inferior olive was demonstrated by Cajal (1909) and more recently by Brodal, Walberg & Blackstad (1950). Using histological techniques, they showed that spino-olivary fibres occupied the ventral and lateral funiculi of the cord and projected from the olive to the vermis of the cerebellum. The projection did not possess a clearcut somatotopic organization and none of the terminal fibres were distributed to the intermediate part of the anterior lobe. Using physiological techniques, Oscarsson (1968, 1969) revealed that there are at least three spino-olivary pathways which convey impulses by climbing fibres to the anterior lobe of the cerebellum:

The ventral spino-olivocerebellar path ascends in the ventral funiculus of the cord with the hind-limb component laterally and the fore-limb component medially. The tract was isolated by the method of partial transection, i.e. after all other pathways to the cerebellum had been cut. The majority of cerebellar responses mediated by the ventral pathway were found in lobules III and IV of the vermis, but Oscarsson (1968) reported a second projection to the intermediate zone following stimulation of skin and muscle nerves. All surface responses had latencies of about 20 msec suggesting the involvement of many relays in the brain stem.

The dorsal spino-olivocerebellar path ascends in the dorsal funiculus of the cord to the dorsal accessory olive. Fibres relayed from the olive are distributed to the vermis and intermediate zones of the anterior lobe. Olivary neurones are activated from wide receptive fields by high-threshold afferents, but the areas of distribution to the cerebellar cortex are restricted to lobules IV and V. This would suggest a high degree of convergence at the level of the olive. The climbing fibre responses mediated by this pathway have relatively long latencies—10–15 msec from the fore-limb and 19–25 msec from hind-limb nerves (Oscarsson, 1969). These findings suggest that the dorsal spino-olivary tract may be one of the pathways through which the A delta group of splanchnic nerve afferents is conveyed to the cerebellum.

The dorsolateral spino-olivocerebellar path ascends in the dorsal part of the lateral funiculus and terminates in the anterior lobe of the cerebellum. It may be described in two parts, dorsal and ventral.

1. The dorsal part relays in the inferior olive. It is used predominantly by cutaneous afferents originating from the ipsilateral limbs. Larson, Miller & Oscarsson (1969a) identified the terminal pathway as climbing fibres distributed to the intermediate zone of lobules IV and V. The mean latency of evoked surface responses was 18–20 msec. From calculations of conduction velocities, there appeared to be only a brief delay in the cord itself, and to account for the relatively long latencies, they considered that the pathway must be interrupted by three or four synapses in the brain stem.

2. The ventral part ascends in the lateral funiculus of the cord to lobule V of the intermediate zone, but its course through the brain stem is uncertain. It is activated by cutaneous nerves from all four limbs and the latencies are rather longer than those for the dorsal part. It is thought that the fibres may carry information from interneurones concerned in reflex arcs and are only indirectly linked to events of the peripheral sense organs (Larson, Miller & Oscarsson, 1969b).

Climbing fibre pathways on the anterior lobe may be shown to be more circumscribed in their distribution when adequate physiological stimuli are used instead of an electrical stimulus. Thus Leicht, Rowe & Schmidt (1973), using controlled mechanical stimuli applied to cutaneous receptors, found inputs from highly restricted cutaneous fields. In lobule V they recorded Purkinje cell responses confined to the distal areas of the ipsilateral forelimb; other climbing fibre responses from the ipsilateral hindlimb had a more extensive distribution.

Climbing fibre projections from the inferior olive

The inferior olive projects to the contralateral cerebellum by means of the climbing fibres. Each climbing fibre terminates on about 10 Purkinje cells and its action here is powerfully excitatory. When an electrical stimulus is applied to the olive, the Purkinje cell discharge has a latency of about 6 msec, whereas direct stimulation of the climbing fibres gives responses with a much shorter latency. Thus Granit & Phillips (1956) observed latencies ranging between 0·35 and 0·8 msec when they stimulated in the region of the fastigial nucleus; other workers, using a juxta-fastigial placement, reported latencies ranging from 1·2 to 5·0 msec. The typical response of a Purkinje cell to a single stimulus is a brief repetitive discharge superimposed on a large primary wave (Eccles, Llinas & Sasaki, 1966a). The repetitive discharge is always observed when the stimulus is applied to the olive, in which there are several synaptic relays or collaterals that excite other olivary cells. In fact the inferior olive may be looked upon as a network of interneurones within the nucleus and this would also account for the much longer latencies compared with direct stimulation of the climbing fibres. In general, each Purkinje cell is supplied by only one climbing fibre which forms synaptic contacts all over the dendritic tree.

THE OUTFLOW FROM THE CEREBELLUM

It is now possible to consider the mode of operation of the cerebellum on the basis of its structural arrangements. Information from the sense organs is derived from two principal afferent systems which eventually converge on the dendritic tree of the Purkinje cells. The climbing fibre afferents drive the Purkinje cells directly, the mossy fibre afferents indirectly. As a result of interaction between these two systems the outflow from the Purkinje cells is continuously controlled. The deep nuclei of the cerebellum receive the axons of the Purkinje cells and they therefore constitute nerve centres on the efferent pathway from the cerebellar cortex to the brain stem and cerebral hemispheres. An attempt to show these arrangements as a working hypothesis is illustrated in Fig. 5.3.

Function of mossy fibres. A good deal of the traffic originates from the sense organs. When the impulses reach the granule cells they are subjected to the inhibitory effects of feed-back from the Golgi cells, thus limiting the distribution of the impulses to a narrow beam of parallel fibres. At the same time the basket and stellate cells are excited and these in turn produce a zone of inhibition on either side of the beam. As a result, for every Purkinje cell excited by the parallel fibres, there is at least one which is inhibited. The output from the cerebellum must therefore be considered in terms of fluctuating patterns of excitation and inhibition in areas defined and selected by the sense organs.

Function of climbing fibres. The climbing fibre impulses are derived from olivary neurones. Their function is to modify the discharges of Purkinje cells, partly by direct excitatory action and partly by inhibition through the activity of basket and stellate cells. Direct

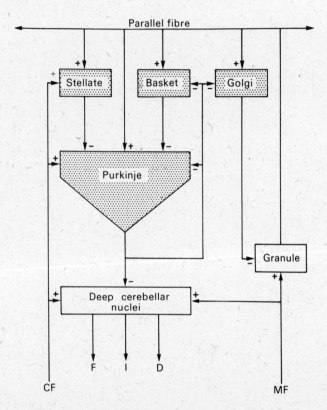

Fig. 5.3. Circuit diagram of input–output relations in the cerebellum. The two input pathways, namely, mossy fibre (MF) and climbing fibre (CF) are shown to have both excitatory (+) and inhibitory (−) actions on the Purkinje cell. The excitatory pathway of the mossy fibre is to the granule cell which discharges along its axon, the parallel fibre, to the Purkinje cell and also to interneurones of the cerebellar cortex. These are stellate and basket cells which give inhibitory synapses to the Purkinje, and the Golgi cell which inhibits the granule. The climbing fibre pathway excites the Purkinje cell by direct action and inhibits it via stellate and basket interneurones. The output pathway along the Purkinje axon gives inhibitory synapses to the deep cerebellar nuclei, namely, fastigial (F), intermediate (I) and dentate (D). Purkinje axon collaterals give feed-back synapses to the Purkinje itself and to the interneurones. The diagram also illustrates the pathway for background excitation of the deep cerebellar nuclei from climbing fibre and mossy fibre collaterals. Purkinje, stellate, basket and Golgi cells are all shaded to indicate their inhibitory function.

excitatory action is produced by each climbing fibre on its chosen Purkinje cell with the result that instructions from the olive can be continuously executed as in the performance of automatic actions. The olive simply samples the excitability of its related Purkinje cells and switches its discharge on or off according to requirements. Reduction of Purkinje cell discharges is assisted by climbing fibre collaterals through the intervention of inhibitory interneurones. Basket, stellate and Golgi cells are all powerfully inhibitory. Thus the olive cells can control all cerebellar output even to the extent of putting temporarily out of action the whole mossy fibre input.

Function of Purkinje cells. The Purkinje cells transmit the output from the cerebellar cortex to the deep cerebellar nuclei and thence to the central nervous system. It is now believed that the action of the Purkinje cells on the cerebellar nuclei is mainly inhibitory as will be explained below.

When a recording microelectrode is inserted into the cerebellar cortex in a lightly anaesthetized animal, it is found that the cellular elements maintain a constant background discharge. Purkinje cells often fire spontaneously at rates which vary from 20 to 50/sec but higher rates may be recorded. Typical discharges appear as positive–negative spikes, 3–5 mV in amplitude peak to peak. Giant spikes with amplitudes 20–40 mV were described by Granit & Phillips (1956). As the spontaneous activity occurs in the absence of peripheral stimulation and even in the chronically deafferented cerebellum, it is possible that the Purkinje cells are self-generating. Nevertheless it is felt that the source of the spontaneous activity may come from the olivary neurones (Eccles, Ito & Szentagothai, 1967).

Function of cerebellar nuclei. The deep nuclei of the cerebellum receive the terminal axons of the Purkinje cells. Although there are various excitatory influences acting on these nuclei, including those from the brain stem reticular formation, inferior olive and mossy fibre collaterals, the outflow to the central nervous system is controlled predominantly by cerebellar inhibition. Nulsen, Black & Drake (1948) reported that the dentate nucleus was responsible for conducting inhibitory effects from the anterior lobe. Ito & Yoshida (1966) showed that Purkinje cells have a direct inhibitory action on the dentate nucleus by recording intracellular potentials following stimulation of the anterior lobe. The IPSP's induced had brief latencies ranging from

0·86 to 1·06 msec. Hence they concluded that the Purkinje axons exerted monosynaptic inhibitory action on dentate neurones. The net result of this discovery indicated that the output of the cerebellum was transmitted by negative signalling, since an increase of Purkinje activity produced greater and more prolonged depression. However, in an extension of this work Ito, Kawai, Udo & Sato (1968) showed that cerebellar stimulation could also have a facilitatory effect on dentate neurones. This would tend to cancel out any inhibitory action of the Purkinje discharges.

It is obvious that the role of the deep cerebellar nuclei is not yet completely understood. The output from the Purkinje cells is a variable output in which increased frequency produces greater inhibition and decreased frequency has the reverse effect. The action on the deep nuclei is complicated by mechanisms which can reduce the excitability of the Purkinje cells or oppose the post-synaptic depression that occurs. In other words the influence of the Purkinje discharges is diminished by a process of disinhibition. It is not known how important these mechanisms may be or whether they are functionally significant. According to Thach (1972), the nuclear cells are engaged in continuous out-going barrages provided by excitatory mossy fibre and climbing fibre collaterals and it is against this background that Purkinje discharges exert their inhibitory influence.

INTERPRETATION OF EVENTS PRODUCED BY IMPULSES FROM VISCERA

It is now appropriate to examine the course of events flowing through the cerebellum from inputs of visceral origin. Various afferent pathways in the spinal cord have been investigated and their projections to the cerebellar cortex identified as two functional systems with distinct electrical and physiological properties. Impulses from the viscera have both excitatory and inhibitory actions on the discharges of single Purkinje cells. As described in the previous chapter, natural stimulation of a viscus, e.g. distension of the gall bladder, produces a remarkable change in cerebellar unit activity. Excitatory effects may be observed in units that are generally silent or fire spontaneously at low discharge rates. The existence of neurones that respond only when evoked by peripheral stimulation suggests the mediation of specific afferent pathways with highly selective terminal projections. Inhibitory effects are observed on spontaneously active units discharging at high frequency. Since the firing can be completely blocked by peripheral stimulation, the impulses arriving in the cerebellum must set up a concentrated inhibitory barrage. This might be brought about by the driving action of parallel fibres on basket and stellate neurones, which give inhibitory synapses to large numbers of Purkinje cells. Comparable results were reported by Eccles, Sabah, Schmidt & Taborikova (1972a) from experiments in which Purkinje cells were tested by controlled stimulation of cutaneous mechano-receptors. They observed three kinds of responses displayed by the Purkinje cells—*excitatory*, in which the firing rate was doubled from about 50 to 100/sec; *inhibitory*, in which a reduced discharge or total silence occurred for about 40 msec or more and *admixtures* in which brief excitation was followed by silence lasting up to 400 msec. Thus there is good agreement that some Purkinje cells respond with a remarkable individuality to a physiological or natural stimulus, indicating a high degree of selectivity with respect to the inputs each receives from a particular afferent. Most other Purkinje cells give response patterns which are more dependent upon the integration of the excitatory and inhibitory influences converging upon them.

Electrical stimulation of the splanchnic nerve evokes characteristic potential changes in a circumscribed region of the anterior lobe. With a microelectrode in the posterior part of the culmen many low-threshold single units have been sampled. It is evident that the A beta group of splanchnic afferents have terminal projections in this region since responses may be recorded with weak stimulation when only a small fraction of the A beta fibres are excited. It can be postulated that low-threshold afferents in the splanchnic nerve have more or less direct access to their chosen Purkinje cells. The latter are apparently unresponsive to most other forms of stimulation, yet discharge with a high degree of probability when evoked by the splanchnic nerve. Stronger stimulation, to excite the A delta fibres, does not increase the response probability. The mean latency of the first spike of the discharge is about 15 msec and this conforms with the view that the impulses ascend in the relatively fast-conducting dorsal columns.

As regards the A delta group of splanchnic afferents, there is general agreement that its fibres ascend bilaterally in the ventrolateral columns of the cord. The cerebellar responses are more easily evoked, more widespread and have a much longer latency (ranging between 20 and 25 msec). Furthermore, the majority of cerebellar units evoked by high-threshold afferents also respond to cutaneous stimulation. This implies a considerable degree of convergence of the two afferent systems on the same neurone. When a conditioning stimulus is applied to one nerve and a testing stimulus to another, the response to the second stimulus is blocked for periods of up to 100 msec or longer. The probability of a unit firing to the testing stimulus is reduced or else the unit ceases to fire altogether. It has been suggested that the depression is due to post-synaptic inhibition of the Purkinje cells by the mediation of basket and stellate synapses or to what was termed 'inactivation of P-cell responses' by Granit & Phillips (1956). A further contribution to the inhibitory action on Purkinje cells may come also from climbing fibre collaterals which make excitatory synapses with the inhibitory interneurones of the cerebellar cortex.

In the normal functioning of the cerebellum account must be taken of the control exerted by the climbing fibre system on the Purkinje cell discharges. The question may be asked, what is the reason for two input systems? At first sight, it might be thought that the two systems are purely antagonistic, the mossy fibres being predominantly inhibitory and the climbing fibres predominantly excitatory since every Purkinje cell is subjected to the influence of both. However, this interpretation can be rejected on the grounds that it does not explain the specific functional role of the climbing fibre mechanism. Recent electrophysiological findings reveal that the parallel fibres excite Purkinje cells directly, inhibit them indirectly and therefore provide changing patterns of neuronal discharge reflecting changes in the sense organs. In other words, the mossy fibre system alone is capable of controlling the output of the Purkinje cell discharges. Eccles, Ito & Szentagothai (1967) gave convincing evidence that the parallel fibres produce a narrow beam of excited Purkinje cells with a zone of inhibition on either side. According to these authors, the climbing fibres have an intense excitatory action on every Purkinje cell and can therefore change the excitability level at any instant. Whatever the background level attained by combination of all mossy fibre influences, whatever may be the existing firing rate of a Purkinje cell, the climbing fibre impulses can modify it. Thus they considered the climbing fibre system as a 'sampling device' for detecting frequency changes in the cerebellar output.

Any hypothesis on the role of the climbing fibres must take into account that in addition to their excitatory effects on Purkinje cells they can also exert inhibitory functions through collaterals acting on basket, stellate and Golgi cells. Such inhibitory functions may contribute in a small way to the general level of Purkinje excitability, but at times their influence may be decisive. They can tip the balance, so to speak, between excitation and inhibition with the result that the Purkinje cell will cease to fire. Murphy & Sabah (1971) recorded silent periods of up to 570 msec following climbing fibre or inferior olive stimulation, pointing out that such prolonged suppression of firing could not be explained on the basis of excess membrane depolarization, since depolarizations usually lasted 8–15 msec by which time the amplitude of the response would have largely recovered. They believed that collaterals to the various interneurones of the cerebellar cortex played a prominent part in this inhibitory response, a view that underlines the dual character of climbing fibre activity. The same authors suggested the need for a 'resetting' mechanism which would be effective in clearing the firing zones of the Purkinje cells should they become blocked by excess excitation or excess inhibition. Similar ideas on climbing fibre mechanisms were expressed in a recent review by Eccles (1973) in which he envisaged automatic clearance of all excitatory effects within 100 msec. According to this concept, 'the cerebellum was engaged in a continuous assessment in much the same way as occurs for a target-finding missile'.

Since the Purkinje cells are mainly inhibitory in action (Ito & Yoshida, 1966), their target cells in the deep cerebellar nuclei will be facilitated by a fall in frequency and inhibited by a rise in frequency. We can therefore regard the action of the climbing fibres as a kind of buffering mechanism, serving the important role of maintaining the output discharges of the cerebellum within a physiological range. A lowered frequency of the Purkinje cell discharges will tend to cause hyperexcitability in the central nervous system; this tendency will be opposed by increasing the activity of the climbing fibres. A raised frequency of the Purkinje cell discharges will tend to cause a depression in the central nervous system and will be opposed by reducing the activity of the climbing fibres. In this way excessive excitation or excessive inhibition is prevented. If this explanation is accepted, the information derived from the sense organs is primarily a function of the mossy fibre system, which records the conditions of the peripheral mechanism at any instant of time. When a particular activity is in progress, for example distension of a viscus or movement of a joint, these conditions will change and will be reflected by changes in the patterns of discharge from the Purkinje cells. The climbing fibre synapses on the Purkinje cells ensure that the output discharges to the deep nuclei of the cerebellum shall fall within a desired range of frequencies. Thus the whole output from the cerebellum can be controlled by lowering or raising the impulse discharge in the climbing fibres. This concept gives functional meaning to the climbing fibre input to the cerebellum and is the basis of smooth performance in nervous activity. If the climbing fibres or their cells of origin in the brain stem are put out of action by injury or disease, all the benefits of a controlled output are lost.

An interesting contribution to ideas on cerebellar function is contained in a theory developed by Marr (1969) that Purkinje cells may have a limited capacity to learn. The theory arose from the fact that the cerebellum is closely concerned with the motor functions of the cerebral cortex and, like the cortex, may be able to learn from experience. The performance of a particular motor skill will call for the same guiding information from the cerebellum every time that skill is repeated. Thus the Purkinje cells may become conditioned by repeated cerebral commands. Assuming that changes in synaptic function are involved in the conditioning process, Purkinje cells are eminently suitable for the purpose by virtue of their dendritic arrangements and neuronal connexions. Their synaptic spines are embraced by two distinct input channels which converge upon them. The theory proposes that a mossy fibre input can be learned provided it is reinforced by a relevant climbing fibre signal. Synaptic modification is achieved when impulses from granule cell and olivary cell are combined in appropriate sequence and time. Unfortunately, experimental testing of this theory has so far failed to show any synaptic modification.

Another problem in the interpretation of cerebellar function is whether the presence of anaesthesia causes a fundamental difference in the processing of information. According to Bloedel & Roberts (1969), there is a considerable difference—in fact the responses in the unanaesthetized animal are the reverse of those generally observed when barbiturates are used. This is clearly a very sweeping statement to make. Their work was based on the antidromic field potentials set up by invasion of impulses from axon to soma of the Purkinje cells and they demonstrated that the potential was facilitated by a preceding stimulus to the parallel fibres. In the presence of anaesthesia, facilitation was not seen and only inhibition was evident as described by other workers. They also claimed that, in the absence of anaesthesia, stimulation of the parallel fibres did not cause basket cells to produce inhibitory affects on the Purkinje discharges—on the contrary, the spontaneous activity of the basket cells was reduced and this would account for the facilitation observed.

In view of these remarkable statements the action of the parallel fibres on Purkinje cells was re-examined by Eccles, Faber & Taborikova (1971) in the decerebrate cat and the results compared with those obtained during the administration of anaesthesia. Facilitation of the antidromic potential was observed in nearly all of the experiments on the decerebrate animal; the effects were maximal at 20–30 msec intervals and facilitation could be detected up to 100 msec after the conditioning stimulus. When the animal was given barbiturate injection, facilitation disappeared and instead a strong inhibitory action was recorded. Thus it appeared that at these brief intervals the results supported the findings of Bloedel & Roberts (1969). However, at longer test intervals, the effects on the antidromic potential were always inhibitory. Maximal inhibition occurred at about 150 msec and was still large at 300 msec. Total durations up to 700 msec were usually observed. Thus it was quite clear that the action of the parallel fibres on Purkinje cells could be powerfully inhibitory whether anaesthesia was present or not; in fact, inhibition was observed in practically all experiments in which the testing interval exceeded 100 msec. The reduction of the antidromic potential by activating the parallel fibres was attributed to the inhibitory action of the basket cells on the Purkinje soma. The administration of anaesthetic depressed the excitability of the Purkinje cells, blocked the invasion of impulses from axon to soma and allowed basket cell inhibition to become dominant. Under these circumstances facilitation was never seen.

The conclusions which can be drawn about this problem will now be summarized:

In the absence of anaesthesia

1. Cerebellar Purkinje cells have a higher level of excitability. As a consequence the antidromic action potential is facilitated by previous conditioning through parallel fibre stimulation.

2. During the first 50 msec or so following invasion of the soma by antidromic impulses, the inhibitory action of the basket cells is submerged by the combined excitatory action produced by conditioning and testing volleys. Facilitation results.

3. At intervals longer than 50 msec the antidromic potential is reduced and finally suppressed. The inhibitory action of the basket cells becomes progressively more dominant and persists for 300 msec or longer.

4. The parallel fibres have both an excitatory and an inhibitory action on Purkinje cells.

In the presence of anaesthesia

1. Facilitation is not seen.

2. The invasion of the Purkinje cells by antidromic impulses is eliminated owing to depressed excitability.

3. The excitatory action of the parallel fibres is neutralized by the larger inhibitory action of the basket cells. Inhibition occurs even at brief test intervals.

4. There is no fundamental difference in the processing of information by the cerebellar neuronal mechanism.

Finally, it seems reasonable to accept that the anaesthetized cerebellum does differ from the unanaesthetized because the excitability of the Purkinje cells will be changed: most barbiturates tend to depress activity. Whilst it appears that no fundamental concepts are invalidated in this particular problem, such differences as are found cannot be ignored in any discussion of cerebellum function.

At the present time, it is considered that the cerebellum behaves as a neuronal machine designed to give all necessary assistance to the actions of the cerebral cortex which it serves. The information flowing into it is derived from a variety of sense modalities—cutaneous, proprioceptive, visceral, etc.—and therefore an assessment of its function cannot be complete if that assessment is limited to its more obvious role in controlling movement and posture. Whilst smooth and effective motor performance depends upon continuous cerebellar discharges to the excito-motor cortex, the projections of the deep cerebellar nuclei via the thalamus suggest involvement of a much wider region of the cerebrum. Again, in the return circuits, corticofugal influences via pontine and olivary nuclei come from an extensive distribution of active points in both cerebral hemispheres (see Chapter 6). Thus on anatomical grounds alone, the concept of a dynamic loop of control postulated by Eccles *et al.* (1972*b*) must be very strongly supported. In conclusion, it seems that all the important operational features of the cerebellum are centred around the Purkinje cells and the resulting output determines what corrections should be made at any instant to ensure that the brain as a whole gives its best possible performance.

SUMMARY

Although in recent years there have been considerable advances in our understanding of cerebellar function, it will be obvious that much of the experimental work has been concentrated on studies of the anterior lobe. In spite of this, it is clear that information derived from electrophysiological investigations is closely linked to our knowledge of the structural organization. In the cerebellum, the structural pattern is regular and uniform. Even though the pathways in and out of the cerebellum are extremely complicated and many remain undefined, they provide an essentially simple framework: the output from the cortex is by the axons of the Purkinje cells and these cells are driven by two different input systems, one direct, the other indirect.

Experiments concerned with tracing the course and destination of splanchnic nerve afferents have revealed some essential differences between the A beta and A delta groups of fibres.

A beta afferents evoke responses in individual Purkinje cells, which are generally silent or fire irregularly in the absence of stimulation. The threshold of the Purkinje cells is extremely low since they will discharge a spike with high probability when only a fraction of the fibres are excited. There is general agreement that access to the cerebellum via the mossy fibre input is through the dorsal columns. After relaying in the gracile and cuneate nuclei, the fibres enter the inferior peduncle and terminate on granule cells situated in the posterior folia of the culmen. The mean latency of the evoked response is about 15 msec. Access to the cerebellum via the climbing fibre input is not definitely known. The available evidence suggests that the impulses are conducted in the dorsal spino-olivary tract and relay in the dorsal accessory olive to be distributed to Purkinje cells in the same folia of the culmen.

A delta afferents may excite or inhibit Purkinje cells. The threshold of excitation is relatively high and facilitatory effects are frequently observed in neurones discharging spontaneously at low rates. In other neurones discharging spontaneously at higher rates, a single afferent volley may produce profound inhibitory effects. Both kinds of responses have been demonstrated by distension of abdominal viscera. The route taken by A delta afferents terminating as mossy fibres is at present unknown. It is not likely to be found in the dorsal or ventral spino-cerebellar tracts where the conduction times are too rapid and the responses are mainly ipsilateral. Likewise the cuneo-cerebellar tract can be discounted since its projections are narrowly confined to the cerebellar vermis whilst the role of the spino-recticular and spino-pontine projections is still undecided. In contrast, it is generally accepted that the A delta afferents which terminate as climbing fibres gain access to the cerebellum through the inferior olive. The findings of Cajal (1909) and of Jansen & Brodal (1954) and many other neurohistologists have established the origin of climbing fibres from the contralateral inferior olive and their terminal synapses have been carefully studied by Scheibel & Scheibel (1954) and by Hamori & Szentagothai (1966). The mean latency of the evoked responses is about 20 msec.

Present ideas on cerebellar function have been constructed on the basis that two essentially different influences control the output of the Purkinje discharges to the deep cerebellar nuclei. The first is the mossy fibre input from granule cells and the second is the climbing fibre input from olivary cells. The mossy fibre influence is a mixture of excitatory and inhibitory effects produced by the activity of the parallel fibres which are axons of granule cells. The excitatory effects are due to direct synaptic contact with the dendrites of Purkinje cells whilst the inhibitory effects are brought about through the mediation of stellate and basket interneurones. The granule cell discharges are effectively controlled through a feed-back loop from Golgi cells which may therefore be regarded as a protective mechanism preventing undue excitation or excessive inhibition. These kind of mechanisms have been appropriately called disfacilitation or disinhibition. The net result of the various interactions which may take place will determine the level of excitability of the Purkinje cells in response to each mossy fibre impulse.

The second major influence on the Purkinje discharges comes from the olivary neurones. Much has been written recently on the function of the climbing fibres and their powerful excitatory synaptic actions. All parts of the cerebellum receive fibres from the olive and most authors stress the importance of the extensive synaptic contacts which each fibre makes over the whole Purkinje dendritic tree. The responses evoked by climbing fibres in the individual Purkinje cells have been investigated in detail, but there are still some difficulties in giving a complete interpretation of their function. According to Eccles *et al.*

(1967), each olivary cell samples the level of excitability of its chosen Purkinje cell and imposes appropriate changes in frequency on that cell. Since the climbing fibre exerts an intense excitatory action, it will tend to oppose any inhibitory effects produced by stellate and basket cells. If the climbing fibre activity is decreased, the frequency of Purkinje cell discharge will be reduced. Thus the climbing fibre impulses have a dominating control of the only output from the cerebellar cortex.

Entirely consistent with this view and an extension of it is the idea that the climbing fibres may operate as a buffer mechanism. For smoothness and efficiency, for example in carrying out a skilled movement, it is essential that impulse discharges be maintained within appropriate limits. The climbing fibres may serve this purpose. A high-frequency discharge of the Purkinje cells will impose severe inhibition on the deep cerebellar nuclei whilst a low frequency will have the opposite effect. The desired level of activity is attained by means of the climbing fibre influence on the Purkinje cell discharges. In this way, the output of the cerebellum is controlled and extremes of excitability or depression are avoided.

As regards the cells of the deep nuclei there is sufficient evidence that they are maintained in a state of excitation by both mossy fibre and climbing fibre collaterals; and their firing rate may be increased or reduced or totally silenced according to the signals conveyed by the Purkinje axons which converge upon them.

REFERENCES

Bloedel, J. R. & Roberts, W. J. (1969). Functional relationship among neurones of the cerebellar cortex in the absence of anaesthesia. *J. Neurophysiol.* **32**, 75–84.

Brodal, A., Walberg, F. & Blackstad, T. (1950). Termination of spinal afferents to inferior olive in cat. *J. Neurophysiol.* **13**, 431–454.

Cajal, S. R. (1909). *Histologie du Systéme Nerveux de L'homme et des Vertèbres.* Maloine, Paris.

Carrea, R. M. E. & Grundfest, H. (1954). Electrophysiological studies of cerebellar inflow. *J. Neurophysiol.* **17**, 208–238.

Eccles, J. C. (1973). The cerebellum as a computer: patterns in space and time. *J. Physiol.* **229**, 1–32.

Eccles, J. C., Faber, D. S. & Taborikova, H. (1971). The action of a parallel fiber volley on the antidromic invasion of Purkyne cells of cat cerebellum. *Brain Res.* **25**, 335–356.

Eccles, J. C., Ito, M. & Szentagothai, J. (1967). *The Cerebellum as a Neuronal Machine.* Springer-Verlag, Berlin.

Eccles, J. C., Llinas, R. & Sasaki, K. (1966a). The excitatory synaptic action of climbing fibres on the Purkinje cells of the cerebellum. *J. Physiol.* **182**, 268–296.

Eccles, J. C., Llinas, R. & Sasaki, K. (1966b). The mossy fiber granule cell relay in the cerebellum and its inhibition of Golgi cells. *Expl Brain Res.* **1**, 82–101.

Eccles, J. C., Sabah, N. H., Schmidt, R. F. & Taborikova, H. (1972a). Cutaneous mechanoreceptors influencing impulse discharges in cerebellar cortex. 11. In Purkinje cells by mossy fiber inputs. *Expl Brain Res.* **15**, 261–277.

Eccles, J. C., Sabah, N. H., Schmidt, R. F. & Taborikova, H. (1972b). Mode of operation of the cerebellum in the dynamic loop control of movement. *Brain Res.* **40**, 73–80.

Fox, C. A. & Barnard, J. W. (1957). A quantitative study of the Purkinje cell dendritic branchlets and their relationship to afferent fibres. *J. Anat.* **91**, 199–313.

Granit, R. & Phillips, C. G. (1956). Excitatory and inhibitory processes acting upon individual Purkinje cells of the cerebellum in cats. *J. Physiol.* **133**, 520–547.

Grant, G. (1962). Spinal course and somatotopically localized termination of the spinocerebellar tracts. *Acta physiol. scand.* **56**, Sup. *193*, 5–45.

Grundfest, H. & Campbell, B. (1942). Origin, conduction and termination of impulses in the dorsal spinocerebellar tract of cats. *J. Neurophysiol.* **5**, 275–294.

Hamori, J. & Szentagothai, J. (1966). Identification under the electron microscope of climbing fibres and their synaptic contacts. *Expl Brain Res.* **1**, 65–81.

Ito, M. & Yoshida, M. (1966). The origins of cerebellar-induced inhibition of Deiters neurones. I. Monosynaptic initiation of the inhibitory postsynaptic potential. *Expl Brain Res.* **2**, 330–349.

Ito, M., Kawai, N., Udo, M. & Sato, N. (1968). Cerebellar-evoked disinhibition in dorsal Deiters neurones. *Expl Brain Res.* **6**, 247–264.

Jansen, J. & Brodal, A. (1954). *Aspects of Cerebellar Anatomy.* Johan Grundt Tanum Forlag, Oslo.

Larson, B., Miller, S. & Oscarsson, O. (1969a). Termination and functional organization of the dorsolateral spino-olivocerebellar path. *J. Physiol.* **203**, 611–640.

Larson, B., Miller, S. & Oscarsson, O. (1969b). Climbing fibre path activated by the flexor–reflex afferents from all four limbs. *J. Physiol.* **203**, 641–649.

Leight, R., Rowe, M. J. & Schmidt, R. F. (1973). Cortical and peripheral modification of cerebellar climbing fibre activity arising from cutaneous mechanoreceptors. *J. Physiol.* **228**, 619–635.

Marr, D. (1969). A theory of cerebellar cortex. *J. Physiol.* **202**, 437–470.

Murphy, J. T. & Sabah, N. H. (1971). Cerebellar Purkinje cell responses to afferent inputs. I. Climbing fiber activation. *Brain Res.* **25**, 449–467.

Newman, P. P. & Paul, D. H. (1969). The projection of splanchnic afferents on the cerebellum of the cat. *J. Physiol.* **202**, 223–237.

Nulsen, F. E., Black, S. P. W. & Drake, C. G. (1948). Inhibition and facilitation of motor activity by the anterior cerebellum. *Fed. Proc.* **7**, 86–87.

Oscarsson, O. (1968). Termination and functional organization of the ventral spino-olivocerebellar path. *J. Physiol.* **196**, 453–478.

Oscarsson, O. (1969). Termination and functional organization of the dorsal spino-olivocerebellar path. *J. Physiol.* **200**, 129–149.

Palkovits, M., Magyar, P. & Szentagothai, J. (1971). Quantitative histological analysis of the cerebellar cortex in the cat. I. Number and arrangement in space of the Purkinje cells. *Brain Res.* **32**, 1–13.

Thach, W. T. (1972). Cerebellar output: properties, synthesis and uses. *Brain Res.* **40**, 89–97.

Scheibel, M. E. & Scheibel, A. B. (1954). Observations on the intracortical relations of the climbing fibres of the cerebellum. *J. comp. Neurol.* **101**, 733–760.

Walberg, F. & Brodal, A. (1953). Spino-pontine fibers in the cat. An experimental study. *J. comp. Neurol.* **99**, 251–288.

6

VISCERAL FUNCTIONS LOCATED
IN THE BRAIN STEM

THE anatomical situation of the brain stem gives this portion of the nervous system a key position for regulating the mass of impulse traffic coursing between the spinal cord, the cerebellum and the cerebral hemispheres. It conveys all the visceral and somatic pathways ascending or descending the cerebrospinal axis or crossing like great highways to and from the cerebellum. In addition, it contains a complex system of minor roads or pathways constituting a structure of immense importance known as the reticular formation. Embedded in this maze of communications lie the cells of origin of the cranial nerves and a host of other nuclei, whose connexions and relationships still remain obscure. However, the brain stem is not just an anatomical centre for communications; nor must it be regarded as a simple pooling of afferent inflows. At all levels of the brain stem and, especially in the medulla, there are many reflex arcs serving as centres for visceral functions. These include the central mechanisms for cardiovascular, respiratory, digestive and temperature regulating systems. Our knowledge of these mechanisms has grown mainly from studies of output systems in the body at rest and also in response to a changing environment; however, the extensive literature on the autonomic nervous system is not being considered in this work. On the other hand, our knowledge of the working relationships between the various reflex circuits is far from complete and therefore an attempt will now be made to define their activities within the brain stem and to trace the pathways which influence them from other parts of the nervous system.

One of the difficulties in experimental work on the brain stem is to secure an adequate exposure and at the same time maintain a normal circulation in the region. The brain stem can be investigated by physiological techniques from either a dorsal or ventral approach. The dorsal approach allows the insertion of microelectrodes using stereotaxic coordinates and is probably far less disturbing to the animal. Mechanical interference is reduced to a minimum by rigid fixation of the head, drainage of the cerebrospinal fluid and, if necessary, by sealing each penetration with a solution of agar or paraffin wax over a layer of mineral oil. Stimulating and recording electrodes may be driven through the substance of the cerebellum to reach any required depth in the brain stem; alternatively, parts of the overlying cerebellum can be removed by suction. The ventral approach is more complicated than the dorsal one since the soft structures of the neck must first be excised to gain access to bone. Extra care must be taken to avoid damage to the basilar artery, which is often tortuous, and the exposure itself is limited to only a narrow strip of medulla and pons (Fig. 6.1).

CARDIOVASCULAR AND RESPIRATORY RESPONSES TO HEATING

Relatively little attention has been given to the role of the brain stem in temperature regulation since this is usually regarded as a function of the hypothalamus. However, the presence of brain stem centres for controlling the circulation and respiration suggests the possibility that the region might also react to sudden changes in temperature. The idea arose from the discovery that both pressor and depressor responses can be elicited from various points in the brain stem and that similar responses affecting heart rate, blood pressure and pulmonary ventilation are often associated with changes of temperature.

Methods of heating the brain

Early attempts to raise the temperature of the brain without heating the whole animal were described by Moorhouse (1911), who surrounded the carotid arteries in containers through which hot water was flowing. As the temperature was gradually raised, increases of heart rate and respiratory ventilation were observed; but precautions had to be taken to prevent the escape of heat to the underlying vagus nerve. Heat is a very effective stimulus on the vagus nerve and a

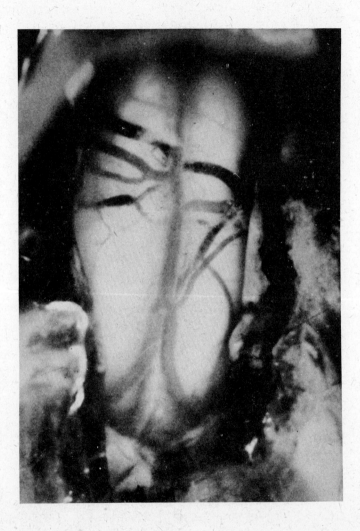

FIG. 6.1. Photograph of ventral surface of brain stem in the cat showing limits of exposure at operation. The two vertebral arteries unite near the anterior border of the foramen magnum to form the basilar artery. Many branches to medulla, pons and cerebellum are given off as the basilar artery is followed rostrally to the upper border of the pons where it divides into the posterior cerebral arteries.

suitable by-pass was usually employed. In one method on the anaesthetized or decerebrate cat, the common carotid artery was cannulated proximally and the blood passed through a glass spiral in a water-bath before being returned through a cannula inserted into the distal end of the artery. As heat was applied to the water-bath, the temperature of the carotid blood was recorded by a thermocouple tied into the lingual artery. A second thermocouple inserted through the skull registered the temperature in the brain stem (Fig. 6.2).

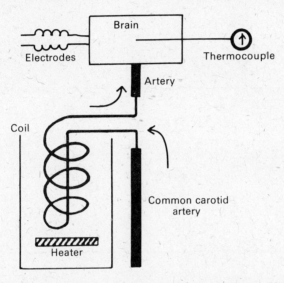

FIG. 6.2. Diagram of a method used for heating the carotid blood. The common carotid artery is cannulated proximally allowing the blood to pass through a spiral glass tube in a heated water-bath before being returned through a cannula inserted into the distal end of the artery. A thermocouple registers the change in temperature within the brain.

Cardiovascular effects of heating

A dramatic fall in blood pressure is the most consistent finding. In Fig. 6.3 it will be seen that the blood pressure recorded from the femoral artery remains unchanged until the temperature in the brain reaches 41·5°C. At this point the blood pressure falls rapidly and remains depressed during the period of heating, but recovers when the brain is cooled by filling the water-bath with cold water. After the

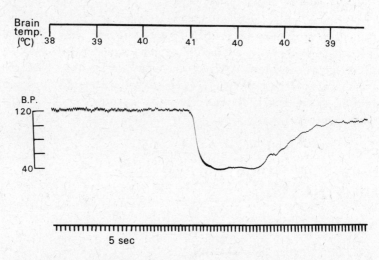

FIG. 6.3. Effect of heating the carotid blood on arterial blood pressure. Cat under sodium pentobarbitone anaesthesia. Femoral blood pressure at 120 mm Hg. When the brain temperature reaches 41°C the blood pressure rapidly falls. As the brain is cooled the blood pressure rises again.

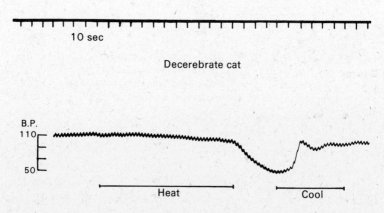

FIG. 6.4. Effect of heating and cooling carotid blood in decerebrate cat. Femoral blood pressure at 110 mm Hg. The changes are not dependent upon the hypothalamus since this had been removed together with the cerebral hemispheres.

blood pressure has returned to its original level, the whole procedure can be repeated many times in the same animal (Newman & Wolstencroft, 1960). Examination of the tracings will show that there is no acceleration of the heart during the period of heating and the only change that is ever recorded in the cat is a slight reduction, e.g. from 210 to 180 beats/min. The response to heating the carotid blood occurs in the intact animal and after bilateral section of the carotid sinus nerves and the cervical vagi. It also occurs in the decerebrate animal with the whole of the hypothalamus removed (Fig. 6.4).

Respiratory effects of heating

As the temperature of the blood in the carotid artery begins to rise, a slight increase in the depth of respiration is usually observed with little or no change in rate. At the critical temperature when the blood pressure falls, there is a marked increase in the depth of respiration sometimes accompanied by an increase of rate. Ventilation returns to its original level as soon as the carotid blood is cooled (Fig. 6.5). The increase in respiration is possibly due to a direct central action of heat on the respiratory neurones. It might be equally contended that the

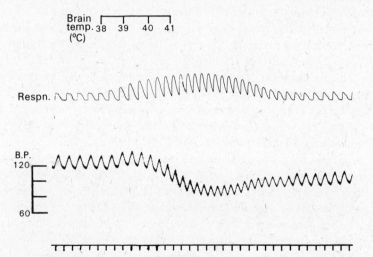

FIG. 6.5. Effect of heating carotid blood on respiration. Cat under sodium pentobarbitone anaesthesia. As brain temperature begins to rise there is an increase in depth of respiration. Note also increase in respiratory rate as blood pressure falls.

increase of respiration is secondary to the fall in blood pressure with consequent rise of CO_2 tension. This is a valid suggestion since it is known that an increase in the CO_2 content of the blood and increased acidity act as a stimulus to breathing. Certainly the effects are not due to reflex stimulation of the carotid chemoreceptors since they are found after section of the chemoreceptor nerves.

A heat-sensitive region in the medulla

Although it is clear that the changes produced by heating the carotid blood involved structures in the brain stem, more precise localization was attempted by direct heating through electrodes introduced at various levels. Experiments were performed on decerebrate cats in which the hypothalamus was completely removed. The heating electrodes were made of fine silver wire, insulated except at the tip and connected to the output of a high-frequency oscillator. The temperature in the region of the electrode tip was recorded by a thermocouple. When the heating current was switched on, the brain temperature rose slowly with gradual spread of heat to adjacent structures; but a second thermocouple placed 1 cm from the tip of the heating electrode showed a temperature at least 1°C lower than that recorded close to the tip. The distribution of responsive points within the brain stem was explored within the limits of the exposed field which extended from the upper pons to the lower medulla (Holmes, Newman & Wolstencroft, 1960).

The temperature recorded by the thermocouple before heating began was usually about 38°C. It was found that heating could be applied until the brain temperature reached 43°C without causing any obvious or irreversible damage to the cells. However, it was unnecessary to heat above 41–42°C in order to obtain consistent responses and heating was then discontinued until blood pressure and respiration had returned to their original state. No effects were ever seen when the heating electrode was in the upper pons or lower medulla. Small responses sometimes observed in the lower pons could have been due to the spread of heat. Figure 6.6 shows that the region of maximal activity was located in the upper part of the medulla. It can be seen that when the temperature recorded by the thermocouple reached 41°C the blood pressure fell about 20–40 mm Hg. Respiration increased with rise in temperature. If the brain stem was sectioned at the junction between pons and medulla, the small responses recorded from points above the section were abolished, but responses from points below the section were unaffected. Similar results were obtained after sections between the upper and middle parts of the medulla. Thus the limits of the responsive region in the upper medulla could be demonstrated.

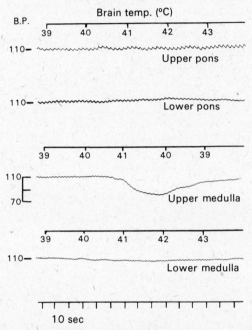

FIG. 6.6. Location of heat-sensitive region in medulla. Decerebrate cat. Direct heating of brain stem to determine distribution of responsive points. With the heating electrode in the pons or lower part of the medulla the blood pressure remains unchanged even when brain temperature reaches 43°C. With the heating electrode in rostral medulla blood pressure falls at 41°C.

Examination of serial sections stained with toluidin blue revealed the track made by the heating electrode. It was found that in each instance in which heating had produced a fall in blood pressure the electrode had entered the medial reticular formation at some point rostral to the hypoglossal nucleus. In experiments giving the largest responses, the tip of the electrode lay surrounded by cells of the nucleus reticularis gigantocellularis in a plane between the rostral part of the nucleus ambiguus and nucleus of the VI nerve (Fig. 6.7). Smaller responses had followed insertions of the electrode into the nucleus reticularis pontis caudalis.

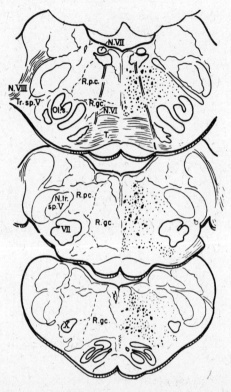

FIG. 6.7. Serial transverse sections through the brain stem of cat. The sections extend rostrally at level of superior olive (01.S.) to nucleus of X nerve caudally. Heat-sensitive points are found in nucleus pontis caudalis (R.p.c.) and nucleus reticularis gigantocellularis (R.gc.). T, trapezoid body; VII, motor nucleus of facial nerve.

Interpreting the results of these experiments, it is clear that certain structures in the brain stem are sensitive to heat and produce their effects in the absence of the hypothalamus. What is the most likely cause of the fall in blood pressure? Our experiments suggest that a group of nerve cells distributed within the medial reticular formation bring about a vasodepressor response when stimulated by a rise of temperature in the carotid blood flow or by the local application of heat. Whichever method is used, the response is the same at a critical temperature of 41–42°C. In the cat, descending fibres arise from the entire nucleus reticularis gigantocellularis, occupy the ventral part of the lateral funiculus and terminate in the thoracic region of the cord (Torvik & Brodal, 1957). It is possible that these fibres serve as a pathway for the mediation of the depressor response.

The anatomical site of the 'heat-sensitive' region corresponds with the position of depressor or vasodilator points described by several investigators. Ranson & Billingsley (1916) explored the medulla with stimulating electrodes, searching for vasomotor reactions. They identified discrete points which either excited or inhibited the functions of the sympathetic system. Wang & Ranson (1939) recorded blood pressure changes following electrical stimulation of the brain stem with fine needle electrodes. This method revealed extensive pressor and depressor regions within the medullary reticular formation. Alexander (1946) used the inferior cardiac nerve as an index of sympathetic outflow to the cardiovascular system in addition to recording arterial blood pressure. A series of maps were constructed to show the distribution of pressor and depressor regions at various levels in the brain stem and it is interesting to note that maximal depressor responses were elicited from the medial reticular formation about the level of the inferior olive. Alexander believed that the depressor points constituted a distinct functional entity operating through a system of descending spinal pathways rather than merely a region which contributed inhibitory afferents to the vasomotor centre. The idea of a distinct vasodilator system which was both anatomically and functionally separate from the medullary vasomotor system was given further support by the work of Lindgren (1955) in the cat. The latter author demonstrated changes in arterial blood pressure and venous blood flow in the muscles, skin and splanchnic area following localized electrical stimulation of the brain stem. The greatest changes were recorded in the skeletal muscles, where increases of blood flow were shown to be due to active vasodilatation and not to inhibition of vasoconstrictor tone. However, since both vasoconstrictor and vasodilator neurones exist in close relationship within the brain stem, it is possible that the vascular responses resulting from electrical stimulation were the result of interaction between the two systems.

The experimental results produced by localized heating do not warrant any conclusions on the neuronal mechanisms involved. Nevertheless the evidence indicates that there is a close link between the medullary heat-sensitive structures and those which are believed to constitute a vasodilator system. In the first place, they share a common site of action in the medial reticular formation of the medulla and both operate after the hypothalamus has been removed. Of course, these centres may not function independently in the intact animal and perhaps they should be regarded simply as relay stations for hypothalamic and cerebral outflow. Secondly, they share the same kind of activities in producing dramatic changes in blood pressure and local blood flow in the tissues. Here, however, there is a difference. The effect of heating the medulla is always a fall and never a rise of arterial blood pressure, whereas electrical stimulation has a variable effect on blood pressure. Low intensities of stimulation generally produce a fall, attended by an increased blood flow in the muscles, and this changes into a rise when the stimulus intensity is increased. Such reversals can be explained by spread of current from vasodilator to vasoconstrictor neurones. The evidence therefore suggests that localized heat applied to the brain stem may actively excite a depressor region in the reticular formation, causing vasodilatation and a fall of blood pressure. The alternative view, which cannot be excluded, is the possibility of direct inhibitory action of heat-sensitive neurones on the vasomotor centre with consequent reduction in vasoconstrictor activity.

As regards the function of these centres in the brain stem, our knowledge is very imperfect. Heat-loss mechanisms in the hypothalamus must obviously play the major role under physiological conditions and the fact that medullary mechanisms can operate after removal of the hypothalamus does not diminish the importance of the higher levels of temperature control. Evidence will be given in Chapter 9 that the orbital cortex has a direct pathway to the medial reticular formation through which the heat-sensitive neurones may be influenced. It is also known that impulses from the motor cortex can elevate or lower the blood pressure and produce other circulatory changes associated with muscular exercise. Even though such changes are probably mediated by the autonomic activities of the hypothalamus, the existence of lower centres in the medulla must not be forgotten. Their role may be limited to emergency states. As the body temperature rises, a redistribution of the circulating blood in viscera, muscles and skin is essential to remove the excessive heat. This object is normally achieved by cutaneous vasodilatation, whilst the blood pressure is maintained at a constant level or even raised by over-compensation. Only when a critical temperature is reached does compensation fail and massive vasodilatation occurs accompanied by circulatory collapse. It is perhaps premature to speculate on the involvement of medullary mechanisms in heat exhaustion although the circulatory events are comparable.

ALIMENTARY REFLEXES

Besides the neural mechanisms in the medulla which are necessary for the regulation of cardiovascular, respiratory and thermal functions of the body, the lower part of the brain stem contains visceral centres for other reflex activities. These include various afferent and efferent pathways belonging to the cranial nerves, in particular, the vagus nerve and scattered zones associated with the functions of vomiting and salivation.

Vomiting

The act of vomiting is a motor effect resulting in compression of the stomach and emptying of its contents through a dilated cardiac orifice; but it is usually preceded and accompanied by a complex series of events indicating widespread involvement of the nervous system. The precise location of a vomiting centre was described by Wang & Borison (1950) following a series of experiments on the decerebrate cat. Using stereotaxic placements of electrodes, they stimulated various points in the tractus solitarius and its nucleus, extending to the dorsolateral border of the reticular formation. No other region of the brain stem yielded vomiting by electrical stimulation. In another series of experiments on chronic animals, the same authors found that bilateral destruction of the lateral reticular formation prevented responses to a central emetic, e.g. apomorphine hydrochloride, in doses which normally produced vomiting after two minutes. Damage to adjacent structures in the medulla was minimized by the use of gold or glass radon seeds, inserted into the desired location. The authors concluded that the central mechanism for vomiting resided in the dorsolateral border of the lateral reticular formation and not in the dorsal sensory nucleus of the vagus nerve. In subsequent work (Wang & Borison, 1952), it became apparent that the region responding to electrical stimulation was not identical to the structures sensitive to the action of chemical emetics. They produced evidence for the separate existence of a 'chemoreceptor trigger mechanism' in the floor of the fourth ventricle, corresponding to the area postrema. The problem was approached in two ways:

1. Bilateral cauterization of this zone in the dog resulted in the loss of centrally induced emesis, e.g. by apomorphine.

2. The administration of copper sulphate demonstrated a powerful emetic response. When copper sulphate was introduced into the stomach of a fasting dog, vomiting occurred within a few minutes, but if the nerves to the stomach were cut, vomiting was delayed for about two hours. If, however, the drug was given intravenously in a dog with a denervated stomach, vomiting occurred within a few minutes. Thus copper sulphate had both a peripheral and a central action. The experiments indicated that impulses from the stomach reached the vomiting centre through afferents in the vagi and sympathetic nerves and, if these nerves were cut, vomiting still occurred after a delay of about two hours. This was presumably the time required for the absorbed copper in the circulating blood to reach an adequate concentration. The authors concluded that there were really two vomiting centres in the medulla—chemical and reflex. Chemical emesis was due to the activity of a chemoreceptor zone which was sensitive to drugs like apomorphine; reflex emesis was due to impulses arising from the stomach or any part of the alimentary tract or from other organs.

The area postrema has been subjected to careful histological examination in an attempt to distinguish elements which might suggest a special chemoreceptor function. Brizzee & Neal (1954) described large 'glialoid' cells resembling astroblasts and arranged in clusters with a prominent capillary network. There were very few nerve fibres associated with these cells. However, loose bundles of nerve fibres were seen arising from smaller cells and terminating in the solitary tract. No definite conclusion was reached about the function of the two types of cells, but the authors supported the view that the area postrema may have a chemoreceptor function. They suggested that the nerve bundles might serve as a conduction pathway from the receptors to the lateral reticular formation. Brizzee (1956) also showed that bilateral lesions of the area postrema in the monkey resulted in loss of the central response to emetic drugs, a finding that would seem to confirm the existence of a chemoreceptor trigger zone.

To summarize briefly, there may be two regions in the brain stem concerned in the act of vomiting—a chemical zone located in the area postrema of the fourth ventricle and a reflex centre in the lateral reticular formation. The former is sensitive only to emetic chemicals; the latter is a target for afferent impulses from the abdominal and pelvic organs. It is likely that the reflex centre can also be influenced by a wide variety of sensory nerves and by impulses from higher centres.

Salivation

A flow of saliva can easily be elicited when the medulla is stimulated with a weak current. Early investigators were able to demonstrate two secretory nuclei which produced effects on the submaxillary or parotid gland. Miller (1913) applied faradic stimulation to the surface of the medulla in the cat. Chatfield (1941), working on dogs, used a concentric bipolar electrode for more accurate location of the salivary centres, which he found scattered through the reticular substance in regions close to the facial nucleus. Submaxillary responses were predominantly in the rostral part and parotid responses in the caudal part. Magoun & Beaton (1942) confirmed these findings in the monkey. Wang (1943) explored both sides of the brain stem for salivary responses in the cat, using a stereotaxic instrument, and constructed maps of submaxillary and parotid points which were afterwards identified histologically. He found that stimulation of the brain stem above the level of the pons or below the level of the inferior olive did not produce an appreciable flow of saliva. Analysis of all the responsive points revealed two regions of maximal activity, but no sharp division between them. The distribution suggested a rostral area supplying the submaxillary glands and a caudal area supplying the parotid glands. Stimulation of the intermediate area, within the lateral reticular formation, yielded both submaxillary and parotid secretion.

It will be clear from the above reports that many of the positive points for salivary secretion overlap the sites for the vomiting reflex. This is not surprising since vomiting is frequently preceded by nausea and salivation. Under normal conditions, the flow of saliva is the result of stimulation of nerves supplying the mouth, palate and tongue. The afferents are carried in the glossopharyngeal and lingual nerves to the medullary salivary centres which serve as a simple reflex mechanism responding to the introduction of food into the mouth. The medullary centres are also controlled by a more complicated cortical mechanism through which behavioural and emotional situations are expressed.

CONTROL OF URINARY BLADDER

As described in Chapter 2, afferents from the urinary bladder gain access to the spinal cord by two routes: fibres concerned with micturition travel with the pelvic nerves to the sacral segments of the cord, whilst those concerned with the sensations of discomfort and pain are carried in the hypogastric nerves to lower thoracic and lumbar segments. The involvement of the spinal cord in bladder reflexes was discussed in Chapter 3 from information based on experimental spinal lesions and from clinical findings. The spinal afferent pathways of the bladder are not so well documented since they are difficult to distinguish in the cord from the descending pathways. According to the studies of Barrington (1933) in the cat, bladder impulses via the pelvic nerves are conveyed in the dorsal half of the lateral columns and, from clinical studies, Nathan & Smith (1951) distinguished two spinal routes, the pathway for pain and temperature lying within the spino-thalamic tract and that subserving pressure or bladder tension within the posterior columns.

The dual nature of bladder innervation, at least in experimental work, is fully maintained at the level of the brain stem. Studies on the reflexes involved in micturition show that not all of them have their centres in the spinal cord; but attempts to produce bladder contractions by brain stem stimulation have not been very successful. However, the results of electrolytic lesions causing localized destruction in the chronic animal can be correlated with the disturbances of function seen in the neurogenic bladder in man. Using a stereotaxic instrument for precise placement of the lesions Barrington (1925) showed that there are two distinct regions in the pons which are employed in the neural control of the bladder. One is situated at the level of the motor nucleus of the V cranial nerve and, when it is destroyed bilaterally, the animal is unable to empty the bladder with consequent retention of urine. It is possible that this is the region served by pelvic afferents ascending in the dorsolateral columns of the cord and the reflex will be evoked by distension of the bladder. The second region is situated in the mid-brain between the mesencephalic root of the V nerve and the aqueduct at the level of the inferior colliculus. It might represent a centre for the relay of afferents from the hypogastric plexus which ascend in the spino-thalamic tracts, since bilateral destruction of the region results in loss of conscious sensation and desire to micturate.

THE INFERIOR OLIVE

Although the olive and its connexions have been studied in great detail by degeneration experiments our knowledge of the relationship between the different afferent systems which converge on it is far from complete. It is only in recent years that the importance of the olive has been recognized following renewed interest in the olivo-cerebellar projections. Once it was shown that the olivary cells gave origin to the climbing fibres, it was realized that the olive must play an essential role in the functions of the cerebellum. The findings from anatomical studies have largely been confirmed by electrophysiological techniques and ideas are now forthcoming about the organization of the units within the olive. In the previous chapter, an account was given of the spinal pathways which are believed to converge on the olive and the possible functions of these pathways discussed. Less is known about the afferent contributions from sources within the brain itself, but there is good reason to believe that impulses are relayed through the olive from such structures as the caudate nucleus, sensorimotor cortex and limbic system.

Anatomy of the olive

In the cat, the position of the olive is found on the ventral surface of the medulla, just lateral to the elevation caused by the pyramidal tract. The greater part of the olive lies dorsal to the pyramid and its surface marking can be represented as an oval area extending at the side of the basilar artery into the pons. In transverse section, the nucleus appears as a curved band of grey matter opening on the medial side for emergence of its fibres; the bulk of these cross immediately to the opposite side intersecting the spinal tract of the Vth cranial nerve and fibres from the opposite nucleus. They form the olivo-cerebellar tract and terminate as climbing fibres in the white matter of the cerebellum. Histological examination of the olive reveals several types of neurones all with relatively simple dendritic processes and orange-staining bodies representing neuroglia (Scheibel & Scheibel, 1955). Axons and dendrites form an interlacing network. Afferent fibres terminating in the olive form two principal projections: (1) a spinal contribution relaying to all parts of the cerebellum from cells in the caudal zone of the nucleus; (2) a cerebral contribution relaying to specific regions of the cerebellum from cells in the cephalic zone of the nucleus. Such fibre distributions suggest the possibility of functional differences between the two systems.

Methods of unit recording

The olive can be explored from either the ventral or dorsal aspect of the medulla with the head fixed firmly in a stereotaxic instrument. Many authors have preferred the ventral approach. In this method, the base of the skull is exposed after removing the soft structures in front of the neck and a small hole is drilled into the bone over the medulla. The bone is nibbled away with fine forceps to expose the area between the auditory bullae and extended caudally to the edge of the foramen magnum. After deflecting the dura, the microelectrodes are inserted under observation of a low-powered microscope in order to avoid branches of the basilar artery. The spontaneous activity of single unit discharges can usually be displayed for long periods of time if respiratory movements are reduced to a minimum by using high oxygen mixtures. Otherwise some of the various methods described in Chapter 1 can be employed to minimize pulsations.

In the dorsal approach, the cerebellum is exposed on both sides to the level of the tentorium. The primary fissure is identified and the microelectrode inserted at right angles to the surface at a point on the primary fissure about 2 mm lateral to the mid-line. In an average size adult cat the depth between the dorsal surface of the cerebellum and the ventral surface of the medulla is about 20 mm and the inferior olive is reached at about 18 mm deep to the pial surface. The position of the electrode tip must be identified after each experiment as shown in Fig. 6.8. In practice, the depth of a penetration is often revealed by the character of the electrical discharges as the microelectrode passes through the various layers of the cerebellum. A quiet period ensues as the tip passes through the fourth ventricle to enter the medullary substance. When using this method, there is comparative freedom from mechanical disturbances and less trauma inflicted on the animal.

Fig. 6.8. Transverse section through brain stem and cerebellum of cat at level of inferior olive. The position of the electrode tip is seen on the left side, resulting from a penetration extending through the substance of the cerebellum. The tract made by the electrode shaft is not shown in this section.

Descending functional pathways

Work is now in progress attempting to sort out the pathways and functions of the descending afferents reaching the inferior olive via the mid-brain. It has been shown by degeneration experiments that fibres descend from different parts of the brain to all subdivisions of the olivary complex and many of these findings have received physiological confirmation. It is believed that the afferent connexions to the olive are important for viscero-somatic interactions and the following account will attempt to evaluate the state of available knowledge.

Projections from the basal ganglia

Contributions from anatomical studies have demonstrated the existence of fibre connexions between the basal ganglia and the olives, but the methods are open to uncertainties in regard to the extent of the damage created by an experimental lesion. Investigating pathways from the globus pallidus in the monkey Woodburne, Crosby & McCotter (1946) traced a discrete bundle through the internal capsule to the periventricular grey behind the red nucleus. In the pons, the fibres occupied a position dorsal to the medial lemniscus and terminated at the level of the upper medulla in the rostral part of the inferior olive. This pallido-olivary pathway appeared to project bilaterally. Walberg (1956) also reported on a pathway between the caudate nucleus and the inferior olive. He found that in the cat, a discrete lesion placed in one caudate nucleus caused degeneration in both olives; the extent of the degeneration was approximately equal on the two sides. The fibres terminated in the dorsal lamella of the inferior olive and the rostral part of the medial accessory olive. According to Walberg, there was no evidence of convergence between the caudate–olivary projections and those ascending to the olive from the spinal cord.

Electrophysiological investigations began with the studies of Snider & Barnard (1949), working on cats and monkeys. Bipolar electrodes were placed stereotaxically in the inferior olive and evoked monophasic responses were recorded following electrical stimulation of the caudate nucleus. All the responses were bilateral, the more prominent being on the ipsilateral side. However, they were unable to obtain results following stimulation of the putamen or globus pallidus. The activity of single olivary neurones responding to caudate stimulation has been reported by Sedgwick & Williams (1967). Most of the units were found in the rostral half of the inferior olive, thus confirming the observations of Walberg mentioned above. The latency of the unit responses fell into two groups—short and long—ranging between 1·0 and 18·4 msec. Recently Gresty & Paul (1970) have monitored the olivary output following caudate stimulation by recording evoked climbing fibre responses of Purkinje cells.

Projections from sensorimotor cortex

It would appear from the results of anatomical investigations that all parts of the cerebral cortex are represented in the olivary complex although the greatest contribution comes from the sensorimotor cortex (Walberg, 1956). However, lesions made by a knife or by suction can hardly be described as discrete and involvement of adjacent structures cannot be excluded. In spite of the limitations of tracing pathways by the method of degeneration, the following important facts may be clearly stated:

1. Each sensorimotor cortex gives a bilateral projection to the olives.
2. The distribution of the terminal fibres within the olive is highly specific.
3. Many descending afferents terminate on olivary cells which are not influenced by spinal cord afferents.

Turning now to physiological evidence, many authors have recorded cerebellar action potentials in response to stimulation of the sensorimotor cortex and recent studies indicate that the olive is a relay station for some of these impulses. Armstrong & Harvey (1966) studied the field potentials and single unit discharges evoked by stimulation of the ipsilateral cerebral cortex in the cat. Maximal effects were obtained from points near the junction of the coronal and anterior sigmoid gyri. The majority of responsive units was located in the ventral lamella of the inferior olive and the latencies ranged between 8·3 and 9·4 msec. Although unit discharges were readily evoked at low intensities of stimulation, shorter latencies were not observed when the stimulus intensity was increased. Their results would therefore suggest that the cortical projection to the olive was by an indirect polysynaptic pathway. However, Sedgwick & Williams (1967) demonstrated the existence of olivary units with short latency responses when stimulating approximately the same region so that the possibility of a direct cortico-olivary connexion cannot be excluded.

Experiments now in progress confirm the bilaterality of descending influences from the sensorimotor cortex. Furthermore, it can be shown that individual cells in the brain stem or cerebellum can be activated by impulses originating in both cerebral hemispheres. In cats under thiopental sodium anaesthesia, a recording microelectrode was inserted into the cerebellum and stimulating electrodes were applied to the pericruciate areas of the cerebral cortex on the two sides. Single shocks delivered to either the contralateral or the ipsilateral cerebral cortex evoked a discharge in the same cerebellar unit. The threshold of the responsive units was found to be the same whichever side was stimulated and both short-latency and long-latency responses were elicited (Hossain & Newman, 1968). However, when comparing the short-latency responses of the two sides, the ipsilateral response was consistently longer. This finding is illustrated in the traces of Fig. 6.9. Obviously it would be interesting to know more about these bilateral influences on the cerebellum; but the pathways and precise structures through which they relay in the brain stem have not yet been

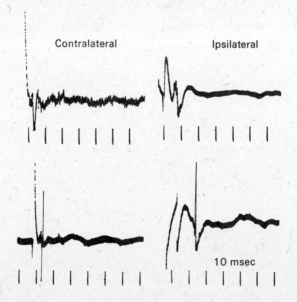

FIG. 6.9. Cerebellar responses to stimulation of cerebral cortex. Cat under sodium thiopentone anaesthesia. Upper traces show evoked primary wave; lower traces, response of single cerebellar unit. Stimulus applied to pericruciate cortex. Note short latency of contralateral responses and relatively longer latency of ipsilateral responses.

determined. It is curious that the ipsilateral response should have a longer latency unless the fibres cross in the brain stem to the opposite side, then recross to reach the ipsilateral cerebellum; alternatively, the impulses may be delayed in the brain stem reticular formation. It is unlikely that projections from one cerebral cortex cross into the opposite cortex before descending into the brain stem since the ipsilateral response is unaffected after section of the corpus callosum

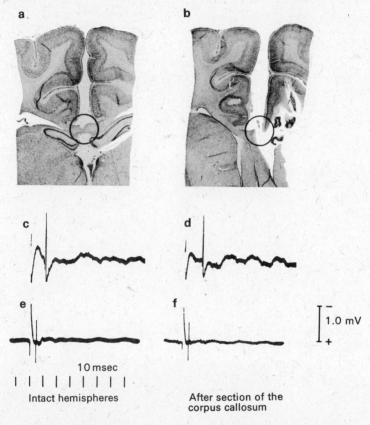

FIG. 6.10. Unit responses recorded from the cerebellum before and after complete section of the corpus callosum. (a), corpus callosum intact; (b) corpus callosum divided. (c) and (d) are comparable ipsilateral unit responses; (e) and (f) are comparable contralateral responses. Stimuli delivered to sensory cortex. The evidence suggests that projections from each sensory cortex converge on identical points in the cerebellum but do not cross before descending into the brain stem.

or even after removal of the entire contralateral cerebral hemisphere (Fig. 6.10).

As regards the questions of convergence and interaction between cerebral and spinal cord afferents, some light is thrown by the results of our experiments. Cerebellar units can be driven by both cerebral and peripheral nerve stimulation. Thus, if a testing stimulus, delivered to the splanchnic nerve, is preceded by a conditioning stimulus to the cerebral cortex, the response to the testing stimulus may be inhibited.

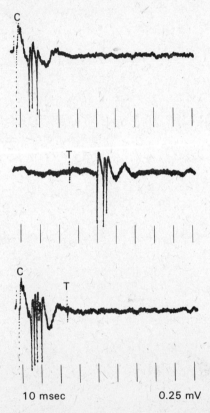

10 msec   0.25 mV

Fig. 6.11. Corticofugal inhibition. Top trace, cerebellar unit response to a single stimulus delivered to the sensory cortex. Middle trace, response of same unit to a single stimulus delivered to the splanchnic nerve. Lower trace, conditioning stimulus (C) to sensory cortex, testing stimulus (T) to splanchnic nerve. C–T interval 25 msec. The test response is inhibited.

The typical effect was a reduction in the probability of response to splanchnic stimulation until complete inhibition was observed (Fig. 6.11). Depression of the test response could last as long as 90 msec. The fact that the same cerebellar unit could be driven from both afferent sources suggests that convergence must occur at a site in the brain stem or in the cerebellum itself. As mentioned above, Walberg (1956) could find no histological evidence of convergence between cerebral and spinal afferents in his studies of the inferior olive. However, several authors have reported the possibility of convergence on single olivary units. Thus Carrea, Ruarte & Volkind (1968) stated that significant convergence and interaction from various sources were the exception rather than the rule since more than half of the units they sampled did not respond to physiological stimulation. They did not attempt any systematic studies of cortico-olivary projections. Crill (1970) reported that 30 per cent of the units studied in his experiments responded to stimulation of both cerebral and spinal inputs, but the majority of the units were located in the dorsal accessory nucleus of the olive. Other evidence for modification of olivary discharges by the cerebral cortex has been based on studies of climbing fibre responses. Thus Miller, Nezlina & Oscarsson (1969) reported on convergence patterns in climbing fibre responses to both peripheral and cortical inputs and Leicht, Rowe & Schmidt (1973) demonstrated similar findings when using controlled mechanical stimuli. Indeed, the observations reported by the latter authors were in close agreement with the experimental results described above. The mechanical stimulation consisted of air jets, vibration, taps and pressure applied to the foot pads of all four limbs and to the hairy skin of the limbs and the body. When such stimuli were preceded by an electrical stimulus delivered to the cerebral cortex, the climbing fibre responses evoked by the skin were inhibited in 65 per cent of all the units tested. Maximal inhibitory effects were observed at conditioning-testing intervals of 30–70 msec and the duration of the inhibition could last up to 125 msec. However, their studies of interaction between the spino-olivocerebellar pathways and the cerebral cortex were limited to the precruciate region only. Accordingly, no definite conclusions can yet be drawn on the mechanisms involved in the sensorimotor projections or on the role of the inferior olive and further information is awaited.

Projections from orbital cortex

The important role of the orbital cortex and other parts of the limbic system in the control of visceral functions will be discussed in subsequent chapters. Very little is known about the influence of the orbital cortex on structures in the brain stem; but evidence of an orbito-cerebellar pathway, possibly mediated by the inferior olive, will be described here.

In cats under sodium thiopentone anaesthesia, responses evoked by orbital stimulation were recorded simultaneously from the brain stem and cerebellum. The stimulating electrodes were fine monopolar wires, insulated except at the tips, which lay about 1–2 mm deep to the pia on the orbital surface. On each side, the most effective point of insertion was found to be in the posterior sigmoid gyrus at the inferior end of the ansate sulcus. Symmetrical points were stimulated, as near

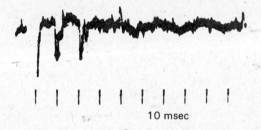

10 msec

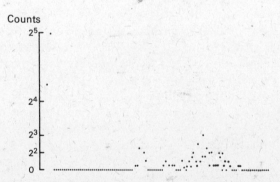

Fig. 6.12. Orbito-cerebellar responses. Cat under sodium thiopentone anaesthesia. Top: early and late evoked responses recorded from posterior culmen of anterior lobe following stimulation of the orbital cortex. Bottom: post-stimulus histogram showing the number of events occurring at two distinct peaks of time during 32 successive sweeps. Inter-point time = 160 μsec.

as possible, in the two hemispheres and the tips identified after each experiment.

Impulses set up by stimulating either the ipsilateral or contralateral orbital cortex evoked responses in single units of the inferior olive and in units located in the anterior lobe of the cerebellum. Olivary unit discharges were initially positive-going, followed by two or three secondary spikes. The threshold of stimulation was about 4 volts, 0·1 msec duration and the characteristic response was usually a multiple

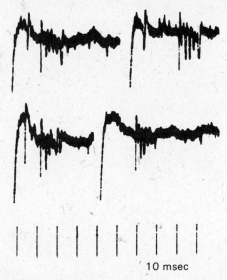

10 msec

Fig. 6.13. Inhibition of short-latency response. Cat under sodium thiopentone anaesthesia. Conditioning stimulus applied to orbital cortex on one side and testing stimulus to a symmetrical point on the opposite side. Responses recorded from anterior lobe of cerebellum. Upper trace shows complete response (short- and long-latency components) following both conditioning and testing stimuli; C–T interval 60 msec. Lower trace shows inhibition of the short-latency component of the test response when C–T interval is reduced to 40 msec. Long-latency component is unaffected.

spike discharge with a latency of about 8·0 msec for the first spike. Cerebellar unit discharges were far more complex. Analysis of the latencies showed that the evoked responses fell into two main groups: early responses with latencies ranging between 4·0 and 8·4 msec and late responses with a latency range from 13·4 to 18·8 msec. It was apparent that the early cerebellar responses did not involve pathways through the inferior olive; but the late responses could have been relayed by olivary neurones and their climbing fibres to reach the cerebellar cortex 3–5 msec later (Fig. 6.12).

The orbital cortex projects bilaterally on the anterior lobe of the cerebellum. When symmetrical points were stimulated in a conditioning-testing sequence, it was found that the conditioning stimulus had a long-lasting inhibitory effect on the test response. Evidence of depression could be detected for periods lasting up to 400 msec. When the early and late components were displayed in the same response, it was possible to block the early discharges whilst the late activity remained unaffected (Fig. 6.13). Interaction between the late components of the responses gave typical inhibitory curves with maximal blocking effects and recovery times as shown in the graph of Fig. 6.14. The results of all these experiments suggest that the orbital cortex may have an important influence on cerebellar unit discharges.

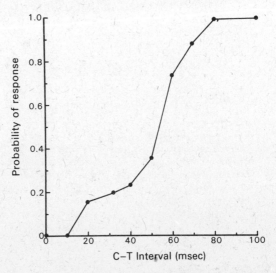

Fig. 6.14. Graph of interaction between late components of orbito-cerebellar responses. Ordinate shows, for the various test intervals, the probability of occurrence of the test response. Probability of response to testing input from orbital cortex is 1·0 with C–T intervals over 80 msec. Prior stimulation of opposite cortex at test intervals indicated on abscissa produced inhibitory effect and reduction of response probability to 0·0. Maximal blocking effects occur at C–T intervals between 10 and 40 msec.

The impulses are mediated by two distinct projection systems—a relatively fast system that may involve the reticular formation and a slower or delayed system relaying in the brain stem via specific olivary neurones.

THE RETICULAR FORMATION

In spite of numerous studies of the reticular structure at various levels of the brain stem, there is no clear picture, except in the broadest sense, of a functional organization. In fact, attempts to trace the pathways of the afferent systems have proved extremely difficult and the emphasis has now shifted to physiological analysis and the coding of impulses. Attempts to subdivide the reticular formation into distinct cell groups have not been convincing although Brodal (1953) in an extensive study identified three collections of nuclei which gave origin to reticular–cerebellar projections. It remains to be seen whether a more extensive knowledge of the reticular pathways will favour the idea of spatial differentiation and the existence of separate systems or whether the various afferent streams which appear to converge on the reticular neurones share a common field of activity. From the evidence of single unit recordings the latter would seem the more likely since the same unit can often be influenced by different sense modalities and by impulses arising from both sides of the body. Indeed, some authors refer to a 'central internuncial system' in which there is no evidence of any kind of sensory representation. Yet the idea is developing that the degree of convergence of afferent impulses is definitely limited; that notwithstanding the complexity of the reticular network, with its many collaterals and bifurcated axons, there may be a large population of neurones with more restricted receptive fields. In this population may be found distinctive firing patterns in which the individuality of the afferent inflows is never completely lost.

2 Effects of stimulating the splanchnic nerve

It is well known that barbiturate anaesthesia tends to depress the activity of reticular neurones; accordingly, experiments were performed on decerebrate preparations or on animals given intravenous chloralose (35 mg/kg). The brain stem was approached from either the ventral or dorsal surfaces by the techniques described above. Microelectrode penetrations in the upper medulla and pons were made at points about 2–3 mm from the mid-line. Many units discharging spontaneously were encountered. They could be held for long periods in the absence of stimulation; their frequency of discharge varied continuously, displaying random bursts followed by short intervals of silence.

A single shock delivered to the splanchnic nerve generally caused an increase in firing rate; other spontaneously active units were inhibited. More detailed observations were made on units which were silent or fired irregularly in the absence of stimulation. When the A beta group of splanchnic nerve afferents was excited by a weak stimulus (1 V, 0·01 msec), the units responded by either single or multiple spike discharges (Fig. 6.15). The latency for the first spike of the discharge often varied with each successive stimulus and with different units sampled. However, the majority of responsive units had a mean latency of about 15 msec. Increasing the strength of the stimulus from threshold to maximal activation of the A beta fibres tended to shorten the mean latency, but stronger stimulation, to excite the A delta fibres, did not shorten the latency further. In some units, the evoked discharges took the form of a double response; the second burst occurring after a delay of about 100 msec. This late discharge was only seen in decerebrate preparations or under very light anaesthesia and may be compared with the findings of Scheibel et al. (1955) in the encéphale isolé cat.

A large percentage of the reticular units responding to A beta splanchnic stimulation also responded to cutaneous stimulation on the same or opposite side. When a conditioning stimulus was given to one afferent source and a testing stimulus to the other, it was usual to show that the test response was inhibited although interaction could not be demonstrated in every unit studied. The results of interaction were comparable to those described for single units elsewhere in the viscero-sensory system, depending upon the relative intensities of stimulation and C–T intervals. Nevertheless, the impression was gained that reticular unit responses were less predictable than the responses of units in the cerebellum or cerebral cortex. It was not possible to isolate any specific units in the reticular formation, i.e. units which responded only to splanchnic nerve afferents. Evoked responses seemed to be more dependent on unexplained influences. Thus in the intact anaesthetized animal the activity of a reticular unit might alter during the course of an experiment and the number of unresponsive units might vary. Again, in the decerebrate animal much depended on the state of the local circulation and the possibility of influences from the cerebellum unless this had been previously removed.

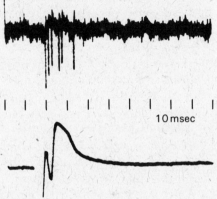

10 msec

FIG. 6.15. Reticular unit response to splanchnic afferent stimulation. Upper trace and time marker show typical multispike discharge following a single stimulus with the latency for the first spike at 20 msec. Lower trace shows the A beta splanchnic nerve action potential simultaneously recorded.

Intracellular recordings from reticular neurones following stimulation of visceral afferents have been reported by Preobrazhensky & Limansky (1969). The early and late responses which they observed would suggest that the impulses reached the reticular neurones by two different spinal routes. Information is lacking on the influence of vagal afferents on the reticular system, but nearly all other sensory modalities, including auditory and visual, are effective forms of stimulation. There is general agreement that reticular units can be influenced from most regions of the body, but at the present time there is little evidence of topographical organization. Some reticular neurones have a wide receptive field, others have a more limited field without being specific and a third group of neurones are apparently uninfluenced by peripheral activity.

Our knowledge of the functions of the reticular formation has been advanced by studying the temporal aspects of neuronal discharges. The variability of latency to a constant stimulus of low threshold suggests that a large number of afferent pathways are available. A reticular unit may be regarded as a target which can be reached from many directions along several neuronal links, some longer than others. When the stimulus intensity is increased or by using repetitive stimulation, the number of available pathways is increased and the target may be reached in a shorter time. The unit will now respond with less variability of latency; impulses can use more direct routes as well as spreading into other synaptic linkages which were previously closed. Hence the early discharges will represent more closely what is happening to the sense organ whilst the late discharges will convey information about the state of surrounding neurones. The idea that changes in temporal patterns of discharge may be used to identify peripheral space has been expressed by several authors, e.g. Amassian & Devito (1954), Fessard (1956), Amassian & Waller (1958), Towe & Amassian (1958). This idea suggests that localization of a peripheral input is not based entirely on anatomical connexions and that temporal patterns of activity may also contribute. For example, two adjacent units responding to the same stimulus input might show quite different response characteristics—differences in latency, number of spikes and interspike intervals. Also, the same unit might alter its response characteristics if the site or the parameters of stimulation are changed or if the experimental conditions have altered. Similar observations on the variability of reticular responses have been reported by Hernandez-Peon & Hagbarth (1955) and by Wolstencroft (1964).

Variability of discharge patterns may have an important bearing on the functions of the reticular formation. It is the site of a great convergence of afferent projections and it constitutes a pool of relays for both ascending spinal and descending cerebral systems. Since its localizing functions are limited, it no doubt uses the information from the sense organs to provide and maintain a controlled output to all other parts of the nervous system. Correlation of the activities of single reticular neurones with the physiology of the reticular formation is obviously linked to the data derived from their discharge patterns. Visceral afferent influences have no distinctive features here since all sensory inputs are sampled on the basis of differential facilitation or inhibition. It is possible, however, that further studies may produce evidence of a greater degree of individually organized patterns within the reticular network.

REFERENCES

Alexander, R. S. (1946). Tonic and reflex functions of medullary sympathetic cardiovascular centers. *J. Neurophysiol.* **9**, 205–217.

Amassian, V. E. & Devito, R. V. (1954). Unit activity in reticular formation and nearby structures. *J. Neurophysiol.* **17**, 575–603.

Amassian, V. E. & Waller, H. J. (1958). Spatiotemporal patterns of activity in individual reticular neurones. *Ret. Form Brain, Henry Ford Hosp. Internat. Symp.*, 69–108.

Armstrong, D. M. & Harvey, R. J. (1966). Responses in the inferior olive to stimulation of the cerebellar and cerebral cortices in the cat. *J. Physiol.* **187**, 553–574.

Barrington, F. J. F. (1925). The effect of lesions of the hind and mid-brain in micturition in the cat. *Quart. Jl exp. Physiol.* **15**, 81–102.

Barrington, F. J. F. (1933). The localization of the paths subserving micturition in the spinal cord of the cat. *Brain* **56**, 126–148.

Brizee, K. R. (1956). Effect of localized brain stem lesions and subdiaphragmatic vagotomy of X-irradiation emesis in monkeys. *Am. J. Physiol.* **187**, 567–570.

Brizee, K. R. & Neal, L. M. (1954). A re-evaluation of the cellular morphology of the area postrema in view of recent evidence for a chemoreceptor function. *J. comp. Neurol.* **100**, 41–59.

Brodal, A. (1953). Reticulo-cerebellar connections in the cat. *J. comp. Neurol.* **98**, 113–154.

Carrea, R., Ruarte, A. & Volkind, R. (1968). Single unit activity at the inferior olive in the cat. *J. nerv. ment. Dis.* **147**, 70–84.

Chatfield, P. O. (1941). Salivation in response to localized stimulation of the medulla. *Am. J. Physiol.* **133**, 637–641.

Crill, W. E. (1970). Unitary multiple-spiked responses in cat inferior olive nucleus. *J. Neurophysiol.* **33**, 199–209.

Fessard, A. (1956). Formes et caractères généraux de l'excitation neuronique. *Review, XXth Internat. Physiol. Cong. Bruxelles*, 35–58.

Gresty, M. & Paul, D. H. (1970). Input–output relations of the inferior olive. *J. Physiol.* **208**, 92–93P.

Hernandez-Peon, R. & Hagbarth, K. E. (1955). Interaction between afferent and cortically induced reticular responses. *J. Neurophysiol.* **18**, 44–55.

Holmes, R. L., Newman, P. P. & Wolstencroft, J. H. (1960). A heat-sensitive region in the medulla. *J. Physiol.* **152**, 93–98.

Hossain, M. A. & Newman, P. P. (1968). Ipsilateral projections between sensory cortex and cerebellum. *J. Physiol.* **200**, 130–131P.

Leicht, R., Rowe, M. J. & Schmidt, R. F. (1973). Cortical and peripheral modification of cerebellar climbing fibre activity arising from cutaneous mechanoreceptors. *J. Physiol.* **228**, 619–635.

Lindgren, P. (1955). The mesencephalon and the vasomotor system. *Acta physiol. scand.* **35**, Suppl. 121, 5–189.

Magoun, H. W. & Beaton, L. E. (1942). The salivatory motor nuclei in monkey. *Am. J. Physiol.* **136**, 720–725.

Miller, F. R. (1913). On the reactions of the salivary centres. *Quart. Jl exp. Physiol.* **6**, 57–72.

Miller, S., Nezlina, N. & Oscarsson, O. (1969). Projection and convergence patterns in climbing fibre paths to cerebellar anterior lobe activated from cerebral cortex and spinal cord. *Brain Res.* **14**, 230–233.

Moorhouse, V. H. K. (1911). Effect of increased temperature of the carotid blood. *Am. J. Physiol.* **28**, 223–234.

Nathan, P. W. & Smith, M. C. (1951). The centripetal pathway from the bladder and urethra within the spinal cord. *J. Neurol. Neurosurg. Psychiat.* **14**, 262–280.

Newman, P. P. & Wolstencroft, J. H. (1960). Cardiovascular and respiratory responses to heating the carotid blood. *J. Physiol.* **152**, 87–92.

Preobrazhensky, N. N. & Limansky, Y. P. (1969). Activation of bulbar reticular neurons by visceral afferents. *Neurophysiol.* **1**, 177–185.

Ranson, S. W. & Billingsley, P. R. (1916). Vasomotor reactions from stimulation of the floor of the fourth ventricle. *Am. J. Physiol.* **41**, 85–90.

Scheibel, M. E. & Scheibel, A. B. (1955). The inferior olive. A Golgi study. *J. comp. Neurol.* **102**, 77–132.

Scheibel, M. E., Scheibel, A. B., Mollica, A. & Moruzzi, G. (1955). Convergence and interaction of afferent impulses in single units of reticular formation. *J. Neurophysiol.* **18**, 309–331.

Sedgwick, E. M. & Williams, T. D. (1967). Responses of single units in the inferior olive to stimulation of the limb nerves, peripheral skin receptors, cerebellum, caudate nucleus and motor cortex. *J. Physiol.* **189**, 261–279.

Snider, R. S. & Barnard, J. W. (1949). Electro-anatomical studies on the afferent projections to the inferior olive. *J. comp. Neurol.* **91**, 243–257.

Torvik, A. & Brodal, A. (1957). The origin of reticulo-spinal fibres in the cat. *Anat. Rec.* **128**, 113–137.

Towe, A. L. & Amassian, V. E. (1958). Patterns of activity in single cortical units following stimulation of the digits in monkeys. *J. Neurophysiol.* **21**, 292–311.

Walberg, F. (1956). Descending connections to the inferior olive. An experimental study in the cat. *J. comp. Neurol.* **104**, 77–172.

Wang, S. C. (1943). Localization of the salivatory center in the medulla of the cat. *J. Neurophysiol.* **6**, 195–202.

Wang, S. C. & Borison, H. L. (1950). The vomiting center. *Arch. Neurol. Psychiat. Chicago* **63**, 928–941.

Wang, S. C. & Borison, H. L. (1952). A new concept on the central emetic mechanism. *Gastroenterology* **22**, 1–12.

Wang, S. C. & Ranson, S. W. (1939). Autonomic responses to electrical stimulation of the lower brain stem. *J. comp. Neurol.* **71**, 437–455.

Wolstencroft, J. H. (1964). Reticulospinal neurones. *J. Physiol.* **174**, 91–108.

Woodburne, R. T., Crosby, E. C. & McCotter, R. E. (1946). The mammalian midbrain and isthmus regions. The fiber connections. *J. comp. Neurol.* **85**, 67–79.

7

VISCERAL PROJECTIONS TO THE MID-BRAIN AND THALAMUS

IN spite of a considerable amount of work devoted to visceral afferent projections to the cerebellum and cerebral cortex, there is only scattered information about visceral functions at subcortical levels. It is true that the hypothalamus plays a key role in the regulation of the viscera and the endocrine glands, but less is known about the neural network in which it lies and the influences which converge upon it. Our knowledge of the specific and diffuse thalamic relays is based on comparatively recent studies and to a large extent the contributions have come from the somatosensory system. The emphasis here is perhaps rather surprising in view of the clinical importance of visceral pain. On the other hand, there have been numerous investigations on the oculomotor nucleus in the mid-brain since it was shown that both somatic and visceral afferents contribute to the pupillary reflexes. Dilatation of the pupil has been used for many years as an index of sympathetic activity and its involvement in emotional excitement would seem to indicate a link between the mid-brain, diencephalon and cerebral cortex.

THE OCULOMOTOR MECHANISM

Pupillary dilatation

The involvement of the mid-brain in visceral integration was first recognized by McDowall (1925) who used the pupil as an index of activity from areas supplied by the autonomic nervous system. In experiments on the chloralosed cat, he found that dilatation of the pupil occurred in all procedures known to cause pain, such as stretching the gut or compression of the urinary bladder. The reaction was abolished after section of the cervical sympathetic and he believed that the pupil remained constricted from over-action of the parasympathetic. The pathways mediating the reflex were not definitely known, although the presence of afferent fibres in the sympathetic nerves had been clearly demonstrated. Bain, Irving & McSwiney (1935) established that afferent impulses conducted in the splanchnic nerves gave rise to marked dilatation of the pupil and that the response was independent of somatic afferent pathways. Evidence was also given that the dilatation was mainly due to inhibition of the third nerve nucleus since it was obtained after section of the cervical sympathetic but not after section of the third cranial nerve. These observations were confirmed by Irving, McSwiney & Suffolk (1937) who used the reaction of the pupil as an index to test the sensitivity of the alimentary tract. Attempts to trace the spinal pathways of the pupillo-dilator fibres were reported by Harper & McSwiney (1937) who made sections at different levels of the spinal cord above the afferent inflow of the splanchnic nerves. They found that pupillo-dilator fibres occupied the lateral columns on both sides of the cord but they could not distinguish the splanchnic afferents from those of the intercostal nerves.

The idea that dilatation of the pupil occurs entirely by inhibition of the oculomotor nucleus was strongly supported by the work of Ury & Gellhorn (1939) and by Seybold & Moore (1940) since no dilatation was observed in the parasympathectomized eye, except under conditions of strong sympathetic excitement. The problem was further investigated by Harris, Hodes & Magoun (1944) in an attempt to trace the more likely pathways responsible for the reflex. The response was evoked by stimulating the sciatic, splanchnic and trigeminal nerves in cats under light nembutal anaesthesia and the effect of acute lesions in the spinal cord and brain was then studied. The results confirmed that the spinal pathway for the pupillo-dilator response was contained in the lateral columns at the 1st cervical level. Sections in the medulla and pons revealed that the fibres coursed through the lateral part of the reticular formation from a ventral to a dorsal position on either side of the mid-line. The pathway was clearly distinct from the lateral spino-thalamic tract. In the mid-brain, the fibres were directed forward to the central grey of the aqueduct to terminate in the oculomotor nucleus. The authors showed that inhibitory action was exerted directly at the level of the mid-brain since destruction of the cerebral cortex or of the entire hypothalamus did not abolish the reflex even in chronic preparations. It was also emphasized that the ascending pupillo-dilator path was quite separate from pathways subserving pain.

An investigation of the types of fibres involved in the pupillo-dilator reflex was carried out by Evans (1961) using cats under chloralose anaesthesia. Changes in the diameter of the pupil were measured on a graticule inserted into a low power microscope. Evans made the interesting observation that low-threshold afferents were not concerned in the reflex since pupillary dilatation occurred only when A delta or C fibres were excited. The placement of lesions at various sites in the spinal cord confirmed the views of earlier workers that the afferent pathways ascended bilaterally in the lateral columns of the cord with little evidence of crossing. The unmyelinated C group of fibres tended to lie dorsal to the A delta group, but the posterior columns of the cord were not implicated.

It would appear from all these investigations that there is a close relationship between the spinal afferents which evoke pupillary dilatation and those which carry pain nerve impulses. The majority of workers agree that although separate conducting systems can be identified within the central nervous system, they have many features in common—bilaterality, diffuse projections and high-threshold fibre components. It is also accepted that the reflex is brought about by inhibition of the parasympathetic supply to the pupil, derived from the oculomotor nucleus, since dilator effects are present after section of the cervical sympathetic trunk.

Pupillary constriction

It is a common observation that animals under moderately deep anaesthesia or during sleep have their pupils highly constricted, whilst in light anaesthesia or during the waking state the pupils remain dilated. These changes in the diameter of the pupil are independent of the light or accommodation reflexes which are initiated by impulses from the eye itself. One must also distinguish the mechanisms that produce dilatation, usually marked dilatation, through sympathetic discharges when the animal is aroused, in emotional states or as part of a generalized defence reaction. Pupillary constriction is brought about by the action of the ciliary ganglion through parasympathetic fibres derived from cells in the oculomotor nucleus. In order to establish precisely the location of these pupilloconstrictor neurones Sillito & Zbrożyna (1970a) recorded potentials evoked by antidromic stimulation of the preganglionic fibres, then mapped the region giving maximal responses by reference to the amplitude of the potentials. They also recorded the activity of single pupilloconstrictor units responding to electrical stimuli delivered to the brain stem and diencephalon. The results obtained indicated that preganglionic pupilloconstrictor neurones were restricted to the small-celled component of the oculomotor nucleus, comprising parts of the Edinger–Westphal and anteromedian nuclei. In another series of experiments (Sillito & Zbrożyna, 1970b), it was shown that the same neurones responded to a light flash with increased activity and to hypothalamic stimulation with decreased activity. As the cervical sympathetic nerves had been cut, the changes in the diameter of the pupil could only have been caused by changes in the discharge frequency of the oculomotor neurones.

The situation regarding our understanding of the pupillary mechanism can be summarized as follows: the diameter of the pupil at any moment is determined by parasympathetic constrictor activity arising from the small-celled component of the oculomotor nucleus. It is not known for certain whether the cells are spontaneously active or whether they are controlled from another region of the mid-brain or diencephalon. If spontaneously active, the pupils will stay partially constricted until modified by some excitatory or inhibitory influence. The light reflex is an excitatory drive increasing tonic activity and constricting the pupil; hypothalamic stimulation on the other hand exerts an inhibitory influence on the oculomotor nucleus and dilates the pupil. Yet there are so many other factors involved in the control of the pupil that the mechanism can hardly operate in isolation. Somatic and visceral afferents from all over the body converge on this region of the brain stem, which may therefore be regarded as an important integrating centre for emergency and defence reactions. Dilatation of the pupil is only one of the changes observed. Vasodilator responses elicited by heat (Chapter 6) or by electrical stimulation of the brain stem (Abrahams, Hilton & Zbrożyna, 1960) constitute additional features of the total body reaction.

VISCERAL RESPONSES IN THE THALAMUS

Since it is believed that impulses entering the thalamus are related to consciousness, explorations to locate the potential fields of the sensory systems have assumed some clinical importance. In animal explorations, the limitations imposed by the use of anaesthetics are partly offset by the accuracy with which electrodes can be guided into the region under study. With chronically implanted electrodes, the placements can be identified histologically after conclusion of the experiment.

Current views on the functional organization of the thalamus point to a detailed representation for those parts of the body with a high innervation density. Hence the stream of impulses from somatic receptors, especially those from the skin and joints, have been carefully traced as they ascend the major tracts of the spinal cord and brain stem. They form the classical sensory systems comprising the dorsal columns, medial lemniscus and the spino-thalamic projections all of which terminate in the contralateral ventrobasal nuclear complex. This is one of several nuclear masses handling information from peripheral structures for relay to the cerebral cortex. Despite the anatomical complexity caused by the inflow of impulses from all over the body, the receiving zone in the thalamus has a discrete topographical arrangement. Furthermore, individual neurones show a preference for a particular form of stimulation suggesting that the thalamus maintains a high degree of specificity for different sensory modalities.

The contralateral surface of the body is represented as a series of segmental projections with the head area placed medially, the trunk laterally and the legs inferiorly; but the overall pattern is somewhat distorted by overlap of dermatomes and by the fact that there is a greater degree of representation for areas with marked sensitivity (Mountcastle & Henneman, 1949). Thus two features about thalamic organization are now clear:

1. Despite the regrouping of fibre systems in the spinal cord and despite synaptic convergence and decussation, the main sensory pathways retain their topographical pattern in the thalamus.

2. Different sensory modalities from receptors in the skin, muscles or joints preserve their functional identity by links with specific thalamic neurones.

Bearing in mind these two features, it is useful to consider how impulses of visceral origin are handled physiologically and the extent with which the relevant data fit into the classical picture.

Primary responses

In cats under sodium pentobarbital anaesthesia, electrical stimulation of the splanchnic nerve evokes an initially positive primary wave in the contralateral ventrobasal nucleus of the thalamus. If the splanchnic nerve is cut, the response is abolished. Patton & Amassian (1951) recorded primary waves with a latency of 5–6 msec following stimulation of the A beta group of splanchnic afferents. The potentials were located in the nucleus ventralis posterolateralis (lateral portion of ventrobasal complex) at points overlapping arm and leg representation. These same points were also responsive to tactile stimulation of the skin. Similar latencies were reported by Aidar, Geohegan & Ungewitter (1952) who traced evoked splanchnic potentials in the ipsilateral dorsal column, gracile nucleus, contralateral lemniscus and contralateral thalamus. Thus evidence was presented of a fast-conducting fibre system carrying impulses from the abdominal viscera to the contralateral thalamus in a pathway closely associated with the proprioceptive system. With stronger stimulation, in order to excite the slower conducting afferents in the splanchnic nerve, the same authors traced a bilateral pathway in the lateral funiculi of the cord to the caudal regions of the thalamus on both sides. They postulated that the higher threshold, slower conducting system might be involved in visceral pain.

Primary responses evoked by stimulation of vagal afferents have been recorded in the thalamus, mainly from the posteromedial nucleus which also serves as a relay station for trigeminal impulses (Ruch, Patton & Amassian, 1952). The central pathways for vagal and splanchnic nerve afferents do not appear to converge at any point in the brain stem or diencephalon. Moreover, their destinations in the cerebral cortex remain distinct in spite of the fact that their impulses arise from the same peripheral organs. Thus vagal representation is found on the orbital surface of the frontal lobe whilst the splanchnic projections go to the primary and secondary areas of the sensory cortex. It is only in the limbic system, which serves as an integrating region, that any degree of overlap occurs. These factors no doubt emphasize topographical and functional differences between the two afferent systems.

Unit responses

The position from which unit responses can be obtained in the thalamus has been determined by microelectrode penetrations of stereotaxic tracts. Composite maps were prepared from the results of a number of experiments in different animals. McLeod (1958) recorded single and multiple spike discharges in the cat following single shocks applied to the contralateral splanchnic nerve. The majority of the units that he sampled were found in the posteroventral nucleus in the area of representation of the abdomen and trunk. Other responsive units were scattered throughout the nucleus indicating a fair degree of overlap into forelimb and hindlimb areas. No evoked responses were recorded from other regions of the thalamus. Over half of the total number of units examined were activated by the A beta group of splanchnic nerve afferents and they had a mean latency of about 12 msec. The remainder of the responsive units were of higher threshold, belonging to the A delta group, and had a mean latency of about 21 msec. Some A delta unit discharges were evoked by stimulation of the ipsilateral splanchnic nerve. Convergence between cutaneous and splanchnic afferents was demonstrated by combination of conditioning and testing stimuli, since the same thalamic unit often discharged when a tactile stimulus was applied to the body surface. McLeod found that the response of a thalamic unit could be blocked by a preceding conditioning stimulus at intervals ranging between 30 and 175 msec. The type of anaesthetic used had no apparent influence on these observations.

The activity of thalamic units was also studied in great detail by Rose & Mountcastle (1954) who observed that a single peripheral stimulus, whether natural or electrical, usually evoked a repetitive discharge. The number of spikes occurring in any discharge was termed its 'modal value'. When the strength of the stimulus was increased, there was generally, though not invariably, an increase of modal value and a progressive shortening of the latency for the first spike. Although the size of individual spikes was not always uniform, the authors concluded that high-frequency repetitive discharges were characteristic of thalamic units and that the various discharge patterns reflected both the site and intensity of the peripheral stimulus. They believed that the discharges were produced by a prolonged excitatory process determined by the number and timing of the presynaptic impulses arriving at a cell (Fig. 7.1).

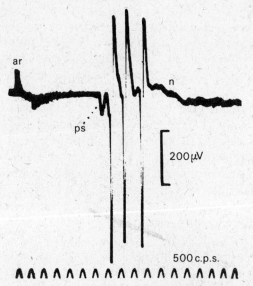

Fig. 7.1. Evoked activity of single thalamic unit. The stimulus was the displacement of a few hairs by a brush applied to the contralateral forepaw of the cat. The unit discharged repetitively. Note presynaptic potential and train of spikes superimposed on a primary wave. ar, stimulus artifact; ps, presynaptic complex; n, slow negative wave. (Rose & Mountcastle, 1954, Fig. 3.)

Poggio & Mountcastle (1963) recorded unit discharges from the ventrobasal complex in unanaesthetized monkeys. It was clear that the functional properties of VBC cells were not affected by barbiturates in the doses used for earlier studies on anaesthetized cats. They confirmed the view that the patterns of thalamic unit discharges represented a response mechanism which faithfully detected variations in the condition of the sense organs. This important relationship between stimulus and response was well demonstrated by Mountcastle, Poggio & Werner (1963) in experiments on position sense and movements of joints. Their results showed that rotation at a joint was signalled not simply by a change of frequency in a single thalamic cell, but by changes in the whole pattern of frequencies in a population of cells.

Role of thalamus in visceral sensation

In considering the role that can be assigned to the thalamus, it will be apparent that visceral and somatic sensory systems have many features in common. In the first place, the fact that impulses in the splanchnic and vagal nerves actually reach the thalamus is itself significant evidence of a higher input system for visceral sensation. This is a relatively new concept since interest in visceral activities has largely been focused on autonomic innervation and output functions of the hypothalamus. Secondly, from the topographically discrete character of the visceral projections, it follows that some localizing and discriminative properties are preserved. The splanchnic projection overlaps the leg and arm areas in the ventrobasal nucleus as would be expected from the segmental level at which the afferent fibres enter the spinal cord. However, the small number of thalamic units that respond exclusively to splanchnic stimulation suggests that discriminative capacity is not well developed. This again is consistent with clinical characteristics. Thirdly, from the point of view of its organization, the visceral afferent system favours a selective role for different sensory modalities. This is evident from the dual pathways of conduction observed in the spinal cord. The mechano-receptors of the mesentery and gut are served by A beta, low-threshold afferents in the dorsal columns whilst impulses producing pain sensation are carried by A delta afferents in the anterolateral columns. The situation is similar in the somatic system where sensory innervation is shared by lemniscal and spinothalamic systems.

Localization

All modalities of visceral sensation are represented in the ventrobasal complex of the thalamus: splanchnic afferents terminate on the posterolateral nucleus and vagal afferents terminate on the posteromedial nucleus. The distribution of splanchnic-evoked neurones occupies a relatively small area in the zone where leg and arm representations overlap. The limited distribution is consistent with the relatively poor afferent supply to the viscera compared to the sensitivity of the body wall. Nevertheless, the existence of an organized thalamic projection is evidence that these fibres serve a localized form of sensation.

Discrimination

Mapping experiments show that A beta and A delta unit responses are randomly distributed. It is difficult to understand why these two functional components are kept apart in the cord if they cannot be distinguished as separate entities at higher levels. In the cerebellum, low- and high-threshold units are encountered in a discrete region of the culmen. They have different latency ranges and respond to natural stimulation with pronounced modal specificity (see Chapter 4). Latency differences between A beta and A delta responses are also features of thalamic recordings and it is evident that they serve quite different functions: the former signal states of distension in the internal organs and the latter are implicated in visceral pain. Apart from this functional division in the afferent projections of the splanchnic nerve, the discriminative capacity of the thalamus is limited. It is clear from microelectrode studies that the majority of units responding to splanchnic stimulation also respond to cutaneous stimulation and evidence of an exclusive splanchnic relay system is scanty. This is not surprising in view of the vague character of visceral sensation described by patients. However, sensory interaction cannot always be demonstrated in conditioning and testing experiments and it may be deduced that some units out of the total population are identified with splanchnic activity alone.

Interaction

When interaction between cutaneous and splanchnic pathways can be demonstrated, the test response may be either diminished or completely blocked. In other words, a unit that discharges to a testing stimulus delivered to one pathway may fail to discharge if a conditioning stimulus is delivered to the other pathway. How can this unresponsive phase be explained? In the spinal cord or at any level of the nervous system below the thalamus, impulses may converge on a common pathway with the result that a period of refractoriness or relative inexcitability is induced. Impulses from a testing source do not discharge the unit because they fail to reach it. However, there is now good evidence (see Chapter 5) that cutaneous and splanchnic impulses ascend the spinal cord in separate anatomical pathways and that the site of convergence is in the thalamus itself. It is believed that impulses reaching the thalamus from a conditioning source produce post-synaptic inhibition of the thalamo-cortical relay cells with resultant depression of their excitability. This idea is supported by the work of Anderson, Brooks, Eccles & Sears (1964) who recorded large positive potentials in the thalamus following conditioning volleys to the radial, median and ulnar nerves. Each positive potential lasting about 120 msec, represented a period of relative inexcitability, which they attributed to the recovery phase at the synaptic relay. During this period, the arrival of a testing volley from any source would be ineffective.

One objection to this hypothesis is that inhibition may still be produced by a weak conditioning stimulus which does not itself cause the unit to discharge. Another difficulty lies in the altered performance of the thalamic unit with changes in the parameters of conditioning or testing stimuli. Accordingly it is suggested that the afferent volleys arriving from the sense organs, while excitatory for some thalamic cells, will tend to inhibit others. If the inhibitory cells have a lower threshold than the excitatory ones, a weak conditioning stimulus will produce a zone of inhibition which will account for the unresponsive period of adjacent cells. During this period a testing stimulus will not evoke activity unless it is strong enough to overcome the inhibition. The hypothesis rests on the assumption that the thalamic relay system is served by inhibitory interneurones. In the cerebellum, inhibitory links through stellate and basket cells account for inhibition of Purkinje cells; but the presence of low-threshold and high-threshold terminals in the thalamus is not so well established.

Inhibition

The problem of explaining the end result of sensory interaction has now been directed to the *modus operandi* of short interneurones as shown in the diagrams of Fig. 7.2. It will be seen that two possibilities are suggested:

1. *Post-synaptic inhibition.* Collaterals from thalamo-cortical relay cells excite the interneurones which in turn inhibit the thalamic relay cell.

2. *Pre-synaptic inhibition.* Collaterals from sensory afferents excite the interneurone which distributes its synaptic knobs on the afferent terminals.

According to Anderson, Eccles & Sears (1964) about 37 per cent of all the thalamic cells they examined were considered to be interneurones on inhibitory pathways. Their evidence indicated that prolonged inhibition of thalamic relay cells could be generated through either type of interneurone. Presynaptic inhibition at the thalamic relay synapses had been proposed by Amassian (1952) and similar conclusions were reached by Purpura & Cohen (1962) and Purpura & Shofer (1963) using the data of intracellular recordings.

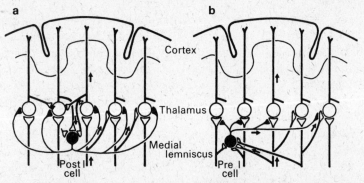

FIG. 7.2. Diagrams of postulated pathways for thalamic inhibition. (a) Postsynaptic action on thalamic relay cells by inhibitory interneurone (Post I cell) which in turn is excited by axon collaterals of the relay cells. (b) Presynaptic action on terminals of lemniscal fibres by inhibitory interneurone (Pre I cell) which in turn is excited by branches of the sensory afferents. (Andersen, Eccles & Sears, 1964, Fig. 18.)

Thus several hypotheses have been developed to account for the effects of afferent impulses on thalamic units and the period of unresponsiveness which follows. Whatever the precise nature of the mechanisms involved, there is no doubt that thalamic inhibition plays an important role in modifying the information carried by the sensory pathways to the cerebral cortex.

VISCERAL PAIN

Pain that arises from the viscera is of great interest to the clinician; he can generally achieve a preliminary diagnosis from the history and symptoms of the patient and afterwards confirm the success of any operative intervention. It is different for the laboratory worker. Experiments on anaesthetized animals can have only a limited value and very often deductions have to be made when nociceptive stimuli are employed. In experiments where the splanchnic nerves are left intact, the possibility that the stimulus may activate fibres subserving pain has led to much discussion and even valid criticism of this exercise. But the same arguments can be applied to any sensory nerve if the stimulus is a strong one. Under effective anaesthesia it must be assumed that the animal has lost its sense of awareness and therefore does not feel pain nor does it manifest any of the motor reactions indicative of pain. Nevertheless, a stimulus applied to the splanchnic nerve must be the starting point of a barrage of impulses flowing into the central nervous system since the course of the impulses can be followed at every level. The experimenter attempts to reduce the undesirable influences by infiltration with local anaesthetic at all operative sites; a careful watch is kept on the diameter of the pupils and the blood pressure is continuously monitored. It is generally found that single shocks delivered to the splanchnic nerve do not cause any changes in systemic blood pressure or in the size of the pupils, even over long periods of time. This fact holds true with strong stimuli when A delta and C components of the splanchnic nerve are excited.

The extent to which pain is a function of the higher threshold afferents in the splanchnic nerve is not yet settled, but a strong stimulus such as over-distension of a viscus is required to excite them. Thus the low threshold A beta fibres that end in the Pacinian corpuscles of the mesentery can be excluded. On the other hand, nociceptive reflexes are elicited by the A delta group of splanchnic nerve afferents and it is this group of fibres which is responsible for the early responses associated with visceral pain. It is now accepted that A delta fibres are carried in the anterolateral columns of the cord to the thalamus on both sides and constitute a separate conducting system with characteristics quite different from the A beta splanchnic components.

Problem of referred pain

At the level of the thalamus, structural organization is not so clearly documented. For example, there is no obvious spatial pattern corresponding to the double spinal pathway for splanchnic nerve impulses. The distribution of A beta and A delta units appears to be identical. In addition, the same thalamic units are generally accessible to impulses from the abdominal skin. This apparent lack of orderly arrangement and functional independence may throw some light on the problem of referred pain. In order to analyse the responses of thalamic units Gaze & Gordon (1954) selectively blocked the fibre groups of the saphenous nerve by the method of cooling with alcohol and acetone. They discovered that over 80 per cent of the total population of units examined were responsive to low-threshold stimulation of the nerve or to a weak tactile stimulus; only a small proportion of the units responded to higher threshold afferents, representing the A delta and C components of the saphenous action potential.

As might be expected from such functional differences, thalamic organization favours the reference of incoming impulses to innervation of the skin. Pain that arises from abdominal viscera is frequently referred to the body surface by the patient. In other words, impulses reaching the sensory cortex from the viscera are interpreted as having come from the skin since the same thalamic relay cells are excited by visceral and cutaneous afferents. It seems likely, therefore, that the terminal pathway for many high-threshold visceral afferents is linked to the cortical destination of the somatic sensory system. This explanation supports the convergence–projection theory of referred pain described by Ruch (1946). As regards the proportion of thalamic units which are driven by high-threshold or nociceptive afferents, no satisfactory conclusions have been reached. Obviously, a stimulus strong enough to cause visceral pain will not only elicit reflex activity, but will discharge the ascending neurones of the anterolateral columns. Some of this activity will be relayed in the thalamus and reach the cerebral cortex independent of the somatosensory system. This suggestion may account for the unreferred component of visceral pain, which is clinically recognized as vague in character and generally poorly localized.

Inhibition of pain

Evidence is provided by conditioning and testing experiments to suggest that thalamic inhibition has a significant role in reducing visceral sensitivity by denying access of impulses subserving pain to consciousness. The time course for sensory interaction shows that the depression imposed by a conditioning volley can last about 200 msec and during part of this time the absence of a second response is complete. Failure of thalamic transmission for conveying afferent impulses will reduce or prevent widespread activity in thalamo-cortical relays. As the majority of thalamic units are responsive to low-threshold stimulation, the arrival of impulses from the skin and body wall will create a constant background of inhibition. Such a background will tend to exclude the higher-threshold impulses originating from the viscera.

Our knowledge, at present, would rule against further speculation. It is not easy to account for pain mechanisms from experiments on anaesthetized animals and the discharge of thalamic units may well have different time relations and patterns in the normal conscious state. There is also good evidence (Anderson, Eccles & Sears, 1964) that in the absence of anaesthesia, the sensory cortex can exert an influence on thalamic relay cells either directly or by antidromic invasion reaching the cells before excitation has occurred. Further evidence will no doubt be forthcoming, but it is a fair assumption that visceral impulses and other high-threshold afferents are substantially modified in behaviour and reference by the thalamic mechanism. It is heartening to note that similar problems of interaction between low- and high-threshold afferents are now being submitted to experimental testing. Thus, in the spinal cord, the 'gate control' theory, first postulated by Melzack & Wall (1965), has attracted a good deal of interest. Convergence of large and small afferent fibres on the same neural pathway is finely balanced by the excitatory and inhibitory effects of their collaterals acting on interneurones. These are provided by the cells of the substantia gelatinosa which in turn depress the outgoing impulses by presynaptic inhibition. The 'gate' is closed by increasing activity in the large fibres with the result that small fibre impulses are blocked. As with thalamic transmission, the output can also be modified by descending influences from the cerebral cortex.

REFERENCES

Abrahams, V. C., Hilton, S. M. & Zbrożyna, A. (1960). Active muscle vasodilatation produced by stimulation of the brain stem; its significance in the defence reaction. *J. Physiol.* **154**, 491–513.

Aidar, O., Geohegan, W. A. & Ungewitter, L. H. (1952). Splanchnic afferent pathways in the central nervous system. *J. Neurophysiol.* **15**, 131–138.

Amassian, V. E. (1952). Interaction in the somatovisceral projection system. *Res. Publs Ass. Res. nerv. ment. Dis.* **30**, 371–402.

Anderson, P., Brooks, C. McC., Eccles, J. C. & Sears, T. A. (1964). The ventro-basal nucleus of the thalamus: potential fields, synaptic transmission and excitability of both presynaptic and post-synaptic components. *J. Physiol.* **174**, 348–369.

Anderson, P., Eccles, J. C. & Sears, T. A. (1964). The ventro-basal complex of the thalamus: types of cells, their responses and their functional organization. *J. Physiol.* **174**, 370–399.

Bain, W. A., Irving, J. T. & McSwiney, B. A. (1935). The afferent fibres from the abdomen in the splanchnic nerves. *J. Physiol.* **84**, 323–333.

Evans, M. H. (1961). The spinal pathways of the myelinated and the non-myelinated efferent nerve fibres that mediate reflex dilatation of the pupils. *J. Physiol.* **158**, 560–572.

Gaze, R. M. & Gordon, G. (1954). The representation of cutaneous sense in the thalamus of the cat and monkey. *Quart. Jl exp. Physiol.* **39**, 279–304.

Harper, A. A. & McSwiney, B. A. (1937). Ascending spinal pathways of the pupillo-dilator fibres. *J. Physiol.* **90**, 395–402.

Harris, A. J., Hodes, R. & Magoun, H. W. (1944). The afferent path of the pupillodilator reflex in the cat. *J. Neurophysiol.* **7**, 231–243.

Irving, J. T., McSwiney, B. A. & Suffolk, S. F. (1937). Afferent fibres from the stomach and small intestine. *J. Physiol.* **89**, 407–420.

Melzack, R. & Wall, P. D. (1965). Gate control theory of pain. *Science* **150**, 971–979.

McDowall, R. J. S. (1925). The reaction of the pupil in the chloralosed animal. *Quart. Jl exp. Physiol.* **15**, 177–180.

McLeod, J. G. (1958). The representation of the splanchnic afferent pathways in the thalamus of the cat. *J. Physiol.* **140**, 462–478.

Mountcastle, V. B. & Henneman, E. (1949). Pattern of tactile representation in thalamus of cat. *J. Neurophysiol.* **12**, 85–100.

Mountcastle, V. B., Poggio, G. F. & Werner, G. (1963). The relation of thalamic cell response to peripheral stimuli varied over an intensive continuum. *J. Neurophysiol.* **26**, 807–834.

Patton, H. D. & Amassian, V. E. (1951). Thalamic relay of splanchnic afferent fibres. *Am. J. Physiol.* **167**, 815–816.

Poggio, G. F. & Mountcastle, V. B. (1963). The functional properties of ventrobasal thalamic neurons studied in unanaesthetized monkeys. *J. Neurophysiol.* **26**, 775–806.

Purpura, D. P. & Cohen, B. (1962). Intracellular recording from thalamic neurons during recruiting responses. *J. Neurophysiol.* **25**, 621–635.

Purpura, D. P. & Shofer, R. J. (1963). Intracellular recording from thalamic neurons during reticulo-cortical activation. *J. Neurophysiol.* **26**, 494–505.

Rose, J. E. & Mountcastle, V. B. (1954). Activity of single neurons in the tactile thalamic region of the cat in response to a transient peripheral stimulus. *Johns Hopkins Hosp. Bull.* **94**, 238–282.

Ruch, T. C. (1946). Visceral sensation and referred pain. *Howell's Textbook of Physiology.* Saunders, London.

Ruch, T. C., Patton, H. D. & Amassian, V. E. (1952). Topographical and functional determinants of cortical localization patterns. *Res. Publs Ass. Res. nerv. ment. Dis.* **30**, 403–429.

Seybold, W. D. & Moore, R. M. (1940). Oculomotor nerve and reflex dilatation of the pupil. *J. Neurophysiol.* **3**, 436–441.

Sillito, A. M. & Zbrożyna, A. W. (1970a). The localization of pupilloconstrictor function within the mid-brain of the cat. *J. Physiol.* **211**, 461–477.

Sillito, A. M. & Zbrożyna, A. W. (1970b). The activity characteristics of the preganglionic pupilloconstrictor neurones. *J. Physiol.* **211**, 767–779.

Ury, B. & Gellhorn, E. (1939). Role of the sympathetic system in reflex dilatation of pupil. *J. Neurophysiol.* **2**, 268–275.

8

VISCERO-SENSORY AREAS IN
THE CEREBRAL CORTEX

THE representation of splanchnic nerve afferents in the sensory areas
of the cerebral cortex was first reported by Amassian (1951) and
Downman (1951), working independently. In cats under light
nembutal anaesthesia, single shocks delivered to the central cut end of
a splanchnic nerve gave an initial surface-positive primary wave
followed by a negative wave or series of waves. With deeper
anaesthesia, only the initial wave was recorded and this was used as
an index to define the projection areas and to map the points of
maximal activity. Both authors agreed that splanchnic afferent
impulses reached the trunk area in contralateral sensory area I and
projected bilaterally on sensory area II. Analysis of the central
pathways of splanchnic afferent impulses has since been the subject of
several papers, but relatively few of these were concerned with the
evoked discharges of cortical neurones (Gardner, Thomas & Morin,
1955; Newman, 1962; Zaraiskaya, Musyaschikova & Chernigovsky,
1965). Indeed, attention was mostly concentrated on topographical
representation and on the results of interaction between cutaneous and
splanchnic nerve afferents. In comparison to our knowledge of the
somatosensory system, including the mass of data now available from
tactile and proprioceptive functions, the viscero-sensory areas in the
cerebral cortex have been surprisingly neglected. Electrical stimulation
of the splanchnic nerve has given some useful clues about the
organization of the afferent projections, but more experiments, using
physiological stimuli, are required in order to demonstrate the changes
evoked in the cerebral cortex by impulses of visceral origin. In general,
the investigations outlined in this chapter indicate that the viscero-
sensory pathway through the thalamus to the sensory cortex involves
a fairly complex projection system. A study of this system has

revealed that there are many similarities between the two systems especially in regard to the principles of their organization. They include common mechanisms of transmission, convergence and interaction of afferent impulses and the properties and firing patterns of individual cells. In investigating the central transmission processes of the visceral afferent system three types of experiments will now be described: the potential changes evoked in the cortex by distension of abdominal viscera; the responses elicited by electrical stimulation of the splanchnic nerve; and the discharge patterns of single cortical units following shocks delivered to the splanchnic nerve alone or in combination with cutaneous stimuli. It will be shown that afferent impulses from abdominal viscera are distributed by the thalamus to somatosensory areas I and II and that the functional differences between low-threshold and high-threshold groups are maintained at the cortical level.

EXPERIMENTAL METHODS

1. Anaesthesia. In experiments recording potentials from the cortical surface, the animals were anaesthetized with sodium pentobarbitone administered intraperitoneally in an initial dose of 40–50 mg/kg body weight. Maintenance doses were given intravenously as required. Anaesthetics chosen by other workers included Dial (Ciba), chloralose, hexobarbitone, or mixtures of chloralose and barbiturate. Single unit recordings were performed on cats under ether followed by sodium thiopentone given in initial doses of 45 mg/kg. Additional doses were administered to maintain the animal under light anaesthesia as indicated by the electrocorticogram which was continuously monitored.

2. Operative procedures. Craniotomy was performed on one or both sides to expose sensory areas I and II (Fig. 8.1). The initial burr hole in the parietal bone was extended forwards to the frontal air sinus and downwards through the temporal bone to the edge of the zygoma. Care was taken to avoid damage to the superior sagittal sinus and to any pial veins adherent to the dura; they could usually be stroked to the side with cotton wool after cutting and deflecting the dura. The ansate sulcus was identified and the pia covered with cellophane strips or immersed under a pool of warm liquid paraffin. To minimize cerebral pulsations, the cerebrospinal fluid was drained through the cisterna magna.

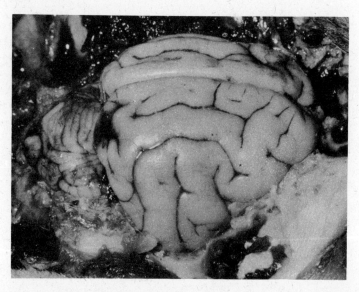

FIG. 8.1. Photograph of exposed cat brain seen from above. The dura has been removed to reveal surface markings of right cerebral hemisphere. Visceral afferent projections are found in the sensory area anterior to ansate sulcus and above Sylvian fissure. Dorsal surface of cerebellum can be seen on left.

In Chapter 2 a brief reference was made to the 'closed head' technique for microelectrode recordings. The principle of this technique (Li & Jasper, 1953) entailed the construction of a sealed chamber which effectively prevented all movements of the electrode tip in relation to the cell membrane. A threaded metal ring was screwed tightly into a trepan hole in the skull; a transparent window was then cemented over the top of the ring with a hollow glass tube through which the microelectrode was inserted. A modification of the method had a plastic cup fixed into position with dental cement. The dura was excised under mineral oil and a metal ring screwed on the cup which was then filled with molten paraffin wax to the top of the ring. Overheating of the cortex was prevented by a layer of mineral oil covering the pia (Amassian et al., 1959).

3. Recording procedures. Surface potentials were recorded in the open-head preparations with either saline wicks or bipolar silver ball electrodes, tips 2–3 mm apart. Unit activity was recorded with glass microelectrodes (tip diameters 0.5–3.0 μ). The micropipettes were filled with 3 M-KCl or 3 M-NaCl and their d.c. resistances ranged between 8 and 15 MΩ. In order to reduce the effects of cerebral pulsations a pressor foot was attached to the manipulator using silver wire buried in the foot for recording the electrocorticogram (Amassian, 1953). Simultaneous recordings from the cerebral cortex and splanchnic or cutaneous nerves were displayed on Tektronix 3 in. indicators mounted side by side and the traces were photographed on a Tektronix 565 split-beam oscilloscope. During exploratory penetrations, the activity of the cortex was monitored with a loud-speaker which, however, was always off during photography in order to eliminate conditioning by sound.

RESPONSES TO VISCERAL DISTENSION

Stimulation

The standard procedure was to insert a balloon into a viscus and to record responses to inflation from the surface of the cortex. Sometimes several exploratory positions were tried before any potential changes were observed. Gall bladder, stomach, loops of small intestine and urinary bladder gave positive results, but most of the experiments described here were performed on the gall bladder and stomach. Balloons of appropriate size were inflated with air or saline by means of a motorized syringe; a polyethylene cannula was fixed to the muscles and skin to reduce movement. After insertion of the balloons, the abdomen was closed in layers and the operative sites were infiltrated with a local anaesthetic. The rate of inflation was controlled and a two-way tap on the cannula allowed quick release. In each experiment, inflation and deflation were repeated several times.

Responses

In lightly anaesthetized animals evoked cortical potentials were superimposed on the electrocorticogram; in deeper anaesthesia spontaneous activity was reduced and the potentials were more easily recognized. They consisted of burst discharges varying in duration and amplitude according to the degree of visceral distension and the site of the recording electrode (Fig. 8.2). Bilateral responses were

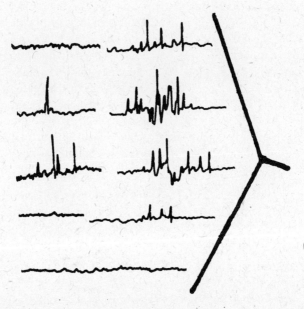

Fig. 8.2. Cerebral cortical responses to distension of the stomach. Cat under deep sodium pentobarbitone anaesthesia. Position of ansate sulcus is indicated on left side to show the extent of the primary sensory area on which electrocorticograms have been superimposed. Localized responses during period of balloon inflation are revealed by the surface potential changes. Note area of maximal activity nearest to the sulcus.

observed following distension of the stomach with the electrodes on symmetrical positions in sensory area I. Maximal responses were recorded at points close to the angle of the ansate sulcus. The responses were not affected after section of the vagi, but were unobtainable in the spinal animal with vagi intact. The results of these earlier experiments suggested what now has been amply confirmed, that impulses released by distension of viscera ascend in the spinal cord to reach their destination in a localized area of the cerebral cortex. Similar results have been reported from the work of Chernigovsky and his associates (1965).

RESPONSES TO STIMULATION OF THE SPLANCHNIC NERVE

The difficulties to be met with in stimulating the splanchnic nerve are well known. The nerve lies buried in fat as it passes through the diaphragm to the coeliac ganglion and it may be too short for the application of more than one pair of electrodes. Above the diaphragm, it lies deep against the vertebral column in close proximity to the great vessels where it is bound by fascia to the thoracic ganglia. Contact between the nerve and electrodes is subjected to the rhythmic movements of the lungs and diaphragm in breathing and escape of current from the electrodes to the body wall is sometimes difficult to avoid. In the experiments described in this section, the right splanchnic nerve was exposed below the diaphragm by a retroperitoneal approach at the level of the kidney. Shielded electrodes were applied to the central cut end of the nerve which was immersed in a pool of liquid paraffin. In experiments on single cortical units, described in the next section, the chest was opened by resection of the lower three ribs. Sufficient length of the nerve was dissected free from all tissue to allow the use of a multiple electrode assembly which was held firmly in position by sutures applied through the body wall. By this method manipulations could be carried out without loss of electrode contact. Stimuli were delivered to a distal pair of electrodes and the compound nerve action potential was recorded from a proximal pair.

Cortical responses

The primary response recorded from the pial surface of the cortex was an initially positive wave evoked by a single shock delivered to the splanchnic nerve. Responses were obtained from both sensory areas I and II (Fig. 8.3). In light anaesthesia or with stronger stimulation the primary wave was frequently followed by three or four 'secondary' waves suggesting a spread of activity from the primary afferent focus. The latency of the cortical response, measured from the beginning of the shock artifact to the beginning of the primary wave, was about 7–10 msec; the duration about 12–15 msec and the amplitude about 100 μV. Variations in the electrical characteristics were attributable to many factors including the level of anaesthesia, general state of the animal, recording site and the parameters of stimulation. However, the responses obtained from sensory area II were generally of shorter latency and of greater amplitude than those from sensory area I. The significance of this finding will be discussed later.

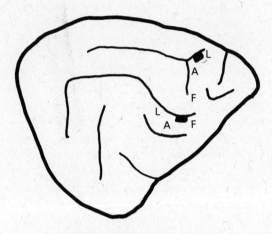

Splanchnic receiving areas in cat

FIG. 8.3. Diagram of right cerebral hemisphere to show splanchnic receiving areas in the cat. L, A, F, leg, arm and face representations in primary and second sensory areas. Primary receiving area for splanchnic afferents lies close to ansate sulcus; second receiving area is below it in anterior ectosylvian gyrus.

Distribution of surface potentials

The somatosensory areas of the cat were first classified by Woolsey (1946) following earlier observations of Marshall, Woolsey & Bard (1941) and of Adrian (1941). From their studies of the cortical projection of peripheral receptors it was shown in many different species that tactile impulses had a double sensory representation. Somatosensory area I (corresponding to the postcentral gyrus in man) was located anterior to the ansate sulcus and was mainly contralateral in function. Somatosensory area II, found on the superior bank of the Sylvian fissure in man, was located in the anterior ectosylvian gyrus of the cat and was bilateral in function.

Primary wave responses to splanchnic nerve stimulation were

mapped in both sensory areas. It will be seen from Fig. 8.3 that the splanchnic afferent projections occupy 1, a discrete area between leg and arm representation for the skin, the points of maximal activity lying close to the ansate sulcus; 2, a smaller area wedged within the trunk representation of somatic sensory area II. The splanchnic projections form only a small part of the sensory cortex, but their distribution was precisely in the position to be expected from anatomical grounds. The consistency of the evoked responses as well as their precise localization were good reasons to believe that the same areas of cortex served a visceral as well as a somatic afferent function.

RESPONSES OF SINGLE CORTICAL UNITS

General considerations

The electrical changes detected from the pial surface are derived from potential fields created by a focus of activity within the brain. Such fields or action currents account for the spontaneous rhythms of the conscious animal and for the modified electrocorticogram observed in light anaesthesia. As distinct from spontaneous activity, the arrival of impulses from a peripheral source causes a localized change in the conducting path and a recording of this change is known as the 'evoked potential'. A microelectrode in contact with the pial surface can detect an evoked potential which appears to be identical to the primary wave recorded with a gross electrode. The electrical changes which occur when the microelectrode is inserted at different depths into the substance of the cortex are illustrated in Fig. 8.4. The initial positive wave becomes a negative wave at depths between 0·4 and 1 mm below the pial surface. During electrode penetration, the firing of single units can be heard on the loud-speaker and seen on the oscilloscope as negative or positive–negative spikes discharging irregularly and without any obvious relationship to the evoked primary wave. Large positive spikes of intracellular origin are also frequently encountered. Two or more units may be recorded in the same trace, but they can be identified as separate units by differences in amplitude and discharge frequencies. In general, the spontaneous activity of unit discharges can be diminished very effectively by increasing the depth of anaesthesia, a procedure that is sometimes necessary.

Properties of the evoked response

Two forms of evoked unit activity were recorded from the sensory cortex, 1, an initially negative spike firing either singly or in short bursts and rarely more than 1 mV in amplitude (Fig. 8.4*c*); and 2, an initially positive spike, 3–5 mV in amplitude, appearing as a single diphasic deflection at threshold intensity of stimulation, but occurring in bursts of two or three spikes with stronger stimulation (Fig. 8.4*d*). Such spikes were quite often initially negative, changing in sign as the

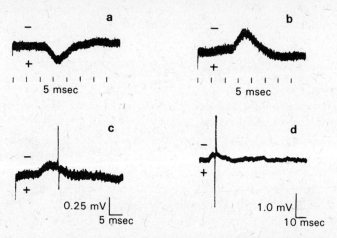

FIG. 8.4. Characteristics of evoked potentials in the cerebral cortex. Cat under sodium thiopentone anaesthesia. (a) surface positive primary wave following onset of stimulus; (b) reversed primary wave recorded at depth 0·4 mm below pial surface; (c) initially negative diphasic spike discharge; (d) initially positive diphasic spike. The sign of the action potential depends on the position of the electrode tip relative to the active elements.

microelectrode was advanced. The theoretical considerations of extracellular field potentials will be discussed below, but it can be mentioned here that with small microelectrode tips, a number of different units could be sampled in a single penetration without injuring the membrane or destroying the cell; often the same unit was identified by its discharge pattern as the microelectrode was withdrawn in the track.

Three effects of splanchnic nerve stimulation on single unit activity were observed:

1. Units that were silent or fired irregularly in the absence of

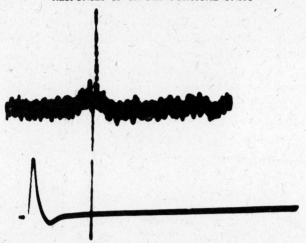

FIG. 8.5. Single cortical unit response to stimulation of contralateral splanchnic nerve. Upper trace shows typical positive–negative spike superimposed on evoked primary wave. Lower trace is simultaneous recording of the splanchnic A beta action potential.

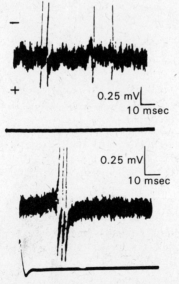

FIG. 8.6. Effect of splanchnic afferent stimulation on spontaneously active units. Cat under light sodium thiopentone anaesthesia. Upper trace, before stimulation, the unit fires irregularly. Lower trace shows how this unit responds to a single shock delivered to the splanchnic nerve.

stimulation became active during the primary response. Figure 8.5 shows a positive–negative spike occurring about the peak of the primary wave following stimulation of the contralateral splanchnic nerve.

2. Spontaneously active units gave an evoked spike discharge similar in latency and form to that observed in silent units (Fig. 8.6).

3. Spontaneously active units showed an increase of firing frequency up to 70/80 per second (Fig. 8.7).

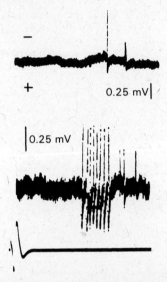

Fig. 8.7. Increased frequency of spontaneous unit discharges. Two units are sampled in the upper trace, each firing singly and at irregular intervals. Lower trace shows how stimulation of the splanchnic nerve causes an increase of firing frequency in each unit.

There was good evidence that 'silent' units were activated by the A beta group of splanchnic nerve afferents since out of a series of 52 units examined, 22 units responded when only a small fraction of the A beta fibres was excited. A further 14 units responded to a larger fraction of the A beta component. Higher intensities of stimulation were required in order to influence spontaneously active units; some responded to maximal excitation of the A beta fibres, but the majority of spontaneously firing units were more easily influenced by the A delta group of splanchnic afferents (Newman, 1962). Thus, as elsewhere in the nervous system, the functional division into low-threshold and high-threshold groupings was strictly maintained.

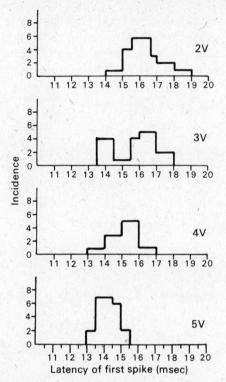

FIG. 8.8. Range of latencies and changes of incidence with increasing intensities of stimulation. Latency of first spike in each evoked discharge plotted on the abscissa, incidence plotted on the ordinate. Note decrease of latency and greater incidence of shorter latencies with increasing stimulus intensities.

Relation between stimulus intensity and latency

It has already been mentioned that the cortical responses and the splanchnic nerve action potential were displayed simultaneously. In this way stimulus intensities were measured simply by reference to the function of afferent fibres excited. The latency of a particular unit was rarely constant at threshold levels of stimulation. Generally, unit responses evoked in sensory area I had longer latencies than those recorded from sensory area II. The range of latencies varied from 19 to 13 msec when only A beta fibres were excited, but shorter latencies occurred with A delta stimulation. In all the units studied it was found that the mean latency for the first spike of the discharge was reduced by increasing the strength of the stimulus above threshold. This relationship is illustrated in the histograms of Fig. 8.8 which also show the range of latencies. With weak stimulation, there was a greater incidence of longer latencies; with stronger stimulation, the shorter latencies were more prevalent.

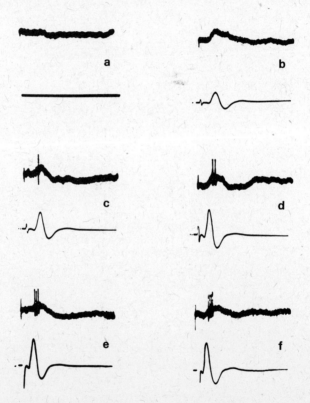

FIG. 8.9. Relation between stimulus intensity and number of spikes. Cat under sodium thiopentone anaesthesia. Upper traces, cortical responses from Sensory Area II; lower traces, splanchnic nerve action potential. (a) Stimulus off; (b) stimulus below threshold of unit but primary wave recorded; (c–f) increasing number of spikes with increasing stimulus intensities.

Relation between stimulus intensity and number of spikes

Both initially negative and initially positive-going units discharged a variable number of spikes in response to a constant stimulus. Low-threshold units responded as a rule with either a single spike or two spikes; high-threshold units often gave a burst of six or seven spikes. A study of the records suggested that increasing the intensity of stimulation caused an increase in the number of spikes per discharge, although this was not an invariable finding. The traces in Fig. 8.9 are from a unit isolated in contralateral sensory area II. A single spike discharge was converted into a three spike discharge with maximal A beta excitation and a fourth spike appeared when A delta fibres were excited in addition. No studies were made in this series on the rate of firing, but apart from the strength of the stimulus, the depth of anaesthesia was equally important. Multiple spike discharges were not consistent with identical stimuli even under very light anaesthesia.

Relation between stimulus intensity and probability

Increasing the intensity of the stimulus above threshold increased the probability that a cortical unit would discharge at least one spike. The data presented in Table 8.1 are from the evoked responses of a

TABLE 8.1. Relation between the intensity of the stimulus and probability of response

Column 1 gives the fraction of A beta fibres stimulated. Columns 2, 3 and 4 express probability functions: P(1), at least one spike will fire; P(2), at least two spikes; P(3), three or more spikes. N, number of responses in each test of 30 trials. P, probability factor

A beta fraction	P(1) N	P(1) P	P(2) N	P(2) P	P(3) N	P(3) P
0·1	—	—	—	—	—	—
0·2	7	0·2	0	0·0	0	0·0
0·3	8	0·2	1	0·0	0	0·0
0·4	9	0·3	2	0·1	0	0·0
0·5	11	0·4	4	0·1	0	0·0
0·6	25	0·8	13	0·4	0	0·0
0·7	27	0·9	17	0·6	2	0·1
0·8	30	1·0	19	0·6	3	0·1
0·9	30	1·0	21	0·7	5	0·2
1·0	30	1·0	22	0·7	10	0·3

typical experiment. It will be observed that the effect of increasing the intensity of splanchnic nerve stimulation was to increase the probability that a single discharge or a number of repetitive discharges would occur. At low intensities of stimulation the number of responses was small compared with the number observed at higher intensities. Figures are given for discharges of at least one spike (P1), at least two spikes (P2) and multiple discharges of three or more spikes (P3). The relationship of stimulus intensity to probability of response for single and multiple discharges is also expressed graphically in Fig. 8.10. It

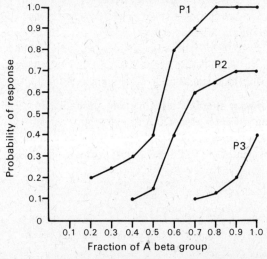

Fig. 8.10. Relation between stimulus intensity and probability of response. The fraction of A beta fibres excited is plotted on the abscissa. The probability factor represented on the ordinate is calculated from the number of occasions the unit fires out of 30 successive trials. The curve P1 expresses the probability that at least one spike will occur following the stimulus; P2, at least two spikes; P3, three or more spikes. Note the effect of increasing the A beta fraction on response probability. Recruitment of delta afferents contributes to the response at the higher stimulus intensities.

can be seen that the change of P1 was gradual over the initial range of intensities and that this was followed by a rapid rise to a high level of probability with maximal excitation of A beta fibres. With greater stimulus intensities, the curves represent a mixed A beta–A delta effect. The curves for P2 and P3, also shown in the figure, follow the same form as P1 but at lower levels of probability.

Comments

The interpretation of the experimental results so far described poses three important problems on cortical function:

1. Do the potential changes recorded from the cerebral cortex reflect changes in the activity of the sense organs? The answer is without doubt in the affirmative. Evoked potentials are electrical events occurring at the site of recording. They are produced only when impulses reach the site after stimulating the sense organ or its afferent pathway and therefore they indicate a neuroanatomical link between the sense organ and a localized region of the brain. The primary response is generated by a large number of cells in a neurone pool and it represents the overall activity of that pool. Since current flows between the somas and the dendrites, the resulting electrical field will be negative in the centre and positive in the periphery of the pool. Thus an electrode resting on the surface of the cortex will record an initially positive deflexion. Phase reversal will occur when the electrode is inserted into the substance of the brain and the recording tip lies in the active region of the pool. These general observations are easy to understand. However, other factors contributing to the evoked primary response must now be considered.

From studies of the cytoarchitecture of the cat cerebral cortex, pyramidal cells form a high proportion of the total, increasing in size as they are traced inwards from the pial surface. Each pyramidal cell has branching dendrites at the base and an apical dendrite ascending into the superficial layers. Axon collaterals and the fibres of smaller non-pyramidal cells also course upwards from the deeper layers and the impulses which they convey are carried to sites above the level of the thalamic afferent terminals. There can be little doubt that the evoked primary response is due to current flowing from the surface towards the deeper layers of the cortex, but the contribution of the thalamo-cortical afferents cannot account for the total evoked response. A distinction must be made between evoked discharges in the deeper layers which are due directly to the arrival of specific afferent impulses and evoked discharges in the superficial layers which are caused by postsynaptic excitation of intracortical neurones (Amassian, Waller & Macy, 1964). In deep anaesthesia the superficial discharges are depressed while the activity of the deeper layers persists. Nevertheless, reversal of the evoked primary wave into an initially negative wave is frequently observed in the superficial cortex even in deep anaesthesia. This would imply that the afferent volley has reached the cortex either by spread from the deeper layers to the surface or is carried there by collaterals or by intracortical neurones. The question is not yet resolved but it can be stated that phase reversal of the primary wave was observed at a depth only 0·4 mm below the pia when recording responses evoked by stimulation of the splanchnic nerve. An excellent review of the extracellular field potentials has been given by Hubbard, Llinas & Quastel (1969).

2. What information about the visceral afferent system can be derived from single unit recordings? The technique of single unit analysis in the cerebral cortex has provided one of the most successful approaches to an understanding of its function since Ling & Gerard (1949) introduced micropipettes with small recording tips. It became possible to isolate the electrical activity of individual cells and to observe their discharge properties under varying conditions of activity. The appearance of the electrical changes largely depends on the location of the electrode tip with respect to the flow of current. Initially negative spikes represent the action potentials generated by the currents flowing across the membrane of the soma and initially positive spikes record current flows radiating from dendrites. In practice, the initial electrical sign is determined by the size of the cell and most negative spikes are recorded in the superficial layers of the cortex where small cells predominate. In the deeper layers of the cortex, where the cells are larger, the microelectrode tip can be placed sufficiently close to the membrane, without penetrating it, to record current flow from the sources and thus an initially positive spike.

In studying the evoked discharges of cortical units a distinction can be made between superficial and deep recordings. In light anaesthesia, the small cells of the superficial layers are spontaneously active, although many of them respond to a sensory stimulus such as touch or light tapping of the body wall. They also respond with low probability to splanchnic evoked impulses by increasing the frequency of their discharge. It seems that the superficial cells belong to a diffuse network of neurones under the influence of thalamo-cortical afferents but without any modality specificity. In contrast, the cells of the deeper layer yield characteristic patterns of discharge according to the site, intensity and frequency of the stimulus and they are not so dependent on levels of anaesthesia. The typical response of a splanchnic-evoked unit is a positive–negative spike, 3–5 mV in amplitude peak-to-peak, superimposed on a reversed primary wave. Many such units are silent in the absence of stimulation or fire only irregularly and they follow successive stimuli with a high degree of probability. These findings confirm earlier statements that impulses from abdominal viscera can influence cerebral activity in specific regions of the cortex. The initial discharges arise in the deeper layers where the receptive fields are fixed and restricted. The impulses are then carried into the superficial layers where the receptive fields are more labile and therefore dependent on intracortical mechanisms. The existence of 'fixed' and 'labile' projections in the sensory cortex suggests the idea of integrative function (Brooks, Rudomin & Slayman, 1961).

3. How does stimulus intensity affect cortical function? It has been noted that an increase of stimulus intensity alters the behaviour of cortical unit discharges by reducing the mean latency of the first spike, increasing the number of spikes and increasing the probability that the unit will discharge at least one spike. At low intensities of stimulation, relatively few afferent fibres are excited. Under such conditions, the unit discharges inconsistently with a greater incidence of long latencies and a low level of response probability. It is suggested that the impulses find their way to the cortex along a multisynaptic pathway involving considerable synaptic delay. Alternatively, the specific afferent input to the cortex is partly blocked by intrinsic activity occurring at the sites of convergence or by the depression resulting from the anaesthesia. By contrast, when the intensity of stimulation is increased, transmission processes are speeded up by synchronous arrival of impulses and greater depolarization at the synaptic junctions. A stronger stimulus excites more afferent fibres and a wider spread of activity through pathways which are not involved at weaker intensities. In summary, variability of response becomes less variable as stimulus intensity is increased—the changing patterns of discharge in the sensory cortex reflect changes in the flow of information from the sense organs.

INTERACTION BETWEEN CUTANEOUS
AND SPLANCHNIC AFFERENTS

It was frequently observed that cortical units responding to stimulation of the splanchnic nerve could also be excited by tactile stimulation applied to the skin on the same side. A pair of stimulating electrodes was inserted at an appropriate site on the body wall and the effects of interaction were demonstrated by conditioning and testing techniques. Single shocks were delivered by two pulse generators over a wide range of intervals. The results of one experiment are illustrated in Fig. 8.11. Record A shows the response of a single shock delivered to the skin; B the response of the same unit to a single shock delivered to the splanchnic nerve. Records C, D, E and F are respectively the responses to conditioning and testing stimuli delivered at progressively diminishing intervals. Indications of interaction between the two sensory inputs were a reduction in the probability that the unit would respond to the testing stimulus and an increase in the mean latency of the test response. In F, with the C–T interval at 20 msec, the test response is absent. The data set out in Table 8.2 show that there was

TABLE 8.2. Relation between conditioning–testing interval and probability of response

Conditioning stimulus to abdominal skin; testing stimulus to splanchnic nerve. Response of unit to either stimulus alone was 30 in each test of 30 trials. Column 1 gives the C–T interval. Column 2 gives the mean latency of the test response. Columns 3 and 4 express probability functions: N, number of occasions in which at least one spike is evoked by 30 successive stimuli to the splanchnic nerve. P, probability factor

Interval (msec)	Latency (msec)	N	P
70	16·2	30	1·0
60	16·5	28	0·9
50	17·8	19	0·6
40	18·2	4	0·1
30	19·5	3	0·1
25	—	0	0·0
20	—	0	0·0

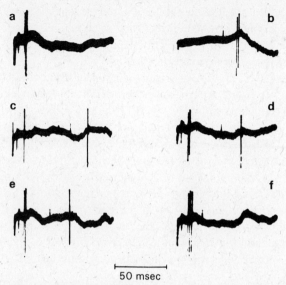

50 msec

FIG. 8.11. Interaction between cutaneous and splanchnic nerve afferents. Cat under sodium thiopentone anaesthesia. (a) Response of cortical unit to cutaneous stimulation alone. (b) Response of same cortical unit to splanchnic stimulation alone; stimulus artifact delayed 50 msec on sweep. (c–f) Test stimuli to splanchnic nerve given respectively at 60, 50, 40 and 20 msec after a conditioning stimulus to the skin. Note absence of test response in (f).

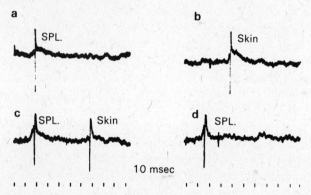

10 msec

FIG. 8.12. Effect of reversing the sequence of stimulation. (a) Unit response to splanchnic stimulation alone. (b) Response of same unit to cutaneous stimulation alone. (c) Conditioning stimulus to splanchnic nerve (SPL); testing stimulus to skin. C–T interval at 50 msec. The unit responds to both stimuli. (d) Occlusion of test response when C–T interval is less than 30 msec.

little evidence of interaction with C–T intervals longer than 50 msec. With shorter intervals, the probability of firing was significantly reduced and at the same time the latency of the test response was increased until the unit ceased to fire.

Reversing the sequence of stimulation yielded comparable results, i.e. conditioning shocks to the splanchnic nerve and test shocks to the skin. In the example shown in Fig. 8.12 the unit failed to respond to skin stimulation with C–T intervals between 20 and 30 msec.

Interaction studies at the thalamic level were discussed in the previous chapter. It was noted that the most prominent change observed was inhibition of the thalamic relay cell by afferents from different sources. Interaction between splanchnic and cutaneous afferents at the cortical level was first reported by Amassian (1952) who demonstrated blocking of the test primary wave with C–T intervals around 20 msec. Amassian believed that the blocking effect should be termed 'occlusion' when both the conditioning and testing volleys evoked the same response and preferred the term 'sensory inhibition' when the conditioning volley did not itself generate a response. This kind of interaction has been encountered in the cerebellum as well as in the cerebral cortex in experiments recording the evoked activity of single units. Thus a weak conditioning stimulus may fail to cause firing of the unit yet effectively block the response of the unit to a strong testing stimulus.

The distinction made between occlusion and inhibition is probably academic since they are both dependent on afferent convergence and neuronal sharing. Nevertheless it is of great significance that impulses arriving in the sensory cortex from distant sense organs not only cause unit discharges, but create a barrier to further discharges. Inhibitory mechanisms occur at all levels in the nervous system and several names have been applied to them. In the sensory cortex interaction performs an important physiological role, at least at the unit level, since cortical representation of peripheral events may be controlled at any instant by the sequence, timing and relative intensities of the sensory input. Depression of the spike generating mechanism of cortical units lasts about 20–50 msec and it is during this period of time that other excitatory influences are unlikely to succeed unless they are extremely powerful.

THE SECOND SENSORY AREA

Adrian (1941) first described dual receiving areas in the cat cerebral cortex. In the same year Marshall, Woolsey & Bard located representative areas of the body in the rostral strip of the anterior ectosylvian gyrus which seemed to be independent of the primary sensory area. The term 'somatic sensory area II' was later proposed by Woolsey (1946) and his nomenclature is now used to define primary and secondary areas for auditory, visual and motor representations. Duality in the cerebral cortex must be regarded as the rule rather than the exception, yet the precise role of the second sensory area is not clear. Indeed, behavioural studies made after complete ablation of the second sensory area indicate that the sensory functions of the animal remain essentially unimpaired.

While there is uncertainty attached to the role of dual representation in the cerebral cortex, it appears that the second sensory area may be an important link in the organization of the splanchnic afferent system. There are several reasons for this belief. First of all, it is known that cells of the posteroventral thalamic nucleus project to discrete points in both cerebral hemispheres and that the splanchnic receiving area is wedged in a narrow strip between arm and leg areas, but overlapping tactile and proprioceptive projections. The major contributions of the splanchnic afferents are found on the contralateral side, a fact that is evident from experience in recording. Contralateral penetrations are usually more successful than ipsilateral recordings but, more significantly, the responses evoked are often larger and more consistent than those obtained from the primary sensory area. This observation emphasizes the relative size of the thalamo-cortical projections and the density of the cell population in the second sensory area. Another observation of interest when recording evoked unit activity is that several units may be encountered in a single penetration while this is not so evident in the primary sensory area. Such an arrangement suggests the possibility of a vertical column of cells belonging to the same modality group and activated by the same peripheral stimulus. The suggestion of functional depth was originally proposed by Mountcastle (1957) on the basis of his work on tactile and joint afferents in the lemniscal projection system.

Secondly, it has been shown that the responses evoked in the second sensory area by stimulation of the splanchnic nerve possess substantially shorter latencies than do those recorded from sensory area I. Evidence from single unit studies shows that at any given stimulus intensity, the mean latency of the first spike of the evoked discharge is comparatively shorter in the second sensory area. The reason for this is not at all clear since fast conducting afferents of the A beta group reach sensory area I as well as sensory area II. Nevertheless, the pathways mediating short-latency responses belong to the dorsal column system which is known to have a low excitatory threshold and to serve discriminative functions. By contrast, somatic sensory inflow is far better organized in the primary receiving area of the cerebral cortex which provides a detailed representation of the contralateral body and serves the principal cortical destination of cutaneous and proprioceptive afferents.

Thirdly, it was shown by Andersson (1962) that cortical responses of short latency were mediated by two spinal pathways, the dorsal columns and the lateral tract. In these studies, unit responses evoked by stimulation of the skin and deeper structures were recorded from the second sensory area. The fact that transection of the dorsal columns did not abolish the evoked responses led to the conclusion that the two spinal pathways represented separate functional systems distinguished by the size and modality of their peripheral fields. This view is quite in harmony with the evidence already presented for the visceral afferent system. It will be remembered that impulses in the splanchnic nerve ascend in the dorsal columns and anterolateral tracts. The A beta group of splanchnic afferents may be compared both anatomically and functionally to the lemniscal division of the somatic sensory system whilst the A delta group may be similarly compared to the spinothalamic division. Although both groups retain their identity as separate functional systems they converge ultimately on the same cortical units in the second sensory area. The A delta group of splanchnic afferents is believed to serve the sensation of pain; it is bilateral in distribution and it has access to all available units in its network.

In summary, the role of the second sensory area is not yet established. Present evidence suggests that it may be concerned more with visceral than somatic functions and that the bilateral character of the A delta splanchnic projections, the size of the receptive fields, the latencies of the evoked responses and other relevant data argue strongly for their participant role in the cerebral organization of visceral pain.

CORTICOFUGAL INFLUENCES
ON THE VISCERAL INPUT

It has been shown by anatomical studies that there are descending projections from the sensory cortex to many different parts of the brain and spinal cord. The pathways were traced to their terminations after lesions were placed at selected points in the cerebral cortex and the fibres allowed to degenerate. Mettler (1935) applied this technique to the monkey and described a succession of descending fibres reaching the thalamus, the hypothalamus and the trigeminal, pontine and olivary nuclei in the brain stem. Jones & Powell (1968) examined the pathways between the sensory areas of the cortex and the thalamus. From histological studies in the cat they identified a topographical arrangement in which the primary and second sensory areas projected to the posteroventral nucleus and to the posterior group of thalamic nuclei. Corticofugal fibres to the trigeminal nucleus and nucleus of the solitary tract were described by Brodal, Szabo & Torvik (1956) and the existence of a pathway from the sensory cortex to the nuclei of the dorsal columns was suggested by the studies of Walberg (1957). This pathway is of great interest. Walberg showed that the fibres descended in the pyramidal tract, then entered the medial lemniscus at the level of the inferior olive to reach the gracile and cuneate nuclei. More recent investigations by Kuypers & Tuerk (1964) indicated that the pathway was not only complicated in its anatomical course but, more significantly, might play an active part in sensory adjustments. They pointed out a preferential distribution of the descending fibres for different cell types in the dorsal column nuclei. On the basis of these findings it is clear that the sensory areas of the cortex need not function as passive receiving mechanisms but, by means of their descending projections, can exercise a modulatory effect at each important level of sensory inflow.

The question of cortical influence on the ascending afferent systems has been amply confirmed by electrophysiological experiment. The potentials evoked at the synaptic relays by stimulation of sensory nerves can often be modified by electrical stimulation of the appropriate region in the cerebral cortex. The responses are sometimes reinforced by facilitation; at other times they are reduced in amplitude or depressed, depending on different anaesthetic conditions. The effect most frequently observed following cortical activation is sensory inhibition. The evidence implies that the central nervous system operates through a number of feed-back circuits whereby the cortical components are able to influence the transmission of impulses that normally flow to them. In Chapter 6 an account was given of the relationship between the sensory cortex and the cerebellum, in particular, the effects of stimulating the sensory cortex on evoked cerebellar discharges. It was shown that descending impulses reached the cerebellum through pontine, reticular and olivary relays and that the pathways exerted a bilateral influence. Evidence will now be given to show that the sensory cortex has a selective action on the relay of afferent impulses transmitted from the thalamus.

Cortico-thalamic relay system

Recent experimental work indicates that the thalamic relay cells are more selective in action than previously believed. What begins as a volley of impulses from a receptor may end in widespread action throughout various parts of the brain; a single peripheral stimulus may give rise to continuous neuronal discharges. On the other hand the impulses evoked in a sensory pathway may be delayed or reduced or lost altogether. Much of this control of sensory input is due to the influence of a cortico-thalamic mechanism. In an analysis of the corticofugal projections from sensory areas I and II Curry (1971) found that 92 per cent of the cells in the posterior group of thalamic nuclei could be influenced by the sensory cortex. On the basis of their structural organization, the influences can be exerted along three different pathways: 1, by direct cortico-thalamic fibres which have been demonstrated anatomically (Jones & Powell, 1968); 2, by means of antidromic invasion of specific afferent fibres arising from the thalamus and terminating by a rich plexus in the deeper layers of the cortex; 3, by the action of collaterals on thalamic interneurones.

Excitatory action. The activity evoked in the thalamus by electrical stimulation of the sensory cortex consists of a multiple spike discharge followed by a rhythmic series of waves or 'burst discharges'. The origin of the 'burst discharges' is in the thalamus itself since they persist after removal of the cortex with the stimulating electrode in the white matter (Adrian, 1951; Anderson, Brooks, Eccles & Sears, 1964). It is also believed that antidromic invasion of the thalamic cells causes the generation of impulses in their axon collaterals which in turn give positive feed-back or excite adjacent thalamic cells. This may account for the repetitive responses observed following cortical stimulation and perhaps explain the facilitatory effects of conditioning stimuli described by Angel & Dawson (1963). The excitatory action of cortico-thalamic discharges has also been demonstrated by Waller & Feldman (1967) from recordings of single thalamic units in the cat. According to these authors a cortical stimulus was set up by the wavefront of a spreading depression which they induced by touching the pia with a capillary tube filled with 2·5 M-KCl. The initial effect observed was desynchronization of the electrocorticogram accompanied by an increase in the discharge rate of the thalamic unit. They postulated that cortico-thalamic fibres excited the unit either directly or via the ascending reticular system and concluded that the responses of thalamic units to a reticular stimulus required cortico-thalamic facilitation. In summary, there is sufficient evidence to show that the sensory cortex can exert an excitatory influence on thalamic relay cells but the problem of its neuronal mechanism is not a simple one.

Inhibitory action. Evidence that the sensory cortex can exert a continuous inhibitory action on thalamic transmission was given by Angel (1963) in a series of experiments on the rat. After the application of strychnine to the primary sensory cortex, the thalamic response to the second of two peripheral stimuli was reduced. In contrast, when the sensory cortex was ablated, the thalamic response was greatly increased. Inhibitory interaction is commonly observed when recording from single thalamic units. Thus if a cortical stimulus is followed by a testing stimulus delivered to a sensory nerve, the response of the thalamic unit may be depressed for about 100 msec. The existence of an inhibitory mechanism within the thalamus was proposed by Anderson, Eccles & Sears (1964) and their conclusions have already been described (Chapter 7). They postulated that a proportion of axon collaterals was distributed to interneurones through which inhibition took place either postsynaptically on the thalamic relay cell or presynaptically on the ascending afferent terminals. Their evidence indicated that postsynaptic inhibition would cause suppression of the thalamic relay cell irrespective of the origin of the arriving impulses—whether they came from the sensory cortex or from the peripheral nerve.

All of these facts confirm the general view that the transmission of impulses by the thalamus to the sensory cortex is subject to modification by the cortex through corticofugal processes of excitation and inhibition.

SUMMARY

Recordings from the sensory areas of the cortex have revealed remarkable parallels of organization between the visceral and somatic afferent systems. There is general agreement that impulses of visceral origin ascend in the central nervous system to reach localized areas in the cerebral cortex. In their ascent they contribute to synaptic mechanisms at all levels of integration—spinal, cerebellar, reticular and thalamic. Under normal circumstances, visceral afferents do not play a major role in conscious sensation although they can dominate the entire nervous system when excited excessively; they are concerned with reflex mechanisms and, as is well known, control the internal environment through their influence on the autonomic nerves and endocrine glands.

Visceral afferents make significant contributions to the second sensory area in both cerebral hemispheres. It is too early to make any definite conclusions about the functions of the second sensory area, but the evidence reported here suggests that it may be especially concerned with the visceral system in the same manner as the primary sensory area is developed for the somatic system. The distinction is fully supported by the clinical characteristics of visceral and somatic sensation since accurate localization and discriminative functions belong predominantly to the somatic system. Electrophysiological evidence also confirms the involvement of the second sensory area with the sense of pain. Thus stimulation of the A delta group of splanchnic nerve afferents yields bilateral responses in the anterolateral conducting system which is known to transmit impulses provoked by painful stimuli.

The sensory cortex is capable of modifying the inflow from peripheral receptors by means of descending influences acting on the various synaptic relays. Neural mechanisms in the thalamus are more complicated than was formerly believed, for axon collaterals have both an excitatory and inhibitory action on adjacent thalamic cells, the latter being mediated by short interneurones. The view is also expressed that cortico-thalamic influences may facilitate the action of ascending reticular impulses in maintaining the excitability of the sensory cortex. It can be concluded that representation of both visceral and somatic sensibility in the cerebral cortex is the product of a series of transmission changes imposed on the ascending systems at the intervening synaptic relays.

REFERENCES

Adrian, E. D. (1941). Afferent discharges to the cerebral cortex from peripheral sense organs. *J. Physiol.* **100**, 159–191.

Adrian, E. D. (1951). Rhythmic discharges from the thalamus. *J. Physiol.* **113**, 9–10P.

Amassian, V. E. (1951). Cortical representation of visceral afferents. *J. Neurophysiol.* **14**, 433–444.

Amassian, V. E. (1952). Interaction in the somatovisceral projection system. *Res. Publ. Ass. Res. nerv. ment. Dis.* **30**, 371–402.

Amassian, V. E. (1953). Evoked single cortical unit activity in the somatic sensory areas. *Electroen. Neurophysiol.* **5**, 415–438.

Amassian, V. E., Berlin, L., Macy, J. Jr. & Waller, H. J. (1959). Simultaneous recording of the activities of several individual cortical neurones. *Trans. N.Y. Acad. Sci.* **21**, 395–405.

Amassian, V. E., Waller, H. J. & Macy, J. Jr. (1964). Neural mechanism of the primary somatosensory evoked potential. *Ann. N.Y. Acad. Sci.* **112**, 5–32.

Andersson, S. A. (1962). Projection of different spinal pathways to the second somatic sensory area in cat. *Acta Physiol scand.* **56**, Suppl. 194, 1–74.

Anderson, P., Brooks, C. McC., Eccles, J. C. & Sears, T. A. (1964). The ventro-lateral nucleus of the thalamus: potential fields, synaptic transmission and excitability of both presynaptic and post synaptic components. *J. Physiol.* **174**, 348–369.

Anderson, P., Eccles, J. C. & Sears, T. A. (1964). The ventro-basal complex of the thalamus: types of cells, their responses and their functional organization. *J. Physiol.* **174**, 370–399.

Angel, A. (1963). Evidence for cortical inhibition of transmission at the thalamic sensory relay nucleus in the rat. *J. Physiol.* **169**, 108P.

Angel, A. & Dawson, G. D. (1963). The facilitation of thalamic and cortical responses in the dorsal column sensory pathway by strong peripheral stimulation. *J. Physiol.* **166**, 587–604.

Brodal, A., Szabo, T. & Torvik, A. (1956). Corticofugal fibres to sensory trigeminal nuclei and nucleus of solitary tract. *J. comp. Neurol.* **106**, 527–555.

Brooks, V. B., Rudomin, P. & Slayman, C. L. (1961). Peripheral receptive fields of neurones in the cat's cerebral cortex. *J. Neurophysiol.* **24**, 302–325.

Curry, M. J. (1971). An electrophysiological study of the somatic posterior group. *J. Physiol.* **216**, 56–57P.

Downman, C. B. B. (1951). Cerebral destination of splanchnic afferent impulses. *J. Physiol.* **113**, 434–441.

Gardner, E. D., Thomas, L. M. & Morin, F. (1955). Cortical projections of fast visceral afferents in the cat and monkey. *Am. J. Physiol.* **183**, 438–444.

Hubbard, J. I., Llinás, R. & Quastel, D. M. J. (1969). *Electrophysiological Analysis of Synaptic Transmission.* Monograph of Physiological Society. Edward Arnold, London.

Jones, E. G. & Powell, T. P. S. (1968). The projection of the somatic sensory cortex upon the thalamus in the cat. *Brain Res.* **10**, 369–391.

Kuypers, H. G. J. M. & Tuerk, J. D. (1964). The distribution of the cortical fibres within the nuclei cuneatus and gracilis in the cat. *J. Anat.* **98**, 143–162.

Ling, G. & Gerard, R. W. (1949). The normal membrane potential of frog sartorius fibers. *J. cell. comp. Physiol.* **34**, 383–405.

Li, C. L. & Jasper, H. (1953). Microelectrode studies of the electrical activity of the cerebral cortex in the cat. *J. Physiol.* **121**, 117–140.

Marshall, W. H., Woolsey, C. N. & Bard, P. (1941). Observations in cortical somatic sensory mechanisms of cat and monkey. *J. Neurophysiol.* **4**, 1–24.

Mettler, F. (1935). Corticifugal fiber connections of the cortex of macaca mulata. The parietal region. *J. comp. Neurol.* **62**, 263–291.

Mountcastle, V. B. (1957). Modality and topographic properties of single neurons of cat's somatic sensory cortex. *J. Neurophysiol.* **20**, 408–434.

Newman, P. P. (1962). Single unit activity in the viscero-sensory areas of the cerebral cortex. *J. Physiol.* **160**, 284–297.

Walberg, F. (1957). Corticofugal fibres in the nuclei of the dorsal columns. *Brain* **80**, 273–287.

Waller, H. J. & Feldman, S. M. (1967). Somatosensory thalamic neurons: effects of cortical depression. *Science* **157**, 1074–1077.

Woolsey, C. N. (1946). Comparative studies on dual somatic afferent areas in cerebral cortex of rabbit, cat, dog, pig, sheep and monkey. *Fedn Proc.* **5**, 116.

Zaraiskaya, S. M., Musyaschikova, S. S. & Chernigovsky, V. N. (1965). Cortical representation of afferent systems of the alimentary tract. *Neurophysiol.* **15**, 405–413.

9

THE ORBITAL CORTEX

THIS chapter is devoted to a description of experimental work on the orbital cortex, a part of the brain that has provoked considerable interest in the field of visceral neurology. It is now abundantly clear that it plays a key role in the autonomic adjustments of the body acting, in the main, through influences on the hypothalamus, but also through projections on visceral centres in the brain stem. As with the functions of the somatic sensory system, the cerebral cortex depends on the coded information which reaches it from receptors; hence the importance of the visceral afferent input which has access to every synaptic level. This fact has not been stressed in the textbooks, which mostly concentrate on the visceral reactions of the autonomic nervous system and tend to neglect the lesser known features of viscero-sensory inflow. There are many reasons for believing that the orbital cortex is a visceral receiving area and integrating centre for somato-visceral reactions. Anatomically, it is part of the limbic complex, which includes the cingulate region and hippocampus, all of which contribute to the complex circuit of neurones feeding into the hypothalamus. With electrophysiological techniques, a variety of pathways has been traced to the reticular formation and cerebellum. Other physiological investigations have revealed widespread influences on the cardiovascular and respiratory systems, gastric functions and temperature regulation, whilst an extensive literature from clinical sources underlines involvement of the orbital cortex in human behaviour. Indeed, it is of great significance to the understanding of visceral disturbances in patients that autonomic responses are manifested in all kinds of emotional stress.

VISCERO-SENSORY INFLOW

The afferent pathways to the orbital surface of the frontal lobe originate from all over the body and are thought to be crossed for the most part. Uncrossed afferents exist, as in the somatosensory system, but topographical patterns which are so characteristic of the sensory areas are lacking. Indeed, there is a marked overlapping of representation for somatic, vagal and splanchnic afferent projections with no corresponding subdivisions for leg, arm and face. This fact supports the attractive hypothesis that the entire region functions as an integrating centre. However, consideration must be given here to the role of the posterior orbital gyrus since the experimental findings suggest it is mainly concerned with visceral control. In the cat the posterior orbital gyrus lies close to the second sensory area, between the orbital sulcus and the olfactory tract; it is continuous rostrally with the anterior orbital gyrus (Fig. 9.1).

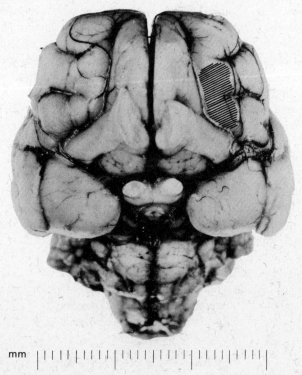

mm

FIG. 9.1. Photograph showing ventral surface of cat brain. Shaded area over posterior orbital gyrus indicates site of visceral afferent projections. The olfactory tract is to the left and the cut optic nerves can be seen centrally.

Somatic functions. There may be a limited degree of localization for face, throat and forelimbs. The evidence is based on experiments by Hess, Akert & McDonald (1952) in unanaesthetized, freely-moving cats with chronically implanted electrodes. According to these authors orbital stimulation gave rise to highly organized bilateral movements which were not attributed to either spread of current or to excitation of the motor areas. Korn, Wendt & Albe-Fessard (1966) confirmed the bilateral character of the movements. They also demonstrated topographical representation for cutaneous and joint afferents, with the forelimbs localized rostrally and the hindlimbs caudally on the orbital gyrus.

Visceral functions. There is evidence that vagal and splanchnic nerve afferents are distributed to the posterior orbital gyrus, but there are surprisingly few accounts in the literature of mapping experiments. Unfortunately the responses are extremely sensitive to the type and depth of anaesthesia and to the parameters of stimulation whilst the degree of overlapping is marked. It is doubtful whether the orbital gyrus should be considered a receiving area comparable to sensory areas I and II and a more instructive analysis on a unitary basis is desirable.

Vagal afferent responses
Although the vagus trunk is accessible in the neck, its use for electrical stimulation must be treated with caution. The wide dispersion of its motor fibres is likely to produce many complex and undesirable effects. Even if the central cut end of one vagus is stimulated, reflex effects in the opposite vagus may be encountered. In their classical experiments on cerebral representation Bailey & Bremer (1938) described the 'isolated encephalon' preparation in which the spinal cord and both vagi were cut in order to eliminate reflex vasodilatation and cardio-inhibition. The animal was kept alive by artificial respiration, the blood pressure fluctuating between 80 and 100 mm Hg. They observed that induction shocks delivered to the central cut end of the vagus nerve produced changes in the cortical potentials recorded from the orbital surface of the frontal lobe. With repetitive stimuli the potentials increased in amplitude and rate. The authors concluded from their experiments that there must be a cerebral

representation of the afferent components in the vagus nerve although at that time the connexions and functions of the orbital cortex were unknown. In 1949 Sachs, Brendler & Fulton attempted to repeat this work, being careful to employ the same techniques with the 'isolated encephalon' preparation. However, they reported only negative results out of a large series of animals. They were unable to offer an explanation of their inability to observe any evoked potentials.

More successful investigations in this field have been reported by Dell & Olson (1951) and by Korn & Massion (1964). In cats under chloralose anaesthesia vagal representation was identified in the medial part of the orbital gyrus, overlapping the responsive zone for somatic afferent projections. A train of stimuli delivered to either the ipsilateral or the contralateral vagus nerve was more effective than single shocks. Interactions between vagal and somatic afferents were also described.

Most of these findings have now been confirmed in the chloralosed cat and it was evident that the administration of Nembutal or Pentothal, even in small doses, tended to reduce or abolish the evoked responses. Primary waves were obtained from all parts of the

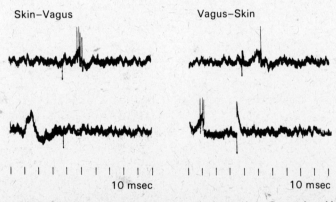

Skin–Vagus　　　　　Vagus–Skin

10 msec　　　　　10 msec

FIG. 9.2. Somato-visceral and viscero-somatic interaction. Cat under chloralose anaesthesia. Responses recorded from orbital cortex. On left, upper trace shows a multiple-spike discharge following a single electrical stimulus to the central cut end of the cervical vagus; stimulus artifact delayed 40 msec on sweep. Lower trace illustrates inhibitory interaction when the vagal stimulus is preceded by a conditioning stimulus to the body wall. On the right, sequence of stimulation is reversed. Upper trace shows response of a unit to cutaneous stimulation alone; lower trace shows depression of the response after presentation of a conditioning stimulus to the vagus nerve.

posterior orbital gyrus following single shocks delivered to the central
cut end of the cervical vagus. Ipsilateral and contralateral stimuli were
equally effective. The same cortical points nearly always responded to
stimulation of the body wall and either occlusive or inhibitory actions
could be demonstrated in conditioning and testing experiments (Fig.
9.2). There was no evidence of topographical representation on the
orbital surface. In good preparations it was possible to record single
unit responses from the superficial layers of the cortex. Typically, the
evoked discharge appeared as a single diphasic deflection at threshold
intensity of stimulation (5 V, 0·01 msec duration), but occurring in
bursts of three or four spikes with stronger stimulation (Fig. 9.3). The
latency for the first spike of the discharge was about 15 msec. The
results indicated that impulses set up by vagal stimulation could evoke

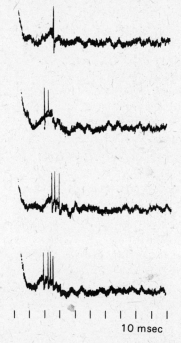

10 msec

FIG. 9.3. Relation between stimulus intensity and number of spikes. Cat under
chloralose anaesthesia. Single unit responses recorded from orbital cortex. From
above downwards, increase in number of spikes per discharge with increasing
intensities of stimuli delivered to central cut end of cervical vagus.

the discharge of single cells in the posterior orbital gyrus. The relatively short latency and high degree of response probability of the evoked discharges were factors suggestive of a projection system having properties essentially similar to those of the somatosensory system. However, vagal representation in the cortex had certain distinguishing features:

1. The afferent projections were bilateral in character and equally effective.

2. The extent of convergence with cutaneous pathways showed almost complete overlap of responsive areas and no evidence of topographical localization.

3. Much difficulty had been experienced by investigators in demonstrating a higher control of the vagus nerve, especially when only single shocks were employed. In view of all these points it is obviously necessary to proceed with caution before attaching any functional significance to the orbital potentials and the subject will be discussed more fully below.

Splanchnic afferent responses

Bilateral responses following electrical stimulation of the splanchnic nerve have been recorded from the orbital surface of the frontal lobe. According to Korn (1969) surface positive primary waves were evoked over an area that was virtually coextensive with the representation for the 12th intercostal nerve in the medial and posterior parts of the orbital gyrus. Unit responses were also recorded when the stimulus was strong enough to excite the A delta group of splanchnic afferent fibres. Korn used cats under chloralose or nembutal anaesthesia and also locally anaesthetized preparations immobilized with Flaxedil. The orbital cortex was approached from the lateral end of the cruciate sulcus by means of an electrode inserted in a rostral–caudal direction. The mean latency for the primary evoked responses was 11·5 msec after stimulation of the contralateral nerve and 13·2 msec after ipsilateral stimulation. No responses were detected when the fibres of the A beta group were excited alone. Unit responses occurred as short bursts of three or four spikes firing at increasing rates with increasing stimulus intensity. Single spike discharges were not seen. Generally, orbital units were activated only when the stimulus intensity was strong enough to set up a motor volley in the intercostal nerve. The same units usually responded to splanchnic and intercostal stimulation, followed occasionally by complete suppression of all spontaneous discharges for periods in excess of 200 msec. It was concluded from these results that the orbital cortex was a zone for the convergence of visceral and somatic afferents but no explanation was offered for the absence of the A beta component.

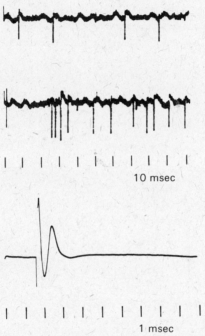

FIG. 9.4. Orbital unit discharges evoked by electrical stimulation of the splanchnic nerve. Cat under chloralose anaesthesia. Upper trace shows irregular firing of the unit in the absence of stimulation. Middle trace shows effect on firing frequency of the unit following a single stimulus delivered to central cut end of contralateral splanchnic nerve. Lower trace is a simultaneous recording of the splanchnic nerve action potential. Note that only the A beta group of splanchnic nerve afferents is excited.

The present author has largely confirmed the above findings using broadly similar methods. In addition it was possible to demonstrate the elusive A beta component but only in animals under chloralose anaesthesia. It can generally be stated that afferents from both sides of the body converge on the orbital cortex and that they appear to have a functionally diverse range. Thus impulses from the skin of leg and arm have both ipsilateral and contralateral actions and are capable of influencing the same units that respond to stimulation of the vagus and splanchnic nerves. In agreement with Korn (1969) responses evoked by splanchnic afferent volleys were produced in the main by A delta activation; but a few units were isolated which gave a marked increase of firing frequency when only A beta fibres were excited. An example of this is shown in Fig. 9.4. Single shocks (2 V, 0·02 msec) were delivered to the central cut end of the right splanchnic nerve and responses from the left orbital cortex were recorded; the splanchnic nerve action potential was displayed simultaneously on a second channel. It can be seen from the waveform of the potential that only the A beta component of the splanchnic fibres was excited. The unit was either silent or fired irregularly in the absence of stimulation but responded with a high level of probability to successive stimulus shocks. The temporal pattern of the evoked discharge is plotted in the

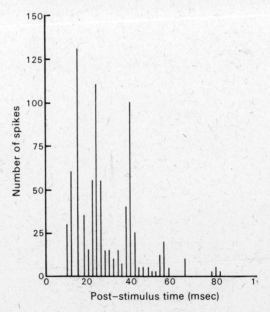

FIG. 9.5. Post-stimulus time histogram of orbital unit influenced by A beta fraction of splanchnic nerve. Periodic firing at the peaks indicated is computed for 128 successive sweeps.

histogram of Fig. 9.5 which shows the post-stimulus events over a time axis of 100 msec. It is of interest that the pattern of discharge usually consisted of a long periodic burst lasting for about 70 msec, with the first spike in the burst occurring at a mean latency of 15·2 msec.

Orbital units responding to stimulation of the A beta group of splanchnic afferents could not be driven by vagal or cutaneous impulses even at greater stimulus intensities. In contrast, all the A delta responses belonged to overlapping fields of representation shared by many peripheral sources. Accordingly, interaction between these various afferent projections could easily be demonstrated. The results of one experiment are illustrated in Fig. 9.6. Inhibition of the response to a testing stimulus was recognized by a decrease in the probability of

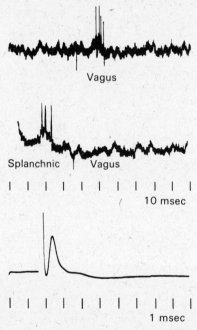

FIG. 9.6. Splanchnic–vagal interaction. Cat under chloralose anaesthesia. Upper trace shows response of orbital unit to vagal stimulation alone; stimulus artifact delayed on sweep. Middle trace shows response of same unit to stimulation of central cut end of splanchnic nerve; when this is presented in a conditioning–testing sequence, the vagal response is inhibited. C–T interval = 30 msec. Lower trace, simultaneous recording of splanchnic nerve action potential showing A beta-delta activation.

firing and a reduction in the amplitude of the test primary wave. Complete inhibition of the test response was sometimes evident for periods as long as 200 msec following a conditioning stimulus delivered to the vagus nerve. Similar forms of interaction were observed between splanchnic and cutaneous afferents.

On the basis of these studies it may be useful to point out certain important differences between the orbital and somatosensory projection systems. Apart from the apparent difficulty in demonstrating A beta influences on the orbital cortex—which may reflect a relative poverty of afferent representation for these low-threshold fibres—all neuronal samplings appear to be susceptible to barbiturate depression to a degree which is not found in other areas of the cerebral cortex. Indeed, successful results seem to depend almost entirely on the choice of anaesthetic. Another difference is the generation of periodic firing by orbital neurones in preference to the single spike or burst discharges characteristic of unit activity in the sensory cortex. Furthermore, the interspike interval distributions are not necessarily affected by increasing the intensity of afferent stimulation. By contrast, unit discharges recorded from the sensory cortex show a remarkably consistent relationship to stimulus intensity, especially in regard to their latency, frequency and probability of firing. The absence of any precise topographical organization in the orbital cortex has also been repeatedly affirmed. All these observations may indicate that the two projection systems operate so differently that there is nothing to be gained by comparing them; but since they are both concerned with inputs from the viscera it is unlikely that they serve completely independent functions. It would be helpful to know more about the contribution of visceral afferent discharges in the conscious animal before making any further pronouncements on functional differences. For the present it will suffice to state that the orbital cortex is not simply an alternative pathway for the inflow of impulses from the viscera, but the problem will be further discussed later in this chapter.

INFLUENCE ON ALIMENTARY SYSTEM

Towards the end of the last century it had become clear that the orbital surface of the frontal lobe was not primarily olfactory in function. However, it was not until the studies of Bailey & Sweet (1940) that this part of the brain was shown to exert an influence on alimentary and other autonomic systems. There followed a number of important papers on the effects of cortical stimulation in the cat, dog and monkey which yielded a good deal of new information although little emerged about the pathways mediating these effects. On the other hand the results of cortical ablation were at first disappointing since they gave only scattered pieces of information and the changes observed were mainly behavioural. Thus bilateral ablation of the orbital gyri was sometimes found to produce no significant changes on the autonomic systems being investigated. A further difficulty in determining the functional role of the orbital surface was the discovery that many other cortical sites were concerned in regulating or influencing visceral function and the relative importance of these areas has still to be worked out. With the information now available from clinical sources it seems likely that the orbital cortex is part of a cerebral network for visceral sensory integration.

Stimulation experiments

1. Gastric movements

Bailey & Sweet (1940) recorded gastric movements in cats and monkeys by means of a balloon connected to a water manometer. They found that electrical stimulation of the orbital gyrus resulted in slowing or arrest of respiration, rise in blood pressure and relaxation of the stomach. Typically, there occurred within 1 sec of the onset of the stimulus a brisk diminution of tone in the gastric wall with a maximum fall after 10–50 sec. The responses were clearcut in the monkey, but inconsistent in the cat. Their functional significance was not discussed. Independent of this work Babkin & Speakman (1950) carried out similar investigations in the dog and found two cortical areas which influenced gastric motility—insular-orbital and anterior cingulate. The responses they obtained were a lowering of gastric tone and inhibition of peristalsis accompanied by slowing of respiration and a fall of blood pressure. The effects were uninfluenced by the type of anaesthetic used and all were abolished after section of the vagi. In a further series of experiments Babkin & Kite (1950a) showed that inhibition of gastric movements was not secondary to the changes in blood pressure and respiration. Another important observation was the fact that increased gastric contractions instead of the usual inhibition were sometimes recorded following orbital stimulation. They believed that the effects were produced by impulses acting on centres in the brain stem and that the orbital cortex had both motor and sensory vagal representations. The motor functions appeared to be well established and independent since they were present after bilateral cingulectomy.

In reviewing the literature on the orbital cortex Kaada (1951) reported experiments he performed on the monkey. He stimulated various points on the limbic cortex with bipolar silver wire or steel electrodes and recorded simultaneously the arterial blood pressure, respiratory movements and gastric contractions. The only significant changes observed were those elicited from the posterior orbital gyrus. Both inhibitory and excitatory effects were encountered but the most prominent change observed was a reduction in amplitude or complete abolition of the rhythmic gastric contractions. This usually occurred after a latency of 5–20 sec and lasted up to 40 sec with strong cortical stimulation. These responses were unaffected by section of the splanchnic nerves, but permanently lost when the vagi were cut in the neck. Thus Kaada's results confirmed the view of earlier workers that the orbital cortex exerted an influence on gastric motility and tone, the principal change being inhibitory.

It is of interest that some authors found difficulty in recording increased responses from the gastrointestinal tract. According to Eliasson (1952) increased gastric movements were elicited only from the rostral part of the anterior sigmoid gyrus and were never obtained from the posterior orbital gyrus if precautions were taken to prevent spread of the stimulus current. He also believed that the optimal parameters of stimulation were different at each cortical site. On the other hand it was clearly stated by Hoffman & Rasmussen (1953) that the characteristics of the stimulating current were not of critical value in determining the type of response. Indeed, they showed that neither the waveform nor the frequency of the stimulus could alter the type of response, at least in the monkey.

At the present time it is recognized that the orbital cortex and the anterior cingulate can each exert their influence on the viscera in the absence of the other. The total picture is probably more complex than is indicated by the above summary but the conclusion that inhibition of gastric movements is the usual result of cortical stimulation seems well justified.

2. Gastric secretion

In the early literature there are reports that electrical stimulation of the cerebral cortex caused an increase in the volume of gastric secretion and in the concentration of HCl and pepsin. According to Davey, Kaada & Fulton (1950) both movements of the stomach and secretion can be regulated at the cortical level. In the monkey, electrical stimulation of the cerebral cortex resulted in a very large increase of gastric juice after the pylorus had been tied off; but the stimulus pulses they used were too long to prevent current spread so that the exact location of the stimulated area could not be verified. In the cat, Klopper (1954) observed changes in gastric acidity after stimulating the rostral part of the anterior sigmoid gyrus whilst stimulation of adjacent points on the cortex was without effect. Anand & Dua (1956) made a detailed investigation of the limbic system in both cat and monkey. The animals were prepared with gastric pouches and measurements of acid concentration and pepsin activity were made before and after stimulation of different cortical areas. They found that the site of the stimulus determined the type and extent of the changes observed; when the orbital cortex was stimulated, there was generally an increase in the volume and composition of the gastric secretions. This finding was confirmed by Sen & Anand (1957) in unanaesthetized cats with chronically implanted electrodes: all the gastric secretions, including total acidity, free HCl and pepsin activity, showed a significant rise above resting level following orbital stimulation. Comparable results were observed when the amygdaloid nuclei were stimulated, but the cingulate and hippocampal regions did not influence the functions of the gastric glands. An important observation was that the pouches often showed evidence of hyperaemia and erosion and haemorrhages in the submucosa.

The literature of more recent years contains numerous reports on the cerebral influences affecting the functions of the stomach. Thus Hockman (1963) showed that a constant current delivered in 20 sec trains caused an immediate increase in volume of the gastric juice from a prestimulation level of 1 ml/30 min to 1 ml/min with a concomitant rise in free acid. This was followed by inhibition of gastric secretion for one hour. Marked increases of gastric secretion with the development of acute lesions in the mucosa were reported by Feldman, Birnbaum & Behar (1961) following stimulation of the preoptic region and anterior hypothalamus. They believed that the gastric lesions were caused by local vascular changes which seemed to them more significant than any rise in acid concentration. A decrease in gastric acidity and pepsin secretion has been reported by Smith & McHugh (1964) in experiments on conscious monkeys. The stimulus was applied to the basal-lateral part of the amygdaloid nuclei and presumably excited the efferent fibres passing via the stria terminalis to the hypothalamus. The role of the amygdaloid nuclei is not completely understood. According to Sheacy & Peele (1957) the maximal excitatory effects on the gastric secretions were obtained from the posterior orbital gyrus and the amygdaloid nuclei; but if the impulses reached the vagal outflow to the stomach by acting first on the hypothalamus, it is not surprising that both increased and decreased influences have been recorded.

In summary, it may be stated that the posterior orbital gyrus can alter the activity of the gastric glands through vagal efferent discharges. Most of the effects are excitatory since electrical stimulation elicits an increase in the volume and concentrations of the gastric contents. On the other hand, when the amygdaloid and anterior hypothalamic nuclei are stimulated, there is evidence of an inhibitory influence resulting in a decrease of the gastric secretions. In order to account for these findings it is suggested that the orbital cortex has a dual outflow to the vagal nuclei—a direct pathway mediated by the brain stem reticular formation and a second one operating through the hypothalamus. The role played by the amygdaloid nucleus is uncertain, but it may constitute a functional unit which integrates the two projection systems. Evidence in support of these possibilities will be discussed later in this chapter.

Ablation experiments

1. Laboratory evidence

One of the earliest reports on the effects of bilateral cortical ablation on gastric motility was that of Babkin & Kite (1950b) who recorded pyloric contractions, blood pressure and respiration in the dog. They found that after cingulate ablation, there was an immediate increase in the rate of contraction suggesting that the cingulate cortex normally exerted a moderating influence on the lower brain centres. In contrast, bilateral removal of the orbital cortex had no significant effect on gastric functions, thus confirming their belief that each component of the limbic complex exercised separate influences on the vagal outflow. Hartzell (1929) gave unequivocal evidence of vagal control of gastric function by demonstrating permanent changes in free and total acidity of the stomach following complete bilateral section of the vagal trunks in dogs. However, it has long been recognized that the vagal outflow is concerned with gastric secretion and peristalsis and that the so-called psychic secretion which precedes the intake of food is due to vagal stimulation of the gastric glands. Gastric secretion occurs in the absence of vagal control due to the release of the hormone, gastrin, from the pyloric glands, but the secretion contributed by 'psychic' stimuli is entirely eliminated after bilateral vagotomy. Certainly there is no lack of evidence about the effects of vagotomy in the laboratory animal, yet the results of cortical ablation are far from consistent. The disturbances, in any case, are often transient or cannot be definitely related to the anatomical lesion.

2. Clinical evidence

Cushing (1932) recognized that neurogenic factors might be responsible for the abnormal persistence of ulcerative processes in the stomach and consequent development of a chronic ulcer. He postulated the existence of a pathway from the cerebral cortex to the vagal nuclei, suggesting that irritative lesions along that tract could lead to gastric ulceration. There is good evidence that hyperacidity and peristalsis are associated with increased parasympathetic activity in a high percentage of cases. If psychic and emotional stimuli are allowed to maintain a prolonged effect without treatment, the patient may develop gastric symptoms and in chronic patients, with a longstanding history of hyperacidity and ulceration, there is often a relevant condition of stress. The association of nervous stress in a highly emotional patient and recurrent gastric or duodenal ulceration is now firmly established and, although the corticofugal pathways have not been defined, many surgeons believe that vagotomy is the most rational approach to the problem. Beattie (1949) published the results of a series of cases in whom bilateral vagotomy had been performed and noted the immediate relief from pain and other ulcer symptoms with rapid increase in weight of the patient and return to work. The total volume and acidity of the gastric secretion were reduced to one third of the pre-operative level whilst the tone and muscular power of the stomach gradually recovered. There were no adverse effects on the abdominal viscera except for mild distension of the stomach during convalescence. Bilateral vagotomy has become accepted as a routine surgical measure in the treatment of chronic gastric and duodenal ulcer.

No conclusions concerning the cerebral influences on the alimentary system can be drawn solely on the basis of ablation experiments. We do not know enough about intracortical relations to be certain that the removal of one area of the limbic complex will necessarily interfere with the functions of the whole. The orbital cortex is no exception despite the fact that experimental stimulation causes changes in the autonomic outflow. The role of the vagi in mediating some of these changes is indicated, especially from clinical studies, by the results of selective vagotomy.

INFLUENCE ON CARDIOVASCULAR AND RESPIRATORY SYSTEMS

It has been known for a long time that changes in both arterial blood pressure and respiration can be produced on electrical stimulation of the orbital surface. Amongst the earliest observations are those of Spencer (1894) who reported slowing and arrest of respiratory movements in the monkey and other species. Alterations in breathing can be obtained from widely separated parts of the cerebral cortex, some being excitatory (sensorimotor, anterior cingulate), others inhibitory. Both kinds of changes were demonstrated by Smith (1938) in an extensive survey on the cat, dog and monkey. He found that the orbital gyrus (gyrus compositus anterior) was the most consistent inhibitory area for respiratory movements. Inhibition of respiration was generally accompanied by a rise in arterial blood pressure. In the work published during the following fifteen years most authors are agreed on the respiratory responses, but the effects on the cardiovascular system are somewhat conflicting. In 1940 Bailey & Sweet gave detailed results of their investigations on the cat and monkey. Using Nembutal anaesthesia, electrical stimulation of the orbital gyrus invariably caused slowing and finally arrest of respiration in the expiratory phase which lasted for about 5–10 sec. Escape from inhibition with shallow breathing then occurred and resumption of the normal rate after the stimulus ended. At the same time there was a gradual rise of blood pressure of 10–20 mm Hg succeeded by a rapid return to the original level. However, in 3 out of 10 experiments on cats no rise of blood pressure was recorded, the results in the monkey being more consistent. Similar results were reported by Delgado & Livingston (1948) in dogs and monkeys under Dial anaesthesia. Using concentric needle electrodes and stimulating currents below threshold for the motor cortex, they also observed arrest of respiration in the expiratory phase for about 5–10 sec after which respiratory escape occurred. Again, the most active region was the posterior orbital gyrus. They demonstrated quite clearly that no current spread was involved since electrocoagulation of the superficial layers abolished the response even when strong intensities of current were used. As regards the effects on blood pressure, a rise of about 10 mm Hg lasting about 30 sec was generally observed, but occasionally a fall in blood pressure was recorded. A further interesting observation was that mechanical, thermal and electrical excitation of the orbital surface frequently resulted in a prompt rise of temperature in the extremities. Although the observation applied to only four monkeys, the authors speculated on the possible role of the orbital cortex in the regulation of body temperature—a topic that will be further discussed in this chapter.

Much the same results were reported by Kaada, Pribram & Epstein (1949) on monkeys under barbiturate anaesthesia. Stimulation of the orbital surface produced a profound inhibition of respiratory movements lasting for 25–30 sec. At the same time there was usually a rise in blood pressure, but a rise could be followed by a fall if the initial systemic pressure was low; or else the blood pressure tended to fall during stimulation and rise afterwards. It might be thought that the changes in blood pressure were secondary to the arrest of respiration but there is good evidence to show that the two responses were independent. Thus Sachs, Brendler & Fulton (1949) obtained cardiovascular responses after paralysing respiratory movements with curare. Stimulation of the orbital surface in cat, dog and monkey produced arrest of respiration in the usual way; when the animal was given curare and artificially ventilated, orbital stimulation invariably caused a rise in blood pressure even after the removal of both adrenal glands. However, in animals under Dial anaesthesia, the blood pressure responses were far from consistent, especially in the cat. Sometimes the results depended upon the frequency of the stimulus or upon the waveform of the current and if the stimulus intensity was reduced to threshold level, the posterior orbital gyrus was the only effective area. In general, the experiments so far described indicate that inhibition of respiration and alterations in the cardiovascular system can be evoked on electrical stimulation of the orbital gyrus. The role of the limbic cortex in the integration of cardiovascular responses will need reappraisal in the light of more recent evidence.

Mechanism of cortical control

In an account of the viscero-somatic activities ascribed to the limbic region of the brain Kaada' (1951) postulated the existence of a continuous stretch of cortex with respiratory and cardiovascular influences. Anatomically it comprises the anterior cingulate and posterior orbital gyri, the anterior insula, the temporal pole and hippocampus. All these structures are now known to exert a control on the visceral systems concerned in emotional expression. For example, alterations in the rate and depth of breathing are part of emotional disturbances in sobbing or weeping, whilst marked changes in blood pressure may accompany the states of anger or fear. Kaada believed that the various points of cortical influence on respiration and blood pressure together formed two independent systems, each having an excitatory and inhibitory component. The conflicting results of electrical stimulation could be explained by the differences in threshold of the cortical points. Such differences depended not only on the species of the experimental animal and the type and depth of the anaesthetic used, but on the relative size of the excitatory and inhibitory components. In any given area of the cortex one of the components could be predominant—thus stimulation of the posterior orbital gyrus generally favoured respiratory inhibition. Extending these ideas to the cardiovascular system Hess, Akert & McDonald

(1951) suggested that excitatory and inhibitory points probably existed side by side in the same cortical region and this would account for the opposite effects on blood pressure that were commonly observed.

Many experimental observations have since confirmed the dual effect exercised by the limbic cortex on the cardiovascular system. Löfving (1961) believed that a clear-cut 'depressor' area was located on the anterior medial surface of the cat brain extending from the cingulate gyrus to the orbital surface. Electrical stimulation in this area produced a marked fall in systemic blood pressure accompanied by an increase in regional blood flow. These effects were obtained when the vagal and aortic depressor fibres had been cut in the neck in order to eliminate the influence of cardiovascular receptors. Relatively well-defined 'pressor' points, causing vasoconstriction, were located more ventrally on the medial and orbital surface of the brain, but there was considerable overlap of the two areas from which both kinds of responses could be elicited.

Apart from the difficulties in identifying the functional components of the limbic cortex owing to close approximation of pressor and depressor elements, there were also regional differences in the extent of the vascular response to cortical stimulation. Thus vasodilatation was always more pronounced in the vascular beds of the skeletal muscles than in the splanchnic area; vasodilatation in the skin was much less marked whilst the effect on the renal vessels was almost negligible. All of these experimental findings are of interest in revealing the complex nature of the cortical mechanism inducing cardiovascular changes in the peripheral organs. According to Löfving (1961) the regional differences in blood flow reflected differences in the discharge rate of the vasomotor centre, which in turn was controlled by a 'sympatho-inhibitory' mechanism in the hypothalamus. The ensuing vaso-dilatations were caused by inhibitory influences exerted on tonic vasoconstrictor discharges. By means of discrete electrolytic lesions in the hypothalamic depressor area, he showed that the effects of limbic stimulation could be selectively abolished and concluded that the cardiovascular adjustments of the limbic cortex were mediated by impulses acting through the hypothalamus.

There is now good evidence that the reticular formation of the brain stem from the hypothalamus to the medulla constitutes a functional unit which integrates the afferent impulses of the cardiovascular receptors and the descending impulses of the limbic cortex. The 'depressor' area in the anterior hypothalamus lies ventral and caudal to the anterior commissure and extends caudally in the dorsal hypothalamus. Stimulation of this area elicits (1) a fall in blood pressure and vasodilatation in the vascular beds caused by inhibition of the sympathetic vasomotor discharge and (2) slowing of the heart and respirations due to vagal activation (Hilton & Spyer, 1971). Stimulation within the reticular network of the brain stem evokes a variety of physiological reactions unless very refined methods are used including histological demonstration of electrode positions. When accurate localization of the site and extent of stimulation are established it is found that vagal effects are induced by the tractus and nucleus solitarius but not by the dorsal nucleus of the vagus (Calaresu & Pearce, 1965). Attempts to trace the descending reticular pathway of the vagal outflow have been reported by Achari, Downman & Weber (1968).

For further details concerning the influence of the cerebral cortex on cardiovascular function the reader is referred to a review by Hoff, Kell & Carroll (1963).

INFLUENCE ON BLOOD PRESSURE
RESPONSE TO HEATING

As was seen in Chapter 6, changes in arterial blood pressure can be recorded when a heating electrode is inserted into the brain stem or the temperature of the carotid blood is raised. At a critical temperature of 41°C the blood pressure will fall rapidly and remain depressed during the period of heating and then recover to its original level as the brain is cooled. This response to heating in the intact anaesthetized animal also occurs in a decerebrate preparation in which the hypothalamus has been completely removed. The experiments to be described here will show that the response can be influenced by electrical stimulation of the orbital cortex.

Methods of exposure

The orbital surface in the cat may be approached by one of the following methods:

1. Enucleation of the eye. A transverse incision is made through the scalp above the orbit extending from the mid-line to the ear; a second incision is made through the soft tissues below the orbit. The extraocular muscles are then clamped and tied and the eye removed. After clearing the contents of the orbital cavity, the frontal lobe is exposed through the orbital plate and frontal air sinus. Bleeding may be troublesome and requires gelatin sponge to control it; shock may also be anticipated in animals with initial low blood pressure; later the dura is incised and deflected. The posterior orbital gyrus is identified lateral to the olfactory tract, which is easily seen on the medial side of the exposure. The cortex is then covered with a cellophane strip to prevent drying.

2. Frontal craniotomy. This method is quicker and not so difficult to perform. The skull is opened by means of a burr hole and extended forwards to the frontal air sinus. The saggital sinus is ligated followed by division of the falx at the cribriform plate. This allows the frontal lobes to fall away from the orbital plate when the animal is placed on its back.

3. Stereotaxic approach. With the head of the animal in a stereotaxic instrument, the frontal lobe is exposed from above and the dura deflected caudally to reveal the ansate sulcus. A stimulating needle electrode, insulated except at the tip, is inserted at a point on the cortex inferior to the lower limb of the ansate. Penetration of the electrode tip to a depth of 12–14 mm will usually reach the deep cellular layers of the orbital gyrus. The position of the electrode is confirmed afterwards by histological examination. When the same method is used for recording purposes the position can be detected on the loud-speaker as the electrode traverses the relatively silent white matter.

Effect of orbital stimulation alone

In cats under sodium pentobarbitone anaesthesia a bipolar stimulating electrode was placed on the orbital surface of the frontal lobe and blood pressure was recorded from the femoral artery. It was found that strong continuous stimulation generally resulted in a rise of blood pressure (20–30 mm Hg) whilst a weaker stimulus produced no significant change in the record. A pressor response was obtained with stimulus parameters 12 V, 0·5 msec and 50/sec. Higher rates (75–100/sec) and longer pulse durations (1–3 msec) did not give any appreciable increase in the response. When the stimulus intensity was reduced to 10 V or less, no changes in blood pressure were observed during or following the period of stimulation. In the experiments which will now be described it should be noted that the stimulus itself did not modify the arterial blood pressure (Newman & Wolstencroft, 1960).

Effects during heating

As the carotid blood was heated a rise in brain temperature was detected by a thermocouple connected to a galvanometer calibrated over the range 35–45°C. The femoral blood pressure remained unchanged until the temperature of the brain had risen to 41·5°C. At this point there was a sudden fall in blood pressure. When heating was discontinued the blood pressure returned to its original level. The rectal temperature did not rise during the period of heating. Using a relatively weak stimulus (6 V, 0·1 msec) applied continuously to the orbital cortex, the femoral blood pressure fell slightly when the temperature of the brain reached 41·5°C but recovered almost immediately to its original level. Thereafter, the blood pressure was maintained during the period of stimulation even when heating continued until the brain temperature reached 43°C and was kept at that level for two minutes (Fig. 9.7). If the experiment was repeated with a stronger cortical stimulus (8 V, 0·1 msec), the blood pressure did not fall at the critical temperature, but remained unchanged throughout the whole period of heating until the cortical stimulus was switched off.

In the experiment illustrated by Fig. 9.8 the femoral blood pressure was 120 mm Hg. The carotid blood was heated until the brain temperature reached 43°C and during this time the orbital cortex was stimulated. It will be seen from the trace that the blood pressure remained unchanged except for minor fluctuations. Heating was then discontinued and the temperature gradually dropped. At 42°C the stimulus was switched off with the result that the blood pressure fell immediately to about 40 mm Hg. With further cooling of the brain the blood pressure returned to its original level. The experiments clearly demonstrated that the depressor response to heating could be inhibited

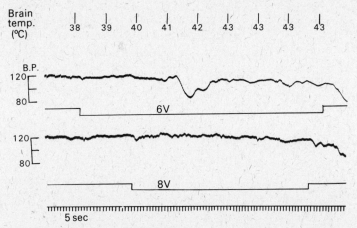

FIG. 9.7. Effect of stimulating the orbital cortex during heating of the carotid blood. Cat under sodium pentobarbitone anaesthesia. Upper trace, inhibitory effect of a weak stimulus (6 V, 0·1 msec, 50/sec)—blood pressure falls slightly when brain temperature reaches 41°C but recovers and is maintained although brain temperature reaches 43°C. Blood pressure falls on cessation of stimulus. Lower trace, stronger stimulus (8 V, 0·1 msec, 50/sec)—blood pressure is maintained at original level throughout the period of heating.

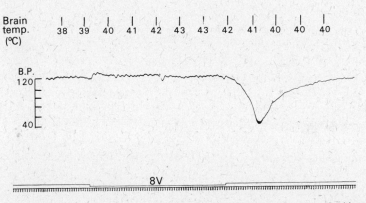

FIG. 9.8. Electrical stimulation of the orbital cortex. Cat under sodium pentobarbitone anaesthesia. Blood pressure recorded from femoral artery. During period of stimulation, carotid blood is heated and brain temperature rises to 43°C. Blood pressure is maintained at 120 mm Hg. When stimulation ceases, blood pressure falls to 40 mm Hg. As the brain is cooled blood pressure rises again. Time intervals at 5 sec.

by electrical stimulation of the posterior orbital gyrus. No other part of the orbital surface gave similar results. For example, when the stimulating electrode was applied to the anterior orbital gyrus, the depressor response to heating was not modified in any way.

The mechanisms responsible for the blood pressure changes produced by heat were discussed in Chapter 6. Evidence was given to show that heat-sensitive neurones were located in the nucleus reticularis gigantocellularis, i.e. within the medial reticular formation of the lower brain stem, a region which has been identified with extensive pressor and depressor points. It was postulated that the depressor points were part of an integrated vasodilator system capable of modifying vasomotor tone in the peripheral blood vessels. Vasodilator neurones have a high threshold to heating, but when exposed to a critical temperature discharge *en masse* with consequent collapse of the circulation. Under normal conditions vasodilator neurones probably exert an inhibitory influence on the vasoconstrictor outflow of the sympathetic. The results of the experiments with heating suggest that the posterior orbital cortex has a powerful control on the vasodilator mechanism since the fall in blood pressure evoked by heating the brain can be effectively prevented.

ORBITO-MEDULLARY PATHWAY

Little attention has been given to the possibility that the orbital cortex may have a direct link with the brain stem autonomic centres since it is commonly assumed that the hypothalamus alone controls both the sympathetic and parasympathetic systems. Spencer (1894) had given the clue to the existence of a higher control when he traced a pathway between the orbital cortex and the upper border of the pons. Rossi & Brodal (1956) obtained evidence of fibre degeneration in the pons and medulla of the cat following certain cortical lesions. One of the lesions described involved the orbital region but unfortunately it was not restricted to the posterior orbital gyrus. Brain stem responses to electrical stimulation and to strychninization of the cerebral cortex were recorded in monkeys by French, Hernández-Peón & Livingston (1955). The cortical areas investigated included the orbital surface of the frontal lobe. Their results revealed a corticofugal projection system to the subthalamus, hypothalamus and mesencephalic reticular formation. However, they did not extend their studies to the pons and medulla.

Medullary responses to orbital stimulation

The experiments described here were undertaken to explore the possibility of a direct link between the orbital gyri and the medulla. In cats under sodium pentobarbitone anaesthesia the cortex was exposed through the roof of the orbital cavity after removing the eye. Access to the brain stem was gained by a ventral approach through the soft structures of the neck followed by removal of the overlying bone. The head was held rigidly by ear bars and a jaw clamp. The area exposed extended from the middle of the pons to the lower medulla and it was covered with warm liquid paraffin. Single shocks from a square wave stimulator were delivered through bipolar silver wire electrodes applied to the orbital surface. Evoked activity was recorded from the brain stem by means of a concentric needle electrode held in a micromanipulator. As a rule no precautions were necessary to limit pulsations from cardiac and respiratory rhythms.

1. Responses evoked by electrical stimulation

Clear-cut responses appeared as an initial negative deflection of relatively large amplitude (300–400 μV) followed usually by secondary deflections of smaller amplitude. The latent period between stimulus and first deflection was of the order of 1·0 msec. The responses were always ipsilateral. The form of the evoked potential varied according to the distance of the electrode tip from the ventral surface as shown in Fig. 9.9. Nothing significant was recorded on surface contact. At a depth of 1 mm below the pia the evoked potential took the form of an initially positive primary wave of low amplitude. As the recording electrode penetrated deeper into the substance of the brain the amplitude of the initial deflexion increased and reversal of polarity occurred when the tip of the recording electrode reached a depth 4 mm below the ventral surface. The largest responses were found in the medulla; the waveform was initially negative and they were generally obtained from points 5–7 mm deep. Such changes in the electrical fields were presumably the result of depolarization occurring at a site deep in the medulla following cortical activation. The suggestion was made that the initial negative wave represented the firing of neurones at the terminals of a descending tract and that the secondary waves were caused by the spread of activity as depolarization was propagated to adjacent neurones. Positivity at the recording electrode would be derived from current conducted outwards to the pial surface.

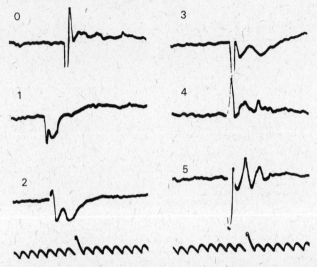

FIG. 9.9. Evoked responses from medulla of cat following single shocks to ipsilateral orbital cortex. Recordings at successive depths, in steps of 1 mm, below ventral surface. Note change in form of potentials with reversal of polarity occurring when electrode tip is 4 mm below pial surface. Time intervals at 1 msec.

To determine the distribution of the evoked potentials the brain stem was explored as far as the exposure would allow. No evoked potentials could be detected in the upper region of the pons or in the caudal third of the medulla. The largest potentials were recorded from the upper third of the medulla within 2·5 mm from the mid-line (Fig. 9.10). Any possibility that they were artifacts seemed excluded by their unilateral and discrete localization nor were they evoked by audible clicks since the sound persisted but the potentials disappeared when the orbital stimulus was reduced below threshold. From an analysis of the electrode positions the site of maximal activity was found near the mid-line below the junction of the medulla with the pons. The position was afterwards identified by histological examination and shown to lie in the medial part of the nucleus reticularis pontis caudalis and the rostral and medial parts of the nucleus reticularis gigantocellularis. These cell groups were described by Brodal (1957) as subdivisions of the brain stem reticular formation, situated near the mid-line and dorsal to the trapezoid body and superior olive.

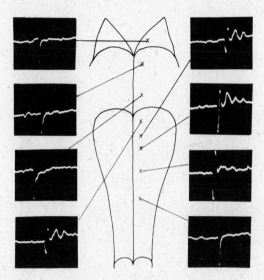

FIG. 9.10. Diagram of brain stem showing distribution of evoked potentials with recording tip 5 mm below ventral surface. No responses following the stimulus artifact are obtained in the pons or caudal medulla. Points giving clear-cut responses are found in the upper third of medulla close to midline. The orbito-medullary projection is unilateral.

2. Medullary responses to orbital strychninization

A small piece of filter paper soaked in 3% strychnine sulphate solution was applied to the orbital surface in proximity to a pair of recording electrodes. The brain stem was explored for strychnine-induced activity by means of a concentric needle electrode. Simultaneous recordings of cortical and brain-stem strychnine 'spikes' were traced on two channels of an ink-writing unit (Newman & Wolstencroft, 1959). Cortical 'spiking' was observed about one minute after the application of the strychnine to the posterior orbital gyrus. Synchronous with the cortical spikes, activity was recorded from the medial reticular formation in the ipsilateral medulla but not from adjacent regions. A typical result is shown in Fig. 9.11(*a*). The evoked activity appeared as bursts of two or three 'spikes', large in amplitude and synchronous with the cortical trace; the effects subsided after about ten minutes. In contrast, records taken from points rostral, lateral or caudal to the responsive region in the brain stem revealed only low voltage waves or else failed to show any changes in background activity (Fig. 9.11*b*).

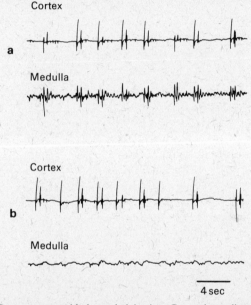

FIG. 9.11. Responses to orbital strychninization. Cat under sodium pentobarbitone anaesthesia. Strychnine applied to orbital cortex; simultaneous tracings from cortex and medulla on two channels of ink-recorder. (a) Upper record, strychnine 'spikes' from posterior orbital gyrus occurring shortly after application of filter paper; lower record, strychnine 'spikes' evoked in ipsilateral medullary reticular formation. (b) Same as (a) except that medullary electrode is outside responsive region.

CONCLUSIONS

The results outlined above point to the existence of descending pathways from the posterior orbital gyrus to the medullary reticular formation. The projections are evidently direct ones since the latent period was of the order of 1·0 msec in animals under light pentobarbital anaesthesia. This suggestion is supported by the results of strychnine neuronography. The responses to electrical and strychnine stimulation were recorded from comparable points in the medulla and the evidence shows that the fibres do not decussate with those of the opposite side. It is not yet clear what role is fulfilled by the orbito-medullary system which is not already performed by projections of the orbital cortex on the hypothalamus.

Considering the evidence from both experimental and clinical sources there is no doubt about the extensive influence that can be exerted by the orbital cortex on the major autonomic systems— alimentary, cardiovascular, respiratory and thermal. By establishing direct connexions with the medullary centres in addition to operating through the hypothalamus, the cortex can send fast reinforcements whenever necessary. It is thus possible to explain some of the remarkable excitatory and inhibitory effects produced by orbital stimulation on visceral functions. These can now be summarized:

Alimentary. Cerebral influences on the functions of the alimentary system are mediated by the vagi and splanchnic nerves. The exact contribution made by the orbital cortex is not known since its action is integrated with the other regions of the brain. However, there are good reasons for believing that the orbital cortex is important for the functions of digestion. Information about the state of the digestive organs is transmitted to this region since both vagal and splanchnic afferent representations have been demonstrated. Electrical stimulation of the orbital cortex usually leads to inhibition of gastric movements and an increase in the volume and concentration of the gastric secretions. On the other hand bilateral ablation of the orbital gyri is relatively ineffective. Permanent changes in gastrointestinal activity, including a reduction in the acidity of the stomach and duodenum, are brought about by the operation of bilateral vagotomy.

Cardiovascular. Stimulation of the orbital cortex generally causes a rise of blood pressure and vasoconstriction when the stimulus parameters are large enough to excite the orbito-hypothalamic projections. The effects are presumably the result of vasomotor sympathetic discharges. Weaker stimuli do not produce any significant changes in arterial blood pressure, but they may prevent a fall in blood pressure resulting from some other cause. This effect may be mediated by orbito-medullary pathways inhibiting vasodilator mechanisms in the reticular formation.

Respiratory. Stimulation of the orbital cortex inhibits respiration with slowing or arrest in the expiratory phase. Similar results are reported from other regions of the limbic system in most species including man and also in conscious patients. This influence is not abolished after bilateral removal of the hypothalamus, a fact that may suggest orbito-medullary involvement.

Thermal. Stimulation of the orbital cortex has a powerful inhibitory effect on vasodilatation induced by a rise in brain temperature. The heat-sensitive neurones are located in the medullary reticular formation. It is significant that the inhibitory action of the orbital cortex is effective without the intervention of the hypothalamus.

REFERENCES

Achari, N. K., Downman, C. B. B. & Weber, W. V. (1968). A cardio-inhibitory pathway in the brain stem of the cat. *J. Physiol.* **197**, 35P.

Anand, B. K. & Dua, S. (1956). Effect of electrical stimulation of the limbic system ('visceral brain') on gastric secretion and motility. *Indian J. med. Res.* **44**, 125–130.

Babkin, B. P. & Kite, Jr. W. C. (1950a). Central and reflex regulation of motility of pyloric antrum. *J. Neurophysiol.* **13**, 321–334.

Babkin, B. P. & Kite, Jr. W. C. (1950b). Gastric motor effects of acute removal of cingulate gyrus and section of brain stem. *J. Neurophysiol.* **13**, 335–342.

Babkin, B. P. & Speakman, T. J. (1950). Cortical inhibition of gastric motility. *J. Neurophysiol.* **13**, 55–63.

Bailey, P. & Bremer, F. (1938). A sensory cortical representation of the vagus nerve. *J. Neurophysiol.* **1**, 405–412.

Bailey, P. & Sweet, W. H. (1940). Effects on respiration, blood pressure and gastric motility of stimulation of orbital surface of frontal lobe. *J. Neurophysiol.* **3**, 276–281.

Beattie, A. D. (1949). The physiological basis of vagotomy. *Br. med. J.* **1**, 607–610.

Brodal, A. (1957). *The Reticular Formation of the Brain Stem, Anatomical Aspects and Functional Correlations.* Oliver & Boyd, Edinburgh.

Calaresu, F. R. & Pearce, J. W. (1965). Electrical activity of efferent vagal fibres and dorsal nucleus of the vagus during reflex bradycardia in the cat. *J. Physiol.* **176**, 228–240.

Cushing, H. (1932). Peptic ulcers and the interbrain. *Surgery Gynec. Obstet.* **55**, 1–34.

Davey, L. M., Kaada, B. R. & Fulton, J. F. (1950). Effects on gastric secretion of frontal lobe stimulation. *Res. Publs Ass. Res. nerv. ment. Dis.* **29**, 617–627.

Delgado, J. M. R. & Livingston, R. B. (1948). Some respiratory, vascular and thermal responses to stimulation of orbital surface of frontal lobe. *J. Neurophysiol.* **11**, 39–55.

Dell, P. & Olson, R. (1951). Projections thalamiques corticales et cérébrales des afférents vagaux. *C. r. Séanc. Soc. Biol.* **145**, 1088–1091.

Eliasson, S. (1952). Cerebral influence on gastric motility in the cat. *Acta physiol. scand.* **26**, Supp. 95, 1–70.

Feldman, S., Birnbaum, D. & Behar, A. (1961). Gastric secretions and acute gastroduodenal lesions following hypothalamic and preoptic stimulation. *J. Neurosurg.* **18**, 661–670.

French, J. O., Hernández-Peón, R. & Livingston, R. B. (1955). Projections from cortex to cephalic brain stem (reticular formation) in monkey. *J. Neurophysiol.* **18**, 74–95.

Hartzell, J. B. (1929). The effect of section of the vagus nerves on gastric acidity. *Am. J. Physiol.* **91**, 161–171.

Hess, W. R., Akert, K. & McDonald, D. A. (1951). Beziehungen des Stirnhimes zum vegetiven system. *Helv. physiol. pharmac. Acta* **9**, 101–124.

Hess, W. R., Akert, K. & McDonald, D. A. (1952). Functions of the orbital gyri of cats. *Brain* **75**, 144–258.

Hilton, S. M. & Spyer, K. M. (1971). Participation of the anterior hypothalamus in the baroceptor reflex. *J. Physiol.* **218**, 271–293.

Hockman, C. H. (1963). Effects of cerebral stimulation of gastric secretion in cats. *Fedn Proc.* **22**, 342.

Hoff, E. C., Kell, Jr., J. F. & Carroll, Jr., M. N. (1963). Effects of cortical stimulation and lesions on cardiovascular function. *Physiol. Rev.* **43**, 68–114.

Hoffman, B. L. & Rasmussen, T. (1953). Stimulation studies of insular cortex of *Macaca mulatta. J. Neurophysiol.* **16**, 343–351.

Kaada, B. R. (1951). Somato-motor, autonomic and electrocorticographic responses to electrical stimulation of 'rhinencephalic' and other structures in primates, cat and dog. *Acta physiol. scand.* **24**, Supp. 83, 1–285.

Kaada, B. R., Pribram, K. H. & Epstein, J. A. (1949). Respiratory and vascular responses in monkeys from temporal pole, insula, orbital surface and cingulate gyrus. *J. Neurophysiol.* **12**, 347–356.

Klopper, P. J. (1954). Influence of the cerebral cortex on gastric secretory function in cats. *Acta Physiol. Pharmac. néerl.* **3**, 420–428.

Korn, H. (1969). Splanchnic projection to the orbital cortex of the cat. *Brain Res.* **16**, 23–38.

Korn, H. & Massion, J. (1964). Origine et topographie des projections vagales sur le cortex antérieur chez le chat. *C. r. hebd. Séanc. Acad. Sci. Paris* **259**, 4373–4375.

Korn, H., Wendt, R. & Albe-Fessard, D. (1966). Somatic projection to the orbital cortex of the cat. *Electroen. Neurophysiol.* **21**, 209–226.

Löfving, B. (1961). Cardiovascular adjustments induced from the rostral cingulate gyrus. *Acta physiol. scand.* **53**, Supp. 184, 1–82.

Newman, P. P. & Wolstencroft, J. H. (1959). Medullary responses to stimulation of orbital cortex. *J. Neurophysiol.* **22**, 516–523.

Newman, P. P. & Wolstencroft, J. H. (1960). Influence of orbital cortex on blood pressure responses in cat. *J. Neurophysiol.* **23**, 211–217.

Rossi, G. F. & Brodal, A. (1956). Corticofugal fibres to the brain stem reticular formation. *J. Anat.* **90**, 42–62.

Sachs, Jr., E. S., Brendler, S. J. & Fulton, J. F. (1949). The orbital gyri. *Brain* **72**, 227–240.

Sen, R. N. & Anand, B. K. (1957). Effect of electrical stimulation of the limbic system of brain ('visceral brain') on gastric secretory activity and ulceration in cats with gastric pouches and implanted electrodes. *Indian J. med. Res.* **45**, 515–521.

Sheacy, C. N. & Peele, T. (1957). Studies on amygdaloid nucleus of cat. *J. Neurophysiol.* **20**, 125–139.

Smith, W. K. (1938). The representation of respiratory movements in the cerebral cortex. *J. Neurophysiol.* **1**, 55–68.

Smith, G. P. & McHugh, P. R. (1964). Gastric secretory response to amygdaloid and hypothalamic stimulation. *Physiologist* **7**, 259.

Spencer, W. G. (1894). The effect produced on respiration by faradic excitation of the cerebrum in the monkey, dog, cat and rabbit. *Phil. Trans. R. Soc.* **185**B, 609–657.

Wall, P. D. & Davis, G. D. (1951). Three cerebral cortical systems affecting autonomic function. *J. Neurophysiol.* **14**, 507–517.

10

CEREBRAL CONTROL OF HYPOTHALAMUS

O UR knowledge of the cerebral influences on hypothalamic activity is still largely at an exploratory stage. This is partly due to the difficulty of sorting out the profuse network of fibre connexions passing into and out of the hypothalamus and partly to the fact that some of the neural mechanisms are regulated by hormones in the blood stream. The present chapter is intended to review the evidence for believing that functions of the hypothalamus are dependent on cerebral activation and, in particular, to look at the contributions from the limbic regions of the brain. The responses attributable to hypo-thalamic discharges are well known. They include the activities of the autonomic nervous system, the neural control of the pituitary glands and involvement of the locomotor system in behavioural reactions. The patterns characteristic of strong emotional excitement also have their origin in the hypothalamus. It is therefore not surprising that emphasis in the literature has been placed on the investigation of these separate functions whilst less is known about the mechanisms of integration. As already suggested, the limbic region is thought to act as an integrating centre for many channels of information, where the necessary adjustments can be made to meet the requirements of environmental change. The hypothalamus could well be the target for this activity. There are, of course, many other aspects to be considered and the danger of over-simplification is only too obvious.

ANATOMICAL DIVISIONS

Boundaries

The hypothalamus extends from the lamina terminalis anteriorly to the mamillary bodies posteriorly. On the medial side it adjoins the lower part of the third ventricle and its lateral boundary is formed by the optic tracts, globus pallidus and internal capsule. Dorsally, it lies below the level of the thalamus. The inferior relations are defined by the optic chiasma, tuber cinereum, median eminence, infundibular stem and hypophysis.

Subdivisions

The hypothalamus may be divided into four regions:

1. The anterior region contains the supraoptic and paraventricular nuclei which give rise to the greater proportion of fibres supplying the posterior pituitary gland.

2. The medial region adjoins the third ventricle; it is highly cellular and contains the ventromedial and dorsomedial nuclei.

3. The lateral region extends from the preoptic region rostrally to the mid-brain caudally. It contains the medial forebrain bundle—a collection of myelinated and unmyelinated fibres through which most of the extrinsic connexions of the hypothalamus are made.

4. The posterior region is marked by a complex of nuclei known as the mamillary bodies lying in front of the posterior perforated substance. Fibres emerging from the mamillary bodies form a distinct tract relaying through the anterior nuclei of the thalamus and terminating in the cingulate cortex.

Connexions

With a few important exceptions, the pathways relating the hypothalamus to other parts of the brain are not clearly established. The cingulate cortex receives impulses via a thalamic relay; the neurohypophysis receives a direct nerve supply from the anterior nuclei; also the adrenal medulla is connected to the hypothalamus by descending tracts which pass out of the spinal cord in the splanchnic nerves and lumbar sympathetic chain. Other descending connexions form a network of fine unmyelinated fibres which cannot easily be separated into afferent and efferent pathways (Raisman, 1966). Similar difficulties apply to the cerebral connexions of the hypothalamus although certain anatomical links have been described. Perhaps the best known is that described by Le Gros Clark & Meyer (1950) in which the hypothalamus serves as a link between the hippocampal and cingulate gyri. This pathway is a very devious one and is believed to form a circuit for impulses carried by the fornix and relating the mamillary division of the hypothalamus to the two cortical areas (Fig. 10.1). Another difficulty encountered is the apparent resistance of cortico-hypothalamic projections to the technique of retrograde degeneration. This may be due to the diffuse character of the cells of origin in the efferent systems where it has already been

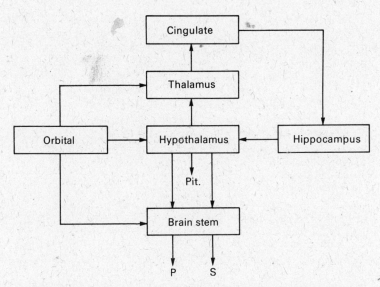

FIG. 10.1. Block diagram showing input–output relations of hypothalamus as discussed in the text. The orbital cortex and hippocampus have direct links with the hypothalamus; the cingulate is connected via thalamus and hippocampus. Output of hypothalamus is distributed to the pituitary gland (Pit.) and autonomic centres of brain stem. A link between orbital cortex and brain stem is also shown, P, parasympathetic outflow; S, sympathetic outflow.

noted that excitatory and inhibitory points on the cortex may be found side by side. Furthermore, staining techniques cannot easily distinguish between terminal fibre degeneration and the degeneration of fibres merely passing through the region to another destination. Thus, in the hypothalamus, where so many different tracts and cells are mingled diffusely, the results of anatomical studies are often difficult to interpret.

FUNCTIONAL DIVISIONS

It has long been known that hypothalamic lesions, even a small discrete lesion, may affect different functions and it is plain that precise topographical arrangements have little place here. Nevertheless it is convenient to classify the various functions according to the following scheme:

The anterior region, including the preoptic and tuberal parts, is traditionally the site controlling the parasympathetic outflow and heat-loss mechanisms. It may influence the release of gonadotrophic hormone from the anterior pituitary. By means of its projections on the neurohypophysis, it controls the release of antidiuretic hormone and oxytocin from the posterior pituitary. It may also be concerned in regulating water intake.

The medial region affects food intake and energy balance. The ventromedial nucleus, in particular, exerts a stabilizing control over the fat stores since obesity is produced after bilateral destruction. It may also secrete a stimulating factor for growth hormone.

The lateral region is associated with emotional behaviour. Its intricate mass of neural elements elaborate the patterned responses of integrated actions involving somatic and visceral output systems.

The posterior region, including the mamillary bodies, is the principal site controlling the sympathetic outflow and heat-conserving mechanisms. It may also elicit vasodilator responses in active skeletal muscle.

A scheme of this kind is of little value in relating different cell groups to specific functions, for the hypothalamus is a compact network of neural, cytochemical and vascular elements with supporting neuroglial material and traversed by innumerable afferent and efferent fibre connexions. But the scheme may help to piece together individual functional patterns and to give an overall picture of a region which seems to influence almost every aspect of bodily activity.

ORBITAL CORTEX AND HYPOTHALAMUS

Visceral afferent impulses are capable of evoking neuro-endocrine responses in the hypothalamus and therefore must play some part in the regulation of normal behaviour. The problem which has not yet been solved is the relationship between the hypothalamus and the cerebral cortex. As the primary and secondary areas of the sensory cortex belong to the afferent projection systems, we must look to other parts of the brain to supply the necessary 'trigger' for the hypothalamic discharges. There is evidence that the limbic regions act together for this purpose, connecting input with output, but in ways that are not fully understood. The possible contribution of each limbic component will now be discussed.

Ward & McCulloch (1947) attempted to unravel the intricate interconnexions between cortex and hypothalamus by the method of strychnine neuronography. In monkeys anaesthetized with Dial, strychnine was applied directly to the orbital surface of the frontal lobe whilst a recording electrode explored distant points in the brain. In this way they demonstrated the existence of pathways from the posterior orbital gyrus to the paraventricular nucleus and to the posterior hypothalamic area on the same side. Using similar methods in different species Sachs, Brendler & Fulton (1949) described diffuse projections to the contralateral orbital cortex and to the ipsilateral caudate nucleus, median forebrain bundle and anterior hypothalamus. Their results were supported soon afterwards by more conventional anatomical studies. Thus Clark & Meyer (1950) produced fibre degenerations in the monkey following lesions of the posterior orbital gyrus; many of the degenerated fibres were traced to the ventromedial nucleus. In discussing the significance of their findings they suggested that afferents from the dorsomedial nucleus of the thalamus formed part of a circuit conveying impulses through the orbital cortex to the hypothalamus; the circuit could serve as a 'trigger' for discharging the autonomic outflow in situations that would generally bring about a defence reaction. On the other hand, any damage to the orbital cortex would be likely to result in autonomic disturbances. Much the same conclusions were reported by Wall, Glees & Fulton (1951). In a preliminary operation, the orbital cortex of the monkey was exposed and undercut; the animal was sacrificed about ten days later and the whole brain examined histologically. The occurrence of nerve degeneration was recognized only when there was a clear contrast between the operated and controlled sides. The authors were able to trace tracts connecting the orbital gyrus to the paraventricular and ventromedial nuclei of the hypothalamus.

It seems from anatomical evidence alone that the orbital cortex and the hypothalamus are strongly linked together and thus have interesting implications in regard to function. Unfortunately, from a physiological point of view, the relationship is not so clearly established. Investigations have taken various forms. In 1953 Pribram & Bagshaw studied behavioural changes in the baboon after removing the posterior orbital gyrus on both sides and considered that the changes were caused by degeneration of cells in the dorsomedial nucleus of the thalamus. This observation supported the idea of Clark & Meyer (1950) that a neuronal circuit involving the thalamus and orbital cortex played a significant part in controlling the hypothalamus. A completely different approach to the problem was made by Turner (1954) on the basis that orbital stimulation was known to have a marked inhibitory effect on respiration. Using this as an index of activity arising in the orbital cortex, he attempted to abolish the response by placing small lesions at various points along the outgoing pathways. As a result, he was able to postulate the existence of an orbito-medullary influence through which the cortex exerted control of pCO_2 in the blood by alterations of the respiratory rate. Although these experiments are extremely interesting he did not state whether the effects were direct or whether they were channelled through the hypothalamus. It would be valuable to know if the response could occur after removal of the hypothalamus. Electrical studies on the orbital cortex, as indicated in the previous chapter, show how widespread is the network of its projections and the consequent difficulty of localizing the sites of its action. In the unanaesthetized animal, prepared with implanted electrodes, Ward & Back (1964) recorded evoked activity from the hypothalamus and from many other parts of the brain too. There seems no doubt that orbital influences can spread through a variety of pathways and reach not only the hypothalamus but many of the lower autonomic centres in addition.

In view of all these uncertainties it may be useful to set out the following proposals:

1. *Effects on sympathetic outflow.* Direct pathways to the ventromedial and posterior nuclei of the hypothalamus have been established mainly through physiological neuronography and fibre

degeneration experiments, but evidence of evoked activity is also available. The idea that the orbital cortex may serve as a link between the thalamus and hypothalamus is favoured by several authors, influenced, no doubt, by the appreciable afferent contributions that come from the dorsomedial nucleus. On the basis of these connexions, it is possible to understand how the orbital cortex is able to participate in activities controlled by the sympathetic nerves.

2. Effects on parasympathetic outflow. There is less information on direct pathways to the anterior nuclei of the hypothalamus and to the system of nerve fibres that join them to the neurohypophysis. It has become apparent that the orbital cortex exerts important effects on gastro-intestinal activity and that they are abolished after bilateral vagotomy. Peristalsis is generally inhibited whilst the volume and concentration of the secretions are increased. These observations suggest that the vagus is capable of two kinds of action or that there are two sets of efferent vagal fibres. As the full range of excitation–inhibition can be brought about by varying the parameters of stimulation, it is postulated that the orbital cortex has a dual outflow to the vagal nuclei, the inhibitory effects operating through the anterior hypothalamus.

3. Effects on other systems. The diffuse character of the orbital projections accounts for the difficulty in assessing which functions are mediated by neural mechanisms in the hypothalamus and which are not. The orbital cortex should not be considered in isolation since so many other cortical areas elicit similar or parallel actions and they will exert a combined effect on the hypothalamus under natural conditions. Another difficulty is the evidence of a direct influence on the brain-stem centres and the possibility that when instructions to the viscera are issued by the cerebral cortex, the hypothalamus may not always be consulted.

ANTERIOR CINGULATE AND HYPOTHALAMUS

Good access to the anterior cingulate is gained if the forebrain on one side is removed by suction; otherwise the two cerebral hemispheres must be separated from each other by division of the vascular bands which connect them. It can then be seen that the gyrus follows the curvature of the corpus callosum on the medial surface of the hemisphere below the cingulate sulcus. It is continuous through the posterior cingulate with the hippocampal gyrus on the inferior surface of the hemisphere. The cellular structure of the anterior cingulate is agranular, resembling that of the motor cortex; in contrast, the posterior cingulate is distinctly granular like the sensory cortex. This feature alone would suggest that the two zones are quite different in function and have different sets of communications. Yet our knowledge of their respective input and output relations is so imperfect that the entire region remains an enigma. At the present time it is believed that the anterior cingulate is necessary as a controlling device for many non-specific cerebral functions, but it seems to have a definite role in conscious behaviour, particularly in the display of integrated somato-visceral reactions induced by emotional excitement.

Anatomical connexions

Although it is now clear that the anterior cingulate and the hypothalamus are closely related, the anatomical pathways are for the most part poorly defined. A notable exception is the tract from the anterior thalamic nuclei conveying impulses from the fornix and mammillary bodies. It is surprising how little we know about the afferent and efferent connexions of the anterior cingulate since it has received a good deal of attention in recent years (Krieg, 1963). It is obviously important to know how it communicates with other parts of the central nervous system, whether, for example, any fibres reach it from the cerebellum or sensory cortex and also to demonstrate the course and distribution of its efferent pathways.

Electrophysiological studies

The results of experimental work on animals show that the anterior cingulate is capable of modifying reactions in many systems of the body. The results, however, are not always consistent and sometimes contradictory or even puzzling. How can one interpret a mechanism when stimulation exerts opposite effects on the same function and ablation causes variable changes that are difficult to reconcile? One of the earliest papers to throw light on the problem was that by Hodes & Magoun (1942). Using the pupillary reflex as an index of evoked activity in the anaesthetized cat, they showed that stimulation of the anterior cingulate generally caused dilatation and the points yielding such changes could be traced to the hypothalamus. However, many of the points overlapped those giving pupillo-constrictor responses. The studies of Smith (1945) are also of great interest. He obtained responses in the monkey following repetitive stimulation of the anterior cingulate, whilst single shocks were ineffective. The responses included slowing or arrest of respiration, dilatation of the pupil, pilo-erection and cardiovascular changes which were manifested either by a rise of blood pressure without affecting heart rate or by a fall of blood pressure with slowing of the heart—the latter being abolished after bilateral vagotomy. In discussing the significance of his observations it was apparent that the cortex produced its effects through both sympathetic and parasympathetic systems and it seemed that the hypothalamus was most likely involved. On this assumption he thought that the anterior cingulate might be concerned in controlling emotional reactions. The same opinion was expressed by Kremer (1947) who obtained suppression of respiratory movements and a fall of blood pressure in the dog. Ward (1948) also believed that the anterior cingulate was part of a central mechanism for emotion. In monkeys under Dial anaesthesia, he showed that repetitive stimulation of the cingulate cortex resulted in arrest of respiration for about 25 sec, slowing of the heart and fall of blood pressure, pilo-erection and dilatation of the pupil. In other experiments, bilateral ablation of the cingulate gyri gave rise to placidity and other changes in social behaviour. Ward concluded that the anterior cingulate was a 'potent autonomic effector area and an integral part of behavioural organization'.

Speakman & Babkin (1949) made the interesting suggestion that both sympathetic and parasympathetic systems could be controlled from the same cortical area and that when one system was put out of action, the opposite effect appeared. Thus a fall of blood pressure of about 30 mm Hg induced by stimulating the cingulate was converted, after vagotomy, to a rise of blood pressure of 30 mm Hg. About the same time Kaada et al. (1949, 1951) were investigating the influence of the limbic cortex on visceral functions and found that changes in activity could be elicited from many different areas. No attempt will be made to summarize here the details of their experimental work, but the conclusions reached are of extreme importance to the analysis of limbic organization, since they indicate the existence of discrete localization which was not previously suspected. The problem was taken a stage further by Babkin & Kite (1950) who found that stimulation of the anterior cingulate in the dog inhibited contractions of the stomach; this response was independent of any cardiovascular or respiratory changes and was not due to activation of the sympatho-adrenal system. Whilst they could not claim that a higher gastric centre existed in the cingulate gyrus, their results pointed to a specific functional action of the cingulate cortex leading to a depression of the parasympathetic outflow. Evidence that the inhibitory effects were mediated by the hypothalamus was suggested by the fact that when the hypothalamus was removed by means of suction, the strength and rate of the gastric contractions increased.

Eliasson (1952) showed that the cingulate gyrus was an active suppressor area, causing inhibition of pyloric motility in the cat. He, too, did not subscribe to the idea of a higher gastric centre but thought that the anterior cingulate might serve as an intermediary between impulses arising from the stomach and the inhibitory effects going back to it. However, he did not find any place for the hypothalamus in this scheme. Further support for the participation of the anterior cingulate in the regulation of visceral activities was provided by the experiments of Showers & Crosby (1958) in the monkey. In addition to obtaining the usual responses to cortical stimulation, namely, cardiovascular and respiratory changes, dilatation of the pupil and salivation, these authors recorded an increased tension in the muscles of the face accompanied by movements and patterns characteristic of emotional expression. Particular interest is attached to this finding because the anterior cingulate is generally regarded as a suppressor area for somatic motor discharges, movements and tone in the skeletal musculature. Evidently the points inhibiting movements and tone overlap those yielding facilitatory responses and it is significant that a combination of visceral and somatic effects can be elicited from the same stimulated site in order to produce a meaningful physiological reaction. Thus increased muscle tension, often the only clinical manifestation of an emotion, is likely to show itself as part of an integrated response pattern. On all the evidence it seems reasonable to believe:

(1) that the anterior cingulate cortex produces visceral excitation and inhibition through effects on the hypothalamus and

(2) that it also serves as a link between the visceral and somatic output systems.

Influence of anaesthesia

Much has been written about the role of the limbic cortex from experimental work on anaesthetized animals, yet a part of the brain which is believed to exert so much influence on emotional behaviour must surely be at a disadvantage when studied under this condition. Even in light anaesthesia, the activity of cortical cells can be so altered as to eliminate low grades of facilitation or inhibition. Accordingly, much importance is attached to the work of Anand & Dua (1956) for their observations on the waking cat and monkey, stimulated by means of implanted electrodes. Their results might possibly explain some of the inconsistencies reported in the literature when different anaesthetics or combination of anaesthetics were administered. Thus in a series of 12 experiments, they recorded a rise of blood pressure in 8 animals and no change in 4; the heart rate was either increased or diminished and the pulmonary ventilation either increased or unaffected. They concluded that the unanaesthetized animal differed from the anaesthetized because under normal conditions the excitability of the cerebral cortex was variable from moment to moment. In other words, anaesthesia altered the level of cortical excitability to such an extent that the responses to stimulation conformed to a narrow and more rigid pattern. Comparable results were reported by Pool & Ransohoff (1949) following a study of visceral reactions in man. Using only local anaesthesia for exposure of the brain, the rostral portion of the cingulate gyrus was stimulated. They recorded a rise of blood pressure of about 60 mm Hg in 8 out of 12 subjects; a fall of blood pressure was recorded in 1 subject and no change in the remaining 3. Changes in respiration were also found to be variable. On the other hand, after the administration of pentothal anaesthesia, the results were quite different: stimulation of the cingulate gyrus generally caused a rise of blood pressure of about 10–20 mm Hg, apnoea lasting 5–45 sec, increased peristalsis and pupillary dilatation. The responses were now more consistent although they could not all be elicited in every subject (Pool, 1954).

It will be apparent that much more information is required before we can be certain about the functions of the agranular cingulate cortex. When the cortex is stimulated, the discharged impulses give rise to widespread autonomic responses which are similar in many respects to those evoked by the hypothalamus itself. It is relevant that the cingulate gyrus receives a large projection from the mammillary bodies and is therefore effectively provided with an information source for carrying out the variety of tasks that it does. Thus up to the present there are good reasons for believing that a close relationship exists between these two regions despite the fact that impulses of cingulate origin do not appear to pursue a direct pathway to any known viscero-motor nuclei in the hypothalamus. Indeed it is becoming increasingly clear that a 'wiring diagram' is more likely to resemble an intricate controlling device rather than a relay system of synaptic connexions. Finally, all evidence based on the results of electrical stimulation must be interpreted with the greatest caution since the balance between facilitation and inhibition is so critical at this cortical level.

TEMPORAL LOBE AND HYPOTHALAMUS

Attention has been paid in recent years to behavioural changes occurring after localized electrical stimulation or following bilateral ablations of the temporal lobes. Certain structures, both cortical and subcortical, are known to occupy key positions in the limbic organization and their functions are of great practical importance because of the steady increase of interventions in clinical work. To evaluate the role of these structures is a most difficult task since many of their activities are shared or work in parallel or spread into other parts of the brain. The structures which will be considered here are the hippocampus and the amygdaloid nuclei and the reason is that they are both concerned in mechanisms that directly or indirectly control the excitability of the hypothalamus.

Influence of the hippocampus

Functional anatomy

The hippocampus is an area of grey matter extending along the entire length of the inferior horn of the lateral ventricle. It consists of two divisions, Ammon's horn and the dentate gyrus; the latter is a narrow strip of cortex on the upper surface, lying under cover of the fimbria. In contrast to other areas of the cerebral cortex, the hippocampus has only three histological layers, the main cell being a large pyramid with long and short apical dendrites. Pyramidal axons with many collaterals run through the molecular layer to occupy the alveus on the ventricular surface. The fibres of the alveus converge to form the fimbria which pass above the dentate gyrus to form the posterior column of the fornix. The two posterior columns come together and follow the under surface of the corpus callosum to form the anterior columns which bend backwards to reach the mammillary bodies. As early as 1937 Papez proposed a mechanism for central emotion based on the functional anatomy of this region. He claimed that impulses from the hippocampus passed by way of the fornix to the mammillary bodies and after relaying through the anterior thalamic nuclei reached the cingulate gyrus. This was the first clear statement to suggest that the hippocampus was not primarily concerned with olfactory functions.

Evoked activity

The functional properties of hippocampal cells have been studied by the evoked potential technique in animals and man. Slow waves were recorded from the surface of the hippocampus in cats and rabbits by Renshaw, Forbes & Morison (1940). The majority of the cells were found to discharge spontaneously, but responded to a peripheral stimulus with rapid negative deflexions. Similar changes were reported by Pribram & Kruger (1954). A more extensive study of hippocampal activity has been reported by Green and his associates in a series of papers and the reader is referred to a review of these publications (Green, 1964). The problem was first taken up by Green & Arduini (1954). Using implanted electrodes in rabbit, cat and monkey, they recorded slow wave discharges from the hippocampus, fornix, mammillary body and the mammillo-thalamic tract. They found that the hippocampus could be 'aroused' from almost any kind of afferent stimulus without any evidence of topographical organization. Comparing these features with the evoked activity of the somato-sensory cortex they concluded that the hippocampus must serve an entirely different function. Single unit activity of the dorsal hippocampus was studied by Green & Machne (1955) in the rabbit and the results generally confirmed earlier findings. They distinguished between spikes discharging spontaneously in irregular bursts and those provoked into prolonged bursts of activity by auditory, visual or tactile stimuli. In subsequent experiments on the cat Green & Adey (1956) found that the latencies of the evoked hippocampal responses were 15–20 msec longer than the latencies of units evoked in the sensory cortex from the same peripheral stimulus. Furthermore, with repetitive stimulation, hippocampal units did not follow increases in stimulation frequency beyond 15/sec. The authors attributed these differences to the fact that many synapses had to be traversed before the afferent volley reached the hippocampal cortex. They left the question open as to the central course of the afferent pathways and whether the primary site of delay was in the hypothalamus–fornix system, which they clearly felt to be most likely. It is interesting that about the same time Gloor (1956) reported that hippocampal discharges could be evoked from the amygdaloid nuclei over pathways terminating on the long dendrites of the hippocampal pyramidal cells.

Further evidence of afferent pathways in the fornix came from the work of von Euler, Green & Ricci (1958). When the fornix was stimulated by single shocks, a postsynaptic potential was recorded in the hippocampus after a brief latency of 4–5 msec. The impulses carried by the fornix entered the hippocampus near the junction of the fimbria and dental gyrus and were then relayed by the granule cells of the dentate gyrus to the hippocampal pyramidal cells. Whilst single shocks produced responses limited to the soma and proximal part of the apical dendrites, repetitive stimulation caused recruitment and massive dendrite depolarization. It was conceivable that similar effects were associated with the mechanism of seizure discharges to which the hippocampus was particularly susceptible. The existence of afferent pathways in the fornix was also demonstrated by Feldman (1962) in the locally anaesthetized cat. Using concentric steel electrodes orientated stereotactically, potential changes were recorded in the hippocampus following stimulation of widely scattered points in the hypothalamus. Whilst no topographical arrangements were observed, the evoked activity took the form of an earlier discharge with a very short latency of 1–3 msec followed almost invariably by a slower wave of 5–10 msec latency. It was noted, additionally, that conduction from the hypothalamus to the hippocampal cortex was facilitated by stimulation of the brain stem reticular formation.

From the above account, it can be stated fairly confidently that apart from the well-known efferent projection from the hippocampus to the mammillary bodies, there is physiological evidence for conduction in the opposite direction. This disclosure is of paramount importance to the problem of disentangling the complex actions of the limbic system; for if it is true that the fornix carries an afferent pathway to the hippocampus, we can guess that it probably operates as a feed-back mechanism allowing the hypothalamus to regulate the inflow of impulses from the periphery to the hippocampal pyramidal cells.

Electrical stimulation

1. Functional changes. The effects of hippocampal stimulation on the various functions of the body are somewhat confusing. Cardiovascular changes were noted by Kaada (1951) and by MacLean & Delgado (1953) in the conscious animal. Stimulation generally resulted in a fall of blood pressure and yet when the fornix was sectioned on both sides the response was unaffected. Respiration was usually inhibited during the period of stimulation; this was shown by Kaada & Jasper (1952) in man, but their patients were often psychotic and under anaesthesia. Dilatation of the pupil was reported by Kaada (1951) and by MacLean & Delgado (1953) who also observed behavioural changes accompanied by lacrimation and salivation. Kaada referred to changes in gastric tone which could be either excitatory or inhibitory and in any case were rather unpredictable. More recently this aspect of hippocampal influence was re-investigated by Feldman, Wajsbort & Birnbaum (1967). In a control series of experiments they showed that stimulation of the posterior hypothalamus caused an increase of potassium concentration in the gastric secretion. They then used this response to study the role of the hippocampus and found that a preceding hippocampal stimulus for a period of 12 minutes resulted in a significantly lower potassium concentration. The hippocampus did not by itself influence gastric secretion. On the basis of their observations the authors suggested that inhibitory impulses from the hippocampus might determine the acid content of the stomach. Other effects of hippocampal stimulation included movements of the body especially those concerned in defence and attack. It was not thought that the hippocampus initiated the movements but it was quite capable of inhibiting cortically induced movements (Vanegas & Flynn, 1968).

In general, we may say that the results of hippocampal stimulation fall into visceral, somatic and behavioural categories. The changes suggest interference with mechanisms rather than specific actions on the structures involved. The hippocampus appears to be a kind of circuit regulator, connecting or disconnecting on a remote line; also, it does not exert control on any particular function.

2. Efferent projections. There is good evidence that the fornix is the principal efferent pathway conducting impulses to the hypothalamus. Pribram & Kruger (1954) described three different projection systems in the temporal region—olfactory tubercle to pyriform cortex, septum to anterior temporal cortex and hippocampus to mammillary body. The course of action potentials originating in the hippocampus was traced by Green & Adey (1956) in the cat: responses were recorded in the fornix, mammillary body, mammillo-thalamic tract and the cingulate gyrus. Thus the impulses followed the classical pathway of anatomy; in addition, evoked responses were recorded in the lateral hypothalamus and in the amygdaloid nuclei. All of these responses had short latencies indicating that complicated routes were not involved.

The effects of repetitive stimulation of the hippocampus were demonstrated by Neimer, Powell & Goodfellow (1960) when they recorded synchronous after-potentials from the hypothalamus. This was an important experiment in view of the well-known seizure activity of the hippocampus and the tendency for the discharges to spread along anatomical paths to adjacent structures. The same technique was used by Feldman (1962) in an attempt to clarify the nature of the influences set up by high-frequency stimulation, which appeared so analogous to epileptiform activity. He was able to show that potentials evoked in the hypothalamus by stimulating the sciatic nerve could be completely inhibited by hippocampal seizure discharges for periods lasting up to 300 msec. Further evidence for hippocampal inhibition came from the work of Redding (1967) who reported a decrease in amplitude of visual and auditory evoked potentials and of reticular potentials in the brain stem. The interaction studies of Dreifuss & Murphy (1968) provided a different technique to unravel the mysteries of the hippocampus. In cats prepared under ether they showed, firstly, that hypothalamic discharges could be elicited by stimuli delivered to the dorsal hippocampus. Secondly, they demonstrated both excitatory and inhibitory forms of interaction with testing stimuli delivered to the amygdaloid nuclei and septal region. Thirdly, they found that the discharge patterns of single hypothalamic units, mainly in the tuberal and lateral regions, could be influenced by hippocampal stimulation and that often the same unit could be driven from the amygdaloid. Thus they gave clear evidence that these limbic structures had a working relationship with the hypothalamus and it seemed reasonable to suppose that they modified the latter's activity.

Possible functional mechanisms

Perhaps the most profitable way to a better understanding of hippocampal function is to recognize that it is different in many respects from other areas of the brain. To begin with, the histological structure is relatively simple and even though electron microscopy may show that the apparent simplicity is misleading, from the standpoint of microelectrode studies, the granule and pyramidal cells together with their dendrites are arranged in a neat, well-defined manner. Next, the anatomical connexions of the hippocampus give few clues about its actual functional role, except for the special relationship which exists with the anterior cingulate gyrus. Thirdly, afferent fibres reach the hippocampus from the brain stem and thalamus but they do not belong to an organized sensory projection system. Indeed, none of the usual characteristics of a cortical receiving area can be applied to the hippocampal cortex—the latencies are too long, there are no specific responses, no topographical representation, no consistent input–output relationship. All these facts suggest that a different functional assignment must be found.

The idea that the hippocampus may serve as a built-in device for controlling visceral functions is developed from the following experimental findings: slow wave responses are induced by virtually any type of stimulus; its discharges can spread into the hypothalamus as well as into adjacent areas of the cerebral cortex; its activity may be influenced by a feed-back mechanism mediated by the fornix; impulses initiated by electrical stimulation produce changes suggesting interference with visceral mechanisms. There are two important clues which may have a bearing on the problem. The first is concerned with hippocampal–cingulate relationships and the second with inhibitory predominance:

Evidence presented by Parmeggiani, Azzaroni & Lenzi (1971) showed that impulses spread from the hippocampus along the Papez loop to the cingulate gyrus and then back again to the hippocampus. The conduction time for the complete cycle was 50–60 msec. When circulation occurred, the primary response recorded from the hippocampus was invariably followed by a smaller secondary response, suggesting that only a fraction of the hippocampal output returned in each cycle. However, the size of the secondary response could be increased by increasing the frequency of stimulation. The theoretical considerations arising from these experiments are very attractive. They suggest that the Papez circuit functions as a positive feed-back mechanism, maintaining a circulation of impulses between the hippocampus and the cingulate cortex. The mechanism would seem to influence target cells outside the circuit in proportion to the rate of the cycle. The faster recycling occurs, the greater the output becomes. In this way, the hippocampus and related structures can exert a modifying influence on the entire hypothalamic output; but the size of this influence will in turn depend upon the afferent contributions from various sources. Thus we are back to the original problem—a search for the links between the visceral afferent and efferent systems and if the Papez circuit can have this sort of action, it can be expected that the limbic organization must be a serious contender for the role.

Turning now to the evidence for inhibition, the results of electrical stimulation show that there is a definite tendency towards inhibitory effects on somatic as well as on autonomic functions. For example, most workers record a fall in blood pressure, arrest of respiration and reduction in gastric secretion. Furthermore, hippocampal stimulation can produce a long-lasting inhibitory effect on potentials evoked elsewhere. Such observations emphasize the predominance of inhibition under experimental conditions but are not exclusive of excitatory influences that may occur in the conscious animal especially in the field of behavioural studies. A clearer understanding of the internal working of the hippocampus is obviously necessary and we cannot do better than recognize that the cytoarchitectural structure itself provides an arrangement for an effective balance between excitation and inhibitition. Anderson, Eccles & Loyning (1964) drew attention to the long-lasting inhibitory potentials derived through basket cell synapses on the soma of the pyramidal cells. Since the basket cells are activated by the collaterals of pyramidal axons a powerful recurrent inhibitory mechanism is established. As with the Renshaw cell in the spinal cord or the Golgi cell in the cerebellum, the output of the hippocampus is controlled by recurrent inhibition. To oppose this self-limiting action of the pyramidal cells excitatory synapses are located on the pyramidal dendritic tree. These excitatory synapses provide background depolarization and discharge their cells only when depolarization reaches the threshold level. This may be expected to follow a fairly strong stimulus such as occurs naturally in emotional stress. The electrophysiological findings of Anderson & Lomo (1967) give ample support to the above views and offer a simple explanation for the selective bias of hippocampal neurones. They observed that a single afferent volley evokes a hyperpolarizing response in a pyramidal cell with the generation of IPSP and consequent depression of the firing level below threshold. On the other hand, stimulus frequencies of about 10–12/sec elicits EPSP and depolarization of the postsynaptic membrane which generates an impulse when sufficiently intense. Increased transmitter release from the dendritic synapses is believed to counteract the recurrent inhibition of the pyramidal cells and thus control the entire output discharge.

In summary, on both anatomical and physiological grounds there is sufficient evidence to show that the hippocampus plays some part in regulating the excitability of the hypothalamus. This by no means excludes many other possible functions, for example, its relation to the various states of consciousness, memory processes and behaviour, but a discussion of such topics is outside the scope of the present work. There is good reason for believing that the hippocampus is a link in a circuit which also includes the thalamus and the cingulate and that the controlled output of this circuit discharges directly to the hypothalamus and along more diffuse paths to segmental and reticular structures in the brain stem. The output influences the firing patterns of all these structures so that the action can switch over to favour facilitation or inhibition according to circumstances (Gergen, 1967). However, because of the more powerful effects of recurrent and forward inhibition, the output remains restricted until excitatory events are intensified.

Influence of the amygdaloid

Functional anatomy

The amygdaloid nuclei lie in the depth of the temporal lobe in the roof of the inferior horn of the lateral ventricle. They form two major groups—baso-lateral and cortico-medial. The globus pallidus is related dorsally, the optic tract and preoptic region anteriorly and the hippocampal cortex posteriorly. According to Fox (1940) the majority of the fibres emerging from the lateral nuclei pass to the anterior commissure whilst all the remaining nuclei contribute to the stria terminalis—the best known pathway connecting the amygdaloid with the hypothalamus (Fig. 10.2). Thus fibres from the basal amygdaloid were traced through the stria to the paraventricular nucleus (Fox, 1943) and other amygdaloid projections to the supra-optic nucleus

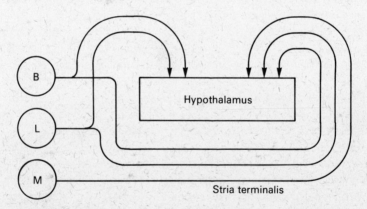

FIG. 10.2. Diagram of links between amygdaloid nuclei and hypothalamus. The basal (B) and lateral (L) divisions have each two efferent pathways, a short route via the anterior commissure and a longer, complex route via the stria terminalis. Efferents from the medial (M) division are conducted by the stria terminalis. To retain simplicity, other amygdaloid projections to subcortical and brain stem structures are not shown.

(Auer & Virgilio, 1953). Pathways to the ventromedial and periventricular nuclei of the hypothalamus were described by Adey & Meyer (1952) who found that many of the fibres passed through the anterior commissure to reach the corresponding nuclei of the opposite side. Hall (1963) has made a detailed study of the baso-lateral connexions in the cat, using electrocoagulation for the placement of discrete lesions; the animals were sacrificed ten days later and the degenerated fibres identified:

(a) *Basal nucleus*—Two efferent pathways via the stria terminalis and the longitudinal association bundle, terminating in the anterior commissure and preoptic region.

(b) *Lateral nucleus*—two efferent pathways via the longitudinal association bundle to the preoptic region and a more diffuse system of fibres to the medial forebrain bundle, terminating in scattered points throughout the lateral hypothalamus. Most of these pathways were confirmed by Valverde (1963) whose findings may be summarized as follows:

The stria terminalis represents the principal efferent projection from the amygdaloid. It conveys fibres to the preoptic region and medial forebrain bundle of the lateral hypothalamus. A second projection pathway known as the ventral amygdalofugal system connects the amygdaloid through the anterior commissure to many telencephalic structures including the preoptic region and hypothalamus. The two systems therefore converge upon the same area, but whether they have any functional differences is not indicated by these degeneration studies.

Evoked activity

Recordings from single units in the amygdaloid nuclei were described by Machne & Segundo (1956) using cats prepared under ether. The majority of the units discharged spontaneously at a steady rate with only occasional 'waxing and waning'. Stimulation of a peripheral nerve usually evoked an increase of the firing rate up to 50 spikes/sec. The latencies of the evoked unit responses ranged between 50 and 200 msec. Many different sense modalities were effective including afferents conveyed by the sciatic, cutaneous and vagal nerves. The authors concluded that the amygdaloid was a convergence centre for somatic and visceral functions without any obvious topographical arrangement of the units concerned. However, they believed that temporal patterns of activity should be taken into account in localization of the peripheral input.

An attempt to demonstrate discriminate functions in the amygdaloid nuclei was reported by Creutzfeldt, Bell & Adey (1963). They distinguished between units influenced by a specific afferent input, e.g. olfactory or sciatic and those which responded to multiple sensory stimuli. The specific responses had a relatively short latency up to 20–30 msec and were reliably reproducible. The unspecific units had variable latencies ranging up to 100 msec and their discharges were either inconsistent or ill-defined. Such units were encountered mainly in the lateral and central nuclei and responded to various forms of stimulation. However, they could find no evidence of true multisensory convergence and no interaction effects were observed. The authors conceded that certain nuclei in the amygdaloid complex may be endowed with specific functions; but the wider distribution of non-specific units suggested that 'arousal' was a more likely role, especially in the mediation of defence reactions.

There is surprisingly little information on amygdaloid responses to visceral stimulation since the paper by Dell & Olson (1951) reporting the central projections of vagal afferent impulses. It may well be that the amygdaloid has no direct input from the viscera, at least in the form of a sensory projection system, or else the distribution of visceral afferent influences is too diffuse for recording evoked potentials in the usual way. Dunlop (1958) drew attention to some of the difficulties he encountered after unsuccessful attempts to obtain amygdaloid responses following stimulation of the marsupial stomach. He did record evoked responses from the dorsal hippocampus although, initially, he suspected current spread to somatic structures. When the strength of the stimulating current was reduced he was able to identify a slow-wave component in the tracing and similar activity was evoked when tension was applied to the stomach wall or acid to the mucosa. However, despite every precaution, the amygdaloid remained unresponsive and there was not even the slightest modification of background activity.

As yet, a good deal of uncertainty remains to be cleared up. The failure to demonstrate evoked responses might have been due to the wrong kind of preparation or inadequate parameters of stimulation or to causes unknown; yet a more plausible explanation is that the amygdaloid is not a direct target for the cerebral destination of visceral afferent impulses and that it will just not accept information which has not been processed. If this indeed be true, then the amygdaloid behaves differently from other components of the limbic system which are apparently accessible to impulses from the periphery. Its non-involvement in stimulus-bound traffic suggests a degree of independence that is perhaps in keeping with the role of a central integrator. The point is well illustrated by Stuart, Porter & Adey (1964) whose experiments clearly emphasized the modulatory character of amygdaloid influence. In cats prepared under ether and locally anaesthetized, penetrations were made into the posterior hypothalamus and over 50 single units were found to respond to distension of the urinary bladder. The frequency of firing of these units was determined primarily by the afferent discharges from the bladder; but the frequency could be increased or diminished by electrical stimulation of the amygdaloid. Whatever interpretations may be given to these effects, the experiments at least indicate that amygdaloid impulses may reach the hypothalamus and presumably have a part to play in controlling its excitability.

Electrical stimulation

A wide variety of visceral and somatic responses may be elicited by electrical stimulation of the amygdaloid nuclei. Often the stimulus results in opposite effects on the same function, but there is little doubt that its influence can be of considerable magnitude. A summary of the principal changes observed will now be given.

(a) Respiration. Inhibition of respiratory movements or complete arrest of respiration was reported by Kaada (1951) from scattered points in the amygdaloid complex; the effects were not abolished after section of the stria terminalis. Similar findings were reported by Poirier & Shulman (1954) and by Anand & Dua (1955, 1956). On the other hand, increased respiratory movements were observed by MacLean & Delgado (1953) from points in the rostral part of the nucleus, although the authors felt it was unwise to identify specific functions with specific regions.

(b) Circulation. Variations in heart rate and blood pressure have been observed by many workers. MacLean & Delgado (1953) found cardiac slowing in cats and monkeys with implanted electrodes. An increase in heart rate accompanied by a rise of blood pressure were seen in man (Chapman *et al.*, 1954). A fall of blood pressure was reported by Poirier & Shulman (1954), using anaesthetized animals, whilst Anand & Dua (1956) obtained a rise of blood pressure in cats and a fall in monkeys. Such lack of consistency in circulatory response may reflect the variety of methods and techniques employed; however, to read any meaning into the results, they should be considered as part of a behavioural pattern which would be valid only in the unrestrained and conscious animal. With these criteria in mind Hilton & Zbrożyna (1963) studied defence reactions and produced a reliable combination of autonomic responses which included a rise in arterial blood pressure and increased blood flow in the skeletal muscles.

(c) Pupillary reactions. Dilatation of the pupil appears to be one of the responses commonly produced by stimulation of the amygdaloid, whatever the conditions or techniques used. The response is an integral part of most defence reactions and can be elicited from almost any input–output circuit in which the 111 nerve nucleus is involved. Zbrożyna (1963) gives a brief but excellent review of his own studies on the pupillary reaction with evidence confirming that the dilatation was not of sympathetic origin but due to inhibition of ciliary nerve discharges. In comparison with the response obtained by stimulating the hypothalamus or mid-brain, the effect of amygdaloid stimulation was always smaller whether the pupil was intact or sympathecto-mized. A lesion severing the stria terminalis on one or both sides did not alter the pupillary dilatation.

(d) Alimentary system. Eliasson (1952) showed that electrical stimulation of the amygdaloid caused an increase in gastric motility in the anaesthetized cat. This was confirmed by Anand & Dua (1955) who also obtained an increase in the volume of the gastric juice, salivation and a rise in blood sugar. They believed that these responses were representative of a behaviour pattern in which sniffing, licking, chewing and swallowing were all associated when the animal was

searching for food. When the site of stimulation or the parameters were altered any one of these responses could be dominant.

(e) Skeletal muscle tension. Organized movements of eating represent a functional pattern in which visceral and somatic motor responses are elicited as mixed effects following amygdaloid stimulation. The movements include contractions of the facial and jaw muscles, accompanied by growling and other signs of vocalized emotion; they may be present even after removal of their representative areas in the motor cortex (Baldwin *et al.*, 1956). Attempts to localize the effects of stimulation to different nuclear divisions have not been too successful since current can easily flow to neighbouring groups of cells concerned in a different behavioural function (MacLean & Delgado, 1953). Possibly the reactions most extensively studied are those of defence and flight. Here, apart from the various autonomic responses described above, changes in the posture of the animal, often merging into aggressiveness, are undoubted signs of an increasing muscular tension generally associated with emotional excitement.

Effects of lesions

Earlier studies carried out by numerous investigators have yielded conflicting results except for the observation that unilateral lesions are inconclusive. Thus Spiegel, Miller & Oppenheimer (1940) found that bilaterally symmetric amygdaloid lesions in the cat and dog resulted in outbursts of ferocity. They also noted that bilateral section of the stria terminalis failed to give similar results, suggesting, therefore, that the stria was not the sole efferent pathway. The same conclusions were reached by Bard & Mountcastle (1948) who described how a placid animal was transformed into a savage beast. On the other hand, Schreiner & Kling (1953) reported that after bilateral removal of the entire amygdaloid complex, their animals exhibited a greater docility, increased sexual activity and a lack of fear or aggression when placed in a background of continuous emotional excitement. Subsequent destruction of the ventromedial nucleus of the hypothalamus produced savage behaviour in the animals.

These early experiments leave no doubt that bilateral lesions of the amygdaloid give rise to profound changes of emotional behaviour and it remains to argue first, whether the changes are excitatory or inhibitory, secondly, which channels mediate the disturbances and thirdly, whether the amygdaloid is likely to be solely responsible. An obvious way to seek an answer to these questions is to consider the entire organization contributing to a behavioural reaction. It remained for Fernandez de Molina & Hunsperger (1962) to perform such experiments in the cat and demonstrate that the 'growling' defence reactions produced by stimulating the dorsomedial amygdaloid nuclei arose because of activation of defence zones in the hypothalamus and mid-brain. The reactions were not abolished by destroying the amygdaloid because the activity of the hypothalamus was maintained by the zone in the mid-brain. Thus they postulated that a subcortical system for defence was organized at three functional levels— amygdaloid, hypothalamus and brain-stem and the arrangement would account for the fact that changes in emotional behaviour would vary according to the level and degree of destruction. Hilton & Zbrożyna (1963) identified the responsive region for defence reactions in the baso-medial nuclei and the adjoining lateral and central nuclei of the amygdaloid complex. Lesions interrupting the stria terminalis on one or both sides did not alter the response and therefore this could not be the efferent pathway to the hypothalamus for the defence reaction. They concluded that another pathway existed to connect the amygdaloid to the hypothalamus and that the same pathway was probably distributed to the defence zone in the brain stem. Impulses mediated by this channel aroused the brain-stem zone for the defence reaction and inhibited the 111 nerve nucleus, causing dilatation of the pupil.

Functional interpretations

It is still perhaps premature to express anything more than broad generalizations on the functions of the amygdaloid nuclei. In a review of the experimental evidence Zbrożyna (1963) believed that stimulation could bring about aggressive behaviour through influences acting on the hypothalamus, but there was no convincing evidence that lesions could produce the opposite effect of docility. Those who claimed increased tameness following amygdalectomy had probably effected a more radical lesion and, on the other hand, increased aggressiveness could be due to the irritative effects of an incomplete lesion. A different interpretation was offered by Egger & Flynn (1967) on the basis of their behavioural studies in cats with implanted electrodes. They found that opposite effects were elicited from anatomically different parts of the amygdaloid complex and, what is perhaps even more significant, that the effects appeared to be related to an increase or slowing down of the firing frequency of hypothalamic neurones. Thus stimulation of the dorsolateral portion of the lateral amygdaloid nucleus facilitated the 'attack' zone of the hypothalamus, whilst stimuli applied to the basal nucleus or to the anteromedial portion of the lateral nucleus caused suppression of the response. As regards the results of bilateral lesions, these depended on differences in the sites and the extent of amygdaloid damage. For example, a lesion in an area which on stimulation produced suppression of attack resulted in facilitation and aggressive behaviour. Lesions in other sites would account for behavioural patterns of an opposite character.

Whether or not it is accepted that the earlier discrepancy of results can be explained by differences in the anatomical site of stimulation or in the location of a lesion, most investigators will agree that an important function of the amygdaloid is modulation: the out-going impulses contribute to the overall excitability of the hypothalamus and brain-stem centres through which the somato-visceral reactions of behaviour are expressed. The amygdaloid is part of an anatomical matrix concerned with the emotional life of the animal. A lot more investigation is needed to find the links and to work out the mechanisms which may show that contributions come from all limbic structures to form a single functional control system.

EMOTIONAL REACTIONS

The various arguments favouring the hypothalamus as a centre for behavioural reactions have been simplified in the present account; but even so, no other part of the brain has such direct influence on the visceral and endocrine outflow. If there are still many unknown factors about the cerebral mechanisms involved in behaviour, at least there is ample evidence that the hypothalamus participates in widespread autonomic activities and in the release of hormones in conditions of stress. Many of these activities such as heart rate, arterial blood pressure, salivary secretion and sweating can be measured accurately, thus relating the physiological reaction to the intensity of the stimulus. Other autonomic responses such as changes in body temperature, size of the pupils, gastric secretions and the chemical composition of the blood and urine give an indication of the extent to which the body can react when the situation demands. Thus the character of the stimulus often determines the nature of the response, e.g. tachycardia in anxiety; sweating in embarrassment. A strong emotional stimulus elicits a complex picture of reactions in most subjects whilst violent emotion may cause an explosion of uncontrollable behaviour.

In comparison with the vast amount of data on the visceral and endocrine responses to emotion in both animals and man, the participation of other physiological systems has not received the same attention. Two of these will now be described; they are, changes in the electrical activity of the cerebral cortex and the increased tension of skeletal muscles.

1. Depression of the alpha rhythm

In most individuals the emotional charge of a stimulus word can be successfully controlled so that no visible reaction is observed. For this reason a variety of methods has been employed to correlate the emotion with a measurable change but most of them have proved unreliable or ineffective. They include the use of transducers and multi-channel polygraphs to record pulse rate, respiration, finger volume changes, electrocardiogram and skin resistance. As long ago as 1934, Adrian & Matthews found that in recording the electroencephalogram depression of the alpha rhythm occurred for most attention stimuli involving intellectual activity. The alpha waves were thought to be controlled by a sub-cortical pace-maker and thus possibly related to subcortical nuclei concerned in emotional responses. To test this relationship Forbes & Andrews (1937) studied cortical activity with simultaneous observations on skin resistance but found no significant relationship between the depression of alpha rhythm and the 'psycho-galvanic' response of the skin. Nevertheless, the method remains of interest to psychologists especially when combined with a word-association test. In the tracings of Fig. 10.3 the subject, who had his eyes closed, reacted in a very definite way to the word 'speech'—depression of alpha rhythm lasted 5–15 secs. Afterwards, he volunteered the information that he disliked the idea of giving a speech owing to a past embarrassing experience.

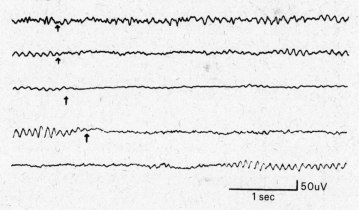

FIG. 10.3. Depression of alpha rhythm. EEG samples from four subjects recorded with their eyes closed. Stimulus word marked by arrow. Top trace shows no change in record after a neutral word. Second trace reveals slight depression following the stimulus word 'quarrel'. Third trace shows depression of alpha rhythm following the stimulus word 'hospital'. Continuous record of lower two traces is from a subject who reacted to the word 'speech'. Note persistence of alpha depression for about 8 sec.

2. Increased muscle tension

Several methods have been tried to assess emotional changes in terms of the muscular system. Luria (1932) measured the response to stress situations by recording muscular activity through a sensitive tambour; the technique showed that muscular tension was directly related to subjective feeling. This principle was applied to studies of handwriting by Ruesch & Finesinger (1943) but with the advance of technical knowledge, more accurate methods have been used. Thus Davis & Malmo (1951) recorded electromyographic changes during interviews of two patients suffering from anxiety states and Lundervold (1952), recording from limb and trunk muscles, noted the appearance of action potentials when the subject was excited. The occurrence of muscle artifacts in the records of standard electroencephalography suggested that this method might also be useful for assessing emotional reactions (Newman, 1953). In practice, recording electrodes were placed over the temporal muscles of the scalp. When the subject was relaxed, no muscle artifacts appeared in the EEG tracings; he was not required to answer to test words but only to listen. It was found that stimulating words or an emotional experience suggested by the operator brought out bursts of muscle spikes superimposed on the EEG traces. The emotional response could then be assessed in terms of amplitude, frequency and duration of the muscle action potentials. Any increase of muscle tension resulting from a stimulus word became immediately evident although the subject was generally unaware of the change and showed no outward sign of emotion.

In Fig. 10.4 it will be seen that positive responses were obtained for

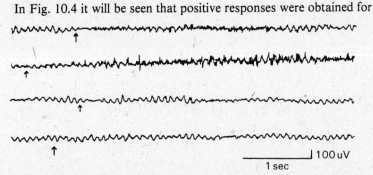

FIG. 10.4. Relation between skeletal muscle tension and emotional excitement. EEG from a female subject who had a history of a severe skin condition. Continuous record, eyes closed. Upper two traces show positive reactions to the words 'skin' and 'rash'. Lower two traces (for comparison) show no reactions to the words 'love' and 'passion'. Stimulus words marked by arrows.

the stimulus words 'skin' and 'rash' whilst there was no change in the electroencephalogram for the neutral words 'love' and 'passion'. Afterwards, this subject stated that she had suffered for many years from an allergic condition affecting her face. In a first series of tests no personal histories were taken, yet in many cases, subjects were able to recall some incident which correlated closely with the electromyographic response. In a second series, records were taken whilst the subjects concentrated on a situation which was particularly distasteful to them. For example, the subject of the traces depicted in Fig. 10.5 had a revulsion for spiders. She was given the serial suggestions that she saw a spider on a wall, that it suddenly jumped on to her leg, crawled on to her arm and neck, that it was a big, hairy spider and she was unable to brush it off, and finally that it was dead and out of sight. Although the electromyographic responses were very marked, the subject showed no other visible sign of emotion; and pulse and respiration rates were constant throughout the experiment. A few sensitive individuals had increased pulse rates and a greater depth of breathing. A striking observation was the rapid disappearance of the .

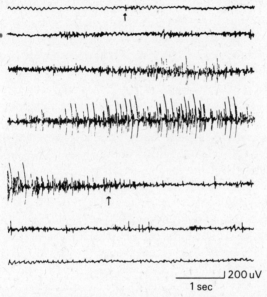

Fig. 10.5. Electromyographic response to suggestion. Continuous record from scalp muscles of female subject, eyes closed. At first arrow, subject 'sees' a spider; it 'jumps' on her leg, 'crawls' over her body, a big, hairy spider; she is unable to brush it off. At second arrow, spider is dead and out of sight. Note disappearance of muscle action potentials and return of normal EEG when emotional stimulus is withdrawn. In sensitive subjects, the tracings can show very clearly periods of emotional excitement and calm induced by suggestion.

spike potentials and restoration of the EEG trace when the stimuli were withdrawn. Another important observation was the apparent lack of physical signs of emotional distress and the calm appearance of the subject even when the suggestions and muscle spikes were at their peak. Thus the method was considered extremely useful for detecting emotional changes and for providing a means of measuring them in an accurate way. It also underlines the practical association of psychological stimuli with muscle tension.

SUMMARY

The regions of the brain which have been studied in this chapter are often taken together under the broad term of 'limbic system' or 'visceral brain' mainly because they have a common interest in the control of certain functions. There is no evidence at all that they behave as a single control unit and very little anatomical information of their interconnections. We do know, however, that they assist in the regulation of the visceral outflow, whatever else they may be concerned with in physiological or psychological fields. It seems that each limbic region can operate in parallel on the same input signals to achieve different purposes, that is to say, they may each exert a degree of independence. The total response, however, must surely be a harmonious one—far removed from the fragmented distortions induced by artificial stimulation. Unfortunately, we know little about the integration of cerebral activity and for the present we must rely upon the analysis of the four principal limbic components.

First, the orbital cortex can be distinguished as a receiving area for vagal and splanchnic nerve afferents although the evidence is scanty and still open to question. In any case, the considerable overlap of somatic and visceral representation would seem to rule out any possibility of discriminative functions. On the other hand, the responses evoked by electrical stimulation are so well known that there can be no doubt the orbital cortex can influence the autonomic outflow to the viscera. A good example of this are the effects on gastric motility and secretions which are so clearly implicated in the treatment of clinical disorders. Whether or not the influence is exerted only through the hypothalamus remains uncertain. There is general agreement that projections from the posterior orbital gyrus terminate on specific hypothalamic nuclei. Thus Ward & McCulloch (1947), using the method of strychnine neuronography, described connexions with the posterior hypothalamus and Sachs, Brendler & Fulton (1949) described connexions with the anterior hypothalamus. Orbital projections to the ventromedial nucleus and pars tuberalis were traced by Clark & Meyer (1950) and to the paraventricular nuclei by Wall, Glees & Fulton (1951) based on fibre degeneration studies. Finally, Ward & Back (1964) established the existence of direct orbito-hypothalamic pathways by means of the evoked potential technique.

Despite all this evidence there are still one or two questions to be answered on this subject. Most of these authors emphasized the diffuse character of the orbital projections suggesting that impulses may spread along a variety of pathways to structures beyond the hypothalamus including the brain stem reticular formation. Therefore it cannot be clear which of these pathways is responsible for mediating a particular function or whether the hypothalamus is necessarily involved. The demonstration of a direct orbito-medullary pathway must also give rise to speculations of this kind.

Secondly, the role of the anterior cingulate remains an enigma. Apart from the well-established anatomical tracts from the mammillary bodies which relay through the anterior nuclei of the thalamus, nothing much else can be claimed. Yet the fact that it receives such an input suggests that it is somehow involved in the higher control of visceral functions. Stimulation studies certainly indicate that the anterior cingulate may have a profound influence on both sympathetic and parasympathetic activities. For example, Showers & Crosby (1958) observed cardiovascular and respiratory changes, accompanied by dilatation of the pupil and salivation, following a stimulus delivered to a single cortical point. But if one takes into account the reports of other investigators, there are so many inconsistencies that it becomes difficult to arrive at any definite conclusion. The same may be said about the effects of bilateral cingulectomy in animals which usually results in disturbances of behaviour, since the disturbances are rarely consistent or permanent. Furthermore, no useful comparison has come from studies on patients since the operation is performed when behavioural disturbances are already present. One clue that may give insight into the problem is the influence of the cingulate cortex on the skeletal musculature, for changes in muscle tone and movements are factors concerned in emotional expression. The cingulate may therefore be regarded as an integrating centre for all the essential physiological activities that accompany a behavioural response.

Thirdly, the hippocampus has been shown to be intimately related both anatomically and functionally to the entire hypothalamic area by two-way pathways. Like the anterior cingulate cortex, its influence on the somato-motor system suggests that it is also programmed for integrated actions such as those involved in defence and attack.

Fortunately, we are better informed about the sources of afferents to the hippocampus for the results of evoked potential experiments have been more successful. Green & Machne (1955) studied the evoked activity of single hippocampal units and found many that responded to auditory, visual and tactile stimuli by an increase of discharge frequency; Green & Adey (1956) recorded evoked hippocampal activity following single shocks applied to the skin and Feldman (1962) demonstrated the appearance of short-latency responses conducted from the hypothalamus. Thus there is good evidence about the inflow of impulses to the hippocampus from both peripheral and central sources. The use which the hippocampus can make of the information is obscure. There is no evidence of any precise topographical organization whilst the long latencies of the responses to peripheral stimuli suggest only an indirect relationship with the sense organs. Likewise, the effects of electrical stimulation of the hippocampus on somato-visceral functions appear to be modulatory rather than specific. That is to say, that the excitability of the hypothalamus and other subcortical structures which are influenced by the hippocampus will perhaps be facilitated, but more usually diminished because of the predominance of inhibition.

Another way of looking at the role of the hippocampus is from the point of view of a visceral control centre which has to deal with unpredictable emotional situations so that a given effect can never be guaranteed to follow a given stimulus. Anderson, Eccles & Loyning (1964) showed that the hippocampal pyramidal cells have a built-in restraining device generated by long-lasting inhibitory potentials mediated through basket cell synapses. The device is operated through a feed-back to the hypothalamus itself and in this way appropriate adjustments of the hippocampal output can be made. The inhibitory synapses are located on the soma of the pyramidal cells. They provide an inhibitory background for any excitatory impulses arriving on the dendritic membrane and effectively block the discharges flowing out of the pyramids when stimulation is weak or moderate. Under conditions of intense excitement, such as occurs in emotional stress, inhibition is overcome by the release of excitatory transmitter and the result is a powerful driving force on the centres controlling the viscero-endocrine output.

Finally, no speculations on the activity of the limbic system can be complete without reference to the role of the amygdaloid. Deep in the temporal lobe is a collection of nuclei, linked to the hypothalamus by the stria terminalis and capable of producing widespread changes in the autonomic nervous system. The problem in the analysis of amygdaloid activity is twofold: on the input side, there is no relationship between central and peripheral impulse patterns and on the output side, entirely opposite effects may be elicited on the same function. Machne & Segundo (1956) demonstrated how impulses from different sensory modalties converged on the same unit without any localizing or discriminative signs and Creutzfeldt, Bell & Adey (1963) revealed that the latencies of evoked unit discharges could be as long as 100 msec. These facts can only mean that the amygdaloid is not directly involved in the events of receptor mechanisms or in their primary discharge patterns. And even if more specific functions are discovered in the future, it is now evident that amygdaloid neurones show an enormous flexibility of response to the majority of incoming signals.

In regard to the output, the way in which the amygdaloid can change the balance point of a hypothalamic discharge is illustrated by the work of Stuart, Porter & Adey (1964) which shows what may happen to the firing pattern of a unit which is responding to a peripheral stimulus. They recorded the evoked activity of a hypothalamic unit following distension of the urinary bladder; the amygdaloid was then stimulated and it was found that the discharge rate of the hypothalamic unit was promptly increased or else reduced. Thus flexibility of action seems to be the keynote of the amygdaloid mechanism. This view appears to be confirmed by the variations and inconsistencies observed in the reactions to electrical stimulation of the amygdaloid or in the character of the behavioural disturbances resulting from lesion experiments. Yet, when all is said, the impression is left that the amygdaloid is only a part of a more extensive functional system whose modulatory influences and flexibility are essential to the organization of conscious behaviour.

REFERENCES

Adey, W. R. & Meyer, M. (1952). Hippocampal and hypothalamic connexions of the temporal lobe in the monkey. *Brain* **75**, 358–383.

Adrian, E. D. & Matthews, B. H. C. (1934). The Berger rhythm: potential changes from the occipital lobes of man. *Brain* **57**, 355–385.

Anand, B. K. & Dua, S. (1955). Stimulation of limbic system of brain in waking animals. *Science* **122**, 1139.

Anand, B. K. & Dua, S. (1956). Circulatory and respiratory changes induced by electrical stimulation of limbic system (visceral brain). *J. Neurophysiol.* **19**, 393–400.

Anderson, P., Eccles, J. C. & Loyning, Y. (1964). Pathway of postsynaptic inhibition in the hippocampus. *J. Neurophysiol.* **27**, 608–619.

Anderson, P. & Lomo, T. (1967). Control of hippocampal output by afferent volley frequency. *Prog. Brain Res.* **27**, 400–412.

Andersson, S. A. (1962). Projection of different spinal pathways to the second somatic sensory area in cat. *Acta physiol. scand.* **56**, Suppl. 194, 1–74.

Auer, J. & Virgilio, di G. (1953). Some afferent connections of the hypothalamus in the cat. *Anat. Rec.* **115**, 277.

Babkin, B. P. & Kite, Jr., W. C. (1950). Central and reflex regulation of motility of pyloric antrum. *J. Neurophysiol.* **13**, 321–334.

Baldwin, M,, Frost, L. L. & Wood, C. D. (1956). Investigation of the primate amygdala: Movements of the face and jaws. *Nature, Lond.* **6**, 288–293.

Bard, P. & Mountcastle, V. B. (1948). Some forebrain mechanisms involved in the expression of rage with special reference to suppression of angry behaviour. *Res. Publs Ass. Res. nerv. ment. Dis.* **26**, 362–404.

Chapman, W. P., Schroeder, H. R., Geyer, G., Brazier, M. A. B., Fager, C., Poppen, J. L., Solomon, H. C. & Yakovlev, P. I. (1954). Physiological evidence concerning importance of the amygdaloid nuclear region in the integration of circulatory function and emotion in man. *Science* **120**, 948–950.

Clark, Le Gros, E. E. & Meyer, M. (1950). Anatomical relationships between the cerebral cortex and the hypothalamus. *Br. med. Bull.* **6**, 341–344.

Creutzfeldt, O. D., Bell, F. R. & Adey, W. R. (1963). The activity of neurons in the amygdala of the cat following afferent stimulation. *Prog. Brain Res.* **3**, 31–49.

Davis, F. H. & Malmo, R. B. (1951). Electromyographic recording during interview. *Am. J. Psychiat.* **107**, 908–916.

Dell, P. & Olson, R. (1951). Projections 'secondaries', mésencéphaliques, diencéphaliques et amygdaliennes des afférences viscérales vagales. *C. r. Séanc. Soc. Biol.* **145**, 1084–1087.

Dreifuss, J. J. & Murphy, J. T. (1968). Convergence of impulses upon single hypothalamic neurones. *Brain Res.* **8**, 167–176.

Dunlop, C. W. (1958). Viscero-sensory and somato-sensory representation in the rhinencephalon. *Electroen. clin. Neurophysiol.* **10**, 297–304.

Egger, M. D. & Flynn, J. P. (1967). Further studies on the effects of amygdaloid stimulation and ablation on hypothalamically elicited attack behaviour in cats. *Prog. Brain Res.* **27**, 165–182.

Eliasson, S. (1952). Cerebral influence on gastric motility in the cat. *Acta physiol. scand.* **26**, Suppl. 95, 1–70.

Feldman, S. (1962). Neurophysiological mechanisms modifying afferent hypothalamo-hippocampal conduction. *Expl. Neurol.* **5**, 269–291.

Feldman, S., Wajsbort, J. & Birnbaum, D. (1967). Effect of combined brain stimulation on gastric secretion and potassium concentration in cats. *Brain Res.* **4**, 103–106.

Fernandez de Molina, A. & Hunsperger, R. W. (1962). Organization of the subcortical system governing defence reactions in the cat. *J. Physiol.* **160**, 200–213.

Forbes, T. W. & Andrews, H. L. (1937). Independent control of alpha rhythm and psychogalvanic response. *Science* **86**, 474–476.

Fox, C. A. (1940). Certain basal telencephalic centers in the cat. *J. comp. Neurol.* **72**, 1–62.

Fox, C. A. (1943). The stria terminalis, longitudinal association bundle and precommissural fornix fibers in the cat. *J. comp. Neurol.* **79**, 277–291.

Gergen, J. A. (1967). Functional properties of the hippocampus in the sub-human primate. *Prog. Brain Res.* **27**, 442–461.

Gloor, P. (1956). Microelectrode analysis of recruiting and potentiation occurring in hippocampal neurones in response to amygdaloid stimulation. *XX Cong. Int. Physiol., Brussels,* pp. 349–350.

Green, J. D. (1964). The hippocampus. *Physiol. Rev.* **44**, 561–608.

Green, J. D. & Adey, W. R. (1956). Electrophysiological studies of hippocampal connections and excitability. *Electroen. Neurophysiol.* **8**, 245–262.

Green, J. D. & Arduini, A. A. (1954). Hippocampal electrical activity and arousal. *J. Neurophysiol.* **17**, 533–557.

Green, J. D. & Machne, X. (1955). Unit activity of rabbit hippocampus. *Am. J. Physiol.* **181**, 219–224.

Hall, E. A. (1963). Efferent connections of the basal and lateral nuclei of the amygdala in the cat. *Am. J. Anat.* **113**, 139–151.

Hilton, S. M. & Zbrożyna, A. W. (1963). Amygdaloid region for defence reactions and its efferent pathway to the brain stem. *J. Physiol.* **165**, 160–173.

Hodes, R. & Magoun, H. W. (1942). Pupillary and other responses from stimulation of the frontal cortex and basal telencephalon of the cat. *J. comp. Neurol.* **76**, 461–473.

Kaada, B. R. (1951). Somato-motor, autonomic and EEG responses to electrical stimulation of rhinencephalic and other structures in primates, cat and dog. *Acta physiol. scand.* **24**, Suppl. 83, 1–285.

Kaada, B. R. & Jasper, H. (1952). Respiratory responses to stimulation of temporal pole, insula and hippocampal and limbic gyri in man. *Archs Neurol. Psychiat.* **68**, 609–619.

Kaada, B. R., Pribram, K. H. & Epstein, J. A. (1949). Respiratory and vascular responses in monkeys from temporal pole, orbital surface and cingulate gyrus. *J. Neurophysiol.* **12**, 347–356.

Kremer, W. F. (1947). Autonomic and somatic reactions induced by stimulation of the cingular gyrus in dogs. *J. Neurophysiol.* **10**, 371–379.

Krieg, W. J. S. (1963). Ch. 8, Cingulate and insular regions in *Connections of the*

Cerebral Cortex, p. 219. N.W. University Medical School. Brain Books, Evanston, Illinois.

Leek, B. F. (1972). Abdominal visceral receptors. *Handbook of Sensory Physiology*, vol. 3. Springer-Verlag, Berlin.

Lundervold, A. (1952). An electromyographic investigation of tense and relaxed subjects. *J. nerv. ment. Dis.* **115**, 512–525.

Luria, A. R. (1932). *The Nature of Human Conflicts or Emotions, Conflicts and Will.* Liveright, New York.

Machne, X. & Segundo, J. P. (1956). Unitary responses to afferent volleys in amygdaloid complex. *J. Neurophysiol.* **19**, 232–240.

Maclean, P. D. & Delgado, J. M. R. (1953). Electrical and chemical stimulation of fronto-temporal portion of limbic system in the waking animal. *Electroen. Neurophysiol.* **5**, 91–100.

Neimer, W. T., Powell, E. W. & Goodfellow, E. F. (1960). The subcortical and hypothalamic after-discharge in the cat. *Electroen. Neurophysiol.* **12**, 345–358.

Newman, P. P. (1953). Electromyographic studies of emotional states in normal subjects. *J. Neurol. Neurosurg. Psychiat.* **16**, 200–208.

Papez, J. W. (1937). A proposed mechanism of emotion. *Archs Neurol. Psychiat.* **38**, 725–743.

Parmeggiani, P. L., Azzaroni, A. & Lenzi, P. (1971). On the functional significance of the circuit of Papez. *Brain Res.* **30**, 357–374.

Poirier, L. J. & Shulman, E. (1954). Anatomical basis for the influence of the temporal lobe on respiration and cardiovascular activity. *J. comp. Neurol.* **100**, 99–109.

Pool, J. L. (1954). The visceral brain of man. *J. Neurosurg.* **11**, 45–63.

Pool, J. L. & Ransohoff, J. (1949). Autonomic effects on stimulating rostral portion of cingulate gyri in man. *J. Neurophysiol.* **12**, 385–392.

Pribram, K. H. & Bagshaw, M. (1953). Further analyses of the temporal lobe syndrome utilising fronto-temporal ablations. *J. comp. Neurol.* **99**, 347–373.

Pribram, K. H. & Kruger, L. (1954). Function of the 'olfactory brain'. *Ann. N.Y. Acad. Sci.* **58**, 109–138.

Raisman, G. (1966). Neural connections of the hypothalamus. *Br. med. Bull.* **22**, 197–201.

Redding, F. K. (1967). Modification of sensory cortical evoked potentials by hippocampal stimulation. *Electroen. clin. Neurophysiol.* **22**, 74–83.

Renshaw, B., Forbes, A. & Morison, B. R. (1940). Activity of isocortex and hippocampus: electrical studies with microelectrodes. *J. Neurophysiol.* **3**, 74–105.

Ruesch, J. & Finesinger, J. E. (1943). Muscular tension in psychiatric patients. *Arch. Neurol. Psychiat., Chicago* **50**, 439–449.

Sachs, Jr., E. S., Brendler, S. J. & Fulton, J. F. (1949). The orbital gyri. *Brain* **72**, 227–240.

Schreiner, L. & Kling, A. (1953). Behavioural changes following rhinencephalic injury in cat. *J. Neurophysiol.* **16**, 643–659.

Showers, H. J. C. & Crosby, E. C. (1958). Somatic and visceral responses from the cingulate gyrus. *Neurology* **8**, 561–565.

Smith, W. K. (1945). The functional significance of the rostral cingulate cortex as revealed by its responses to electrical excitation. *J. Neurophysiol.* **8**, 241–255.

Speakman, T. J. & Babkin, B. P. (1949). Effect of cortical stimulation on respiratory rate. *Am. J. Physiol.* **159**, 239–246.

Spiegel, E. A., Miller, H. R. & Oppenheimer, M. J. (1940). Forebrain and rage reactions. *J. Neurophysiol.* **3**, 538–548.

Stuart, D. G., Porter, R. W. & Adey, W. R. (1964). Hypothalamic unit activity: central and peripheral influences. *Electroen. Neurophysiol.* **16**, 248–258.

Turner, E. A. (1954). Cerebral control of respiration. *Brain* **77**, 448–486.

Valverde, F. (1963). Amygdaloid projection field. *Prog. Brain Res.* **3**, 20–30.

Vanegas, H. & Flynn, J. P. (1968). Inhibition of cortically elicited movement by electrical stimulation of the hippocampus. *Brain Res.* **11**, 489–506.

Von Euler, C., Green, J. D. & Ricci, G. (1958). The role of hippocampal dendrites in evoked responses and after discharges. *Acta physiol. scand.* **42**, 87–111.

Wall, P. D., Glees, P. & Fulton, J. F. (1951). Corticofugal connexions of posterior orbital surface. *Brain,* **74**, 66–71.

Ward, Jr., A. A. (1948). The cingular gyrus: area 24. *J. Neurophysiol.* **11**, 13–23.

Ward, Jr., A. A. & McCulloch, W. S. (1947). The projection of the frontal lobe on the hypothalamus. *J. Neurophysiol.* **10**, 309–314.

Ward, J. W. & Back, J. B. (1964). Responses elicited from orbital cortex of cats: overt activity and related pathways. *Am. J. Physiol.* **207**, 740–749.

Zbrożyna, A. W. (1963). The anatomical basis of autonomic and behavioural response effected via the amygdala. *Prog. Brain Res.* **3**, 50–68.

11

GENERAL CONCLUSIONS

WHEN an author comes to the end of his story he is probably faced with the most difficult part of his work—the tasks of putting together an assortment of projects in the development of a theme and convincing the reader that it has been worthwhile. In selecting the material for this work it is convenient to make a distinction between input and output functions and to regard the hypothalamus as the region from which the output commences. The distinction appears to be justified since there is a wealth of literature on the hypothalamus and its neuro-endocrine influences whereas little attempt has been made, at least in the textbooks, to describe the visceral afferent contributions in a comparable way.

Visceroceptors and their afferent fibres supply the internal organs. Their localization and the reactions which result when they are stimulated have long occupied the attention of workers in the field of visceral sensibility. New features continue to be described, including evidence from electron microscopy, and a very full review of the subject by Leek (1972) will be found in the *Handbook of Sensory Physiology*. The Pacinian corpuscle is probably the best known of the mechanical receptors since it can be dissected and studied in isolation, but tension-signalling receptors are also found in abundance throughout the alimentary tract and in the wall of the urinary bladder. Free nerve endings, possibly subserving pain sensations, are located in the muscular walls and mucous membranes. There is less information about chemical and thermal receptors in the abdomen although recent work has added to our knowledge of their sites of action and function.

The afferent fibres travel in autonomic nerve trunks and strands but do not belong to the autonomic system. Like other sensory fibres, they have their cell bodies in the dorsal root ganglia, enter the central nervous system and participate in reflex arcs. Afferents in the cranial and sacral outflow of the parasympathetic supply the stomach and pelvic viscera; a high proportion of these fibres are non-myelinated. Fibres travelling in the splanchnic nerves supply most of the abdominal viscera and are generally classified into groups A, B and C. The classification is useful in defining differences of function although some overlap occurs within the spectrum of the sub-groups. For example, it is believed that the A beta and A delta groups of splanchnic nerve afferents form two distinct functional systems—the former constitutes a fast-conducting ipsilateral pathway in the dorsal column and the latter is a more scattered, bilateral pathway through which many spinal reflexes are mediated. However, if the argument is taken a little further than this, firstly there are fibres of the A beta group which do not ascend in the dorsal column and some of the A delta group which do. Secondly, there are many other ascending tracts in the spinal cord whose composition and functional role are not yet determined. Thus there is far from being a secure basis for supposing that different groups of visceral afferent fibres are sharply segregated by function.

The reflexes mediated by visceral afferents form a substantial part of conventional physiology if all the cardiac and respiratory effects are included. Reflexes resulting from distension of abdominal and pelvic viscera are of particular interest since they are important in clinical conditions and at the same time demonstrate, even at spinal level, the phenomenon of viscero-somatic interaction. It is difficult to know what value can be placed on the viscero-vascular reflexes or whether they serve any function at all. Many authors have reported a large rise of arterial blood pressure following visceral stimulation but the circulation must surely be well protected from such drastic changes in the intact body. The experiments are significant only to the extent that they indicate how splanchnic afferent impulses can spread through many segments of the cord and operate reflex chains, more effectively when supraspinal influences are depressed.

It is likely that splanchnic afferents of all fibre groups can reach the level of the cerebral cortex. As yet, however, the contributions made by high-threshold 'C' fibres are insufficiently known. Current views on the functional organization of the thalamus point to a high degree of specificity, that is to say that despite the arguments still prevailing about the routes of conduction and the bilateral character of high-threshold afferents, a topographical pattern of representation is preserved. The splanchnic projection of the thalamus overlaps the leg and arm areas in the posterolateral nucleus and vagal afferents are believed to terminate in the posteromedial nucleus. However, the limited distribution of units responding to visceral stimulation alone is consistent with the relatively poor localizing function of the viscera compared with the muscles and body wall. A beta and A delta unit responses cannot be distinguished as separate entities at thalamic level.

In the cerebral cortex impulses of splanchnic origin reach well-defined points on both sensory areas. Primary wave and unit responses are found exactly in the position to be expected from anatomical grounds and they can be recorded not only following electrical stimulation of the nerves but, what is more significant, when a physiological stimulus is delivered to the viscus itself. Such influences may cause a profound change in the discharge patterns of the sampled units and thus convey to the cortex a very definite impression of a peripheral event, especially in regard to the intensity and localization of the stimulus. It seems, therefore, that the flow of information from the viscera is channelled along a functionally identified projection system through the thalamus to the sensory cortex. Unfortunately, things are not so simple as this. There is still no real evidence that A beta and A delta fibre systems operate independently, the one mediating rapid responses and the other serving more slowly conducted responses. The concept of two functional systems applies equally to the somatosensory system which, of course, is much better organized. None the less we cannot ignore the fact that any stimulus strong enough to excite A delta afferents will also excite the A beta component. For the moment it would seem wiser to accept only such differences as can be demonstrated by experiment without placing too much emphasis on implied function. The same caution should be expressed in discussing the role of the second sensory area. There is still nothing useful to say about the duality of representation in the cerebral cortex except to confirm the fact of its existence and to point out the comparative ease with which unit discharges can be evoked by splanchnic afferent stimulation. This is a good indication of the density of the cell population in the second sensory area and it may be of interest to ideas on the cerebral organization of visceral pain. There is now ample evidence that both sensory areas are capable of modifying the sensory inflow through excitatory and inhibitory effects on their synaptic relays. This influence on the ascending sensory systems has been shown by recording at various sites and finding that cortical stimulation can impose significant alterations in the patterns and rates of discharge; the dominant effect on the synaptic relays is a prolonged inhibition. Anatomical methods have also established the existence of descending pathways, some obviously direct to brain stem relay zones and others organized diffusely to complete feed-back loops. Perhaps the most interesting of these influences on the activity evoked by sensory stimulation is to be found in the thalamus itself. Whilst there is much to work out on the cortical mechanisms influencing afferent transmission, it will be apparent that the sensory areas of the cerebral cortex are not passive fields of representation for impulses evoked from the sense organs.

The next problem is to fit into the picture and explain the action of two highly complex circuits or control systems—the cerebellum and the reticular formation. Taking the cerebellum first, it is evident that this organ does not mediate conscious sensations, but can we finally discard the idea that it is primarily concerned with the regulation of muscular activity? The cerebellum also receives a continuous stream of impulses from the viscera which modify the output of the Purkinje cells; yet we know very little about the influence of the cerebellum on visceral functions or whether there is a clinical relationship between visceral disturbances and cerebellar disease. Another question, still unresolved, regarding the dual character of the input to the cerebellum, is how mossy fibre and climbing fibre systems must work together in signalling sensory events to the cerebellar cortex.

The mossy fibre pathway to the cerebellar granule cells originates from the spinal cord, pontine nuclei and the reticular formation. The axons of the granule cells form the parallel fibres which have excitatory action by direct contact with the dendrites of Purkinje cells and inhibitory action through basket and stellate interneurones. As a consequence, the Purkinje cell discharge is finely graded. Since the parallel fibres distribute impulses over a considerable area, the net result will be that a large number of Purkinje cells will be excited or 'on-beam' and many others will be inhibited or 'off-beam'. It is therefore important to distinguish between the complex synaptic changes occurring at the site of each Purkinje cell and the simpler efferent discharge patterns that represent the total Purkinje output to the cerebellar nuclei. The climbing fibre pathway from the inferior olive also produces excitatory and inhibitory effects on the cerebellar cortex. The excitatory effects, by extensive monosynaptic contacts with Purkinje cell dendrites, are powerful and prolonged; the inhibitory effects, through collaterals acting on interneurones, account for long pauses in Purkinje firing. Both these events occur after the development of the response to the mossy fibre input and presumably contribute in an important way to its control. That is to say that some kind of regulating system is imposed by the olivary neurones, but nothing final can be said on this matter. All we can be certain about is that the output from the cerebellum does not depend exclusively on the mossy fibre-granule cell system—the output at any particular time and in any particular zone will be influenced by the prevailing bias in the climbing fibre network. In other words climbing fibre impulses ensure a degree of stabilization by maintaining the output of the cerebellum within a desired range of frequencies.

A second major control system is to be found in the reticular formation. Here are situated many of the important components of the visceral reflexes and the neural links which enable them to participate in a higher order of physiological reactions. Single units located in the medial reticular formation respond to stimulation of the splanchnic nerves. Some show an increase of firing rate, often followed by a delayed burst under light anaesthesia; other units, discharging spontaneously, are inhibited by splanchnic nerve stimulation. As the same units can also be influenced by afferents from various sources, e.g., cutaneous, auditory, it is doubtful whether any topographical representation exists. Furthermore, the latencies and characteristics of the evoked responses are so variable that it seems unlikely there can be any distinction between the visceral and somatic afferent systems at the reticular level. Recently, the lack of any obvious spatially organized function within the medial reticular formation has encouraged studies on the temporal aspects of the unit discharges. How to untangle the complex functional arrangements within the reticular formation remains an important problem of present day research. It would certainly be helpful if we could identify some of the structures concerned in the regulation of visceral functions in spite of the intricate interconnexions of the region. It would also be useful if we could trace the afferent collaterals of the ascending sensory systems and work out the pathways for the irradiation of impulses from one functional centre to another. Finally, a problem which is currently being investigated concerns the activity of corticofugal impulses on the discharge patterns of single reticular neurones.

Many parts of the cerebral cortex have been shown to participate in the neuro-endocrine adjustments of the body. Evidence now indicates that the most significant changes are mediated by the limbic system, a fact which may justify the use of the term 'visceral brain'. Analysis of the effects which may be elicited by electrical stimulation discloses that each limbic component has certain affinities, for example, the gastric and respiratory influences of the orbital cortex or the behavioural responses attributed to the amygdaloid. The important point is that collectively they exert a powerful control on the entire autonomic nervous system extending from the hypothalamus to the brain stem and spinal cord. Visceral afferent impulses have no easy access to the limbic structures and it is clear that we can do little more than guess about the central mechanisms which operate the limbic machine. It appears unlikely, however, that any great progress can be made to explain cerebral function in physiological language or to understand disorders of behaviour without a detailed knowledge of the afferent information provided by the viscera themselves.

The future may well bring new horizons to the neuro-endocrine field as the nature of the central mechanisms is unfolded. The possibility of voluntary control of visceral functions by feed-back or conditioning techniques could have far-reaching clinical application. Since many psychosomatic conditions involve the autonomic nervous system, is it too much to hope that a clearer understanding of the brain machine may one day help in the training of a subject to overcome his own physiological maladjustments?

AUTHOR INDEX

SUBJECT INDEX